THE
HONEYWOOD
FILE

THE
HONEYWOOD
SETTLEMENT

H B CRESWELL

Jane Pendergast.

THE ARCHITECTURAL PRESS   LONDON

The Honeywood File first published in 1929
The Honeywood Settlement first published in 1930
Both volumes reissued individually and as a boxed set 1983
Reissued in one volume 1986
by The Architectural Press Ltd
9 Queen Anne's Gate
London SW1H 9BY

ISBN 0-85139-867-7

Publisher's note
*Since this book was written there have been significant
developments in the legal position of the architect:
readers are therefore warned not to regard the text as
a precise guide to today's legal, contractual and
professional relationships.*

Printed and bound in Great Britain by
Biddles Ltd, Guildford and King's Lynn

THE
HONEYWOOD
FILE

an adventure in building

TO

C.B.
Q.A.G.
W.

PREFACE

Although *The Honeywood File* is designed to engage aspirants to architectural practice with a lively presentment of the adventures that await them, a picture in which men and women rather than architects and builders occupy the canvas, and which is more concerned with the fabric of life than with the fabric of houses, will perhaps amuse those who have fallen under the spell of bricks and mortar or who are curious of the unexplored.

H.B.C.

CONTENTS

Contents

THE FILE IS OPENED

The Honeywood File is to be read as an architect's correspondence file. It consists of a folder endorsed "Honeywood". Within it letters received and carbon copies of those sent out are clipped together in order of date. An actual file taken from an architect's office would, of course, convey little: it would be prolix; raise questions it did not answer and answer those it did not raise; give no clear impression of events and shadowy presentiments, only, of persons; and it would be loaded with superfluities: in a word, it would be tedious and unintelligible.

Any file, therefore, which is to present to the reader such a clear picture of characters and events as it would awaken in the memory of the architect who conducted the correspondence, if he is imagined as perusing it months or years after it was closed, must be stripped of redundancies; subjected to selection and arrangement; given order and proportion and, in addition, the letters themselves must have a colour brighter than reality.

The Honeywood File is put forward as representing an actual file that has been reorganized in this way; but such reorganization does not necessarily involve a departure from verisimilitude. It may enhance verisimilitude, and this has been the author's endeavour; and as the whole value of, and much of the interest in *The Honeywood File* depends upon acceptance of the picture as a true one, he wishes to state that his chief concern has been to make it so.

He also wishes to state that before setting pen to paper he engaged with himself that all characters should be imaginary and all incidents fictitious. There was no virtue in keeping this engagement, for in no single instance was he impeded by the restriction, and only once or twice, when invented incidents awakened memories, was he reminded of it. Now that all is done he can affirm that, though some incidents are paralleled in his experience, none of the events are so; and that no character in the book is associated in his mind with any person alive or dead he has ever known or, for that matter, heard of or read about.

9

The File is Opened

The Honeywood File was first opened when the author sat down before a blank sheet of paper, and James Spinlove, a complete stranger, announced himself at the point of the pen. Sir Leslie Brash, who was apparently standing next in queue in the unknown, then inked himself down; and his temperament and social level were settled at once and for ever by a facile— and apparently meaningless—alliteration which fell on the paper to close a sentence. That fine fellow Grigblay, the graceless Potch, the humble Bloggs and the rest, all happened in the same way; and why they should be themselves and not others, or, being themselves, should think, act, and speak as they do, is beyond the author's comprehension. Where, he asks, have they all come from? The only answer to this question seems to be—the inkpot.

As with the characters, so, very much, with the events: the author has not generally known from one page to another, and often from one sentence to the next, what was going to happen nor how the cat would jump or an entanglement unravel. From week to week, keeping pace with serial publication in *The Architect's Journal*, the broken end of the last number was usually his sole incentive to the next.

Thus, no author ever posed as editor of his own lucubrations with a much better claim to indulgence than here. The detachment of this "editor's" commentary; his quickness to pounce upon and claw out on the carpet and publicly dismember everything that attracts his attention, and his eagerness to reprove or commend, are no elaborate affectations, but the reactions of an imperfect nature to personalities and events with whose creation he has had nothing to do.

To him, as has been said—and now to the reader—enters James Spinlove, the architect from whose hypothetical office *The Honeywood File* is supposed to derive. He proves to be an Associate of the Royal Institute of British Architects which marks him as decently educated and technically well-equipped; and the indications are that he has been in practice half a decade, so that his years do not count much more nor much less than thirty. He has probably built various small houses, a village hall, and so forth. He employs an assistant and a boy clerk.

We open the file at the back—for each succeeding letter is, properly, filed on the top of the preceding one—and we find the following:

THE COMMISSION

FREDERICK DALBET TO JAMES SPINLOVE

Dear Jim,   15.1.24.

I accidentally ran into an old friend of my father's the other day. He told me he had bought land in Kent with the idea of building himself a house and was looking about for an architect. I told him what an incompetent ass you are and of that house of yours which is getting ready to fall down at Ightham, so he may write to you. The name is Sir Leslie Brash (Knt. Bac.). He and my father were lifelong friends, so take care of him. He is an expert economist and financier; you can read of his crimes in *Who's Who*: recreations—conger fishing and cursing; however, though peppery, he is a real good sort, but you must mind your "p's" and "q's" with "dear Maude", as my mother calls her. I have not seen her since she became her ladyship, and shall be amused to see how she wears it. When are we two going to meet?

                                                     Yours,

SIR LESLIE BRASH TO JAMES SPINLOVE

Dear Sir,   17.1.24.

I write on the introduction of Mr. Frederick Dalbet, from whom you have, I anticipate, received intimation. I have purchased property at Thaddington, near Marlford, and am contemplating erecting a residence upon it. The location to be occupied by the mansion I should request your advice upon. The fall of the ground I apprehend to suggest a south-east aspect, but Lady Brash desires the edifice to face in the opposite direction as there is a chimney—a pumping station, if I am correctly

11

informed—some two miles distant on the S.W. which interferes with the prospect. These matters, however, Lady Brash and myself desire to discuss with you. I should be glad to be advised whether you would be prepared to act for me in the capacity of architect if we decide to proceed; or perhaps you will consider it advisable for me to get rid of the property and purchase another as I entirely failed to observe the chimney when I acquired it. In the event of your expressing willingness to act for me I will suggest an appropriate date when we may meet on the property.

Yours faithfully,

SPINLOVE TO BRASH

Dear Sir, 18.1.24.

I beg to thank you for your esteemed favour of the 17th inst., and it will give me great pleasure acting for your good self and meeting you on site as per your letter. I am free Tuesday and Thursday and every day the following week as advised at present if suitable to your convenience and will thank you to let me know re same.

Thanking you in anticipation,
Yours faithfully,
JAS. SPINLOVE.

This is terrible! Is it possible that Spinlove would sign himself "Jas.", and beg to thank and be ungrammatical and guilty of solecisms and prostrate himself like a shopkeeper? It is not likely, but it is in some degree possible and that is why I have, for this one occasion only, played off a practical joke on the reader.

This letter is not on the file, but has been substituted by me in order to pillory a style of letter-writing which, because it is adopted in certain business circles, is supposed by some to be businesslike and to give an impression of efficiency. Needless to say, no diction is businesslike which is not lucid; and faulty grammar and the use of such expressions as "as per" and "re same", implies ignorance and not efficiency. An architect has to correspond with many different kinds of persons under a great variety of circumstances, and no letters are of greater importance than

12

The Commission

those addressed to his clients, where not only are lucidity, firm-
ness, and self-control called for, but frankness, sincerity, tact,
and—if he possesses that gift of the gods—charm. Spinlove will
be likely enough to make mistakes: but he is a decently educated
man and socially, if not in rank, Brash's equal. What Spinlove
did, in fact, write, as recorded on his file, is as follows:

SPINLOVE TO BRASH

Dear Sir,   18.1.24.

I have to thank you for your letter of yesterday and to say
that I shall be most glad to act for you in the matter you speak
of. I can go with you to the site on any day next week, except
Tuesday and Thursday; or on any day during the following
week except Saturday if you will be so good as to name day
and hour and place of meeting. From your description the site
seems to be most attractive. I think that the chimney of which
you speak may not prove su h a serious annoyance as you now
suppose.

Yours faithfully,

This is all right, but if the last three words had been "is now
supposed", it would be happier. In formal correspondence it is
well to avoid the personal "you". Spinlove, however, ought not to
have referred to the chimney. I myself know nothing of what
lies ahead—I had no idea of any chimney till Brash referred to it
—but Spinlove ought to have divined that he will hear quite
enough about this chimney without introducing the subject him-
self. The indications are that Spinlove is not socially astute. It is
Lady Brash who objects to the chimney;—and did not Spinlove's
friend, Dalbet, warn him of "dear Maude"? Spinlove will get into
the lady's bad books if he does not take care. The arrangements
seem to have been completed by telephone and Spinlove does not
record and file telephone messages as he would do if his office of
organization was more thorough, for we next read:

SKETCHES AND ESTIMATES

Dear Sir Leslie Brash (*sic*),   25.1.24.

I have roughly worked out the dimensions of the house for the purpose of giving you an idea of the probable cost, as you asked. I enclose on a separate sheet a list of the rooms with approximate sizes following the instructions you gave me. Assuming that the house is built of brick with tiled roof, iron casements in oak frames, the stairs in oak, and reception rooms panelled in oak and with oak floors, and the whole house well, but not extravagantly, fitted and decorated, I think the figure you should have in mind is from twenty to thirty thousand pounds. This does not include entrance road, fencing, terrace, if any; nor, of course, laying out of garden, nor the cottages you spoke of. It does, however, include—as you will see— garage, stable, and kennels.

As I told you, I think the site an excellent one in every way. If you keep the house well up on the N.W. side, with entrance from the upper road and through the wood, you will be close to the highway, though screened from it. You will have an almost level approach, and the fall of the ground towards the S.W. will admit of readily forming a terrace and give the house a most attractive setting. The wood upon the N. and curving towards the East, will shelter the house and, as I pointed out to Lady Brash, will prevent the chimney being seen from any of the windows. I hope Lady Brash will be reconciled to the chimney as there are insuperable objections to placing the house in any other position, or setting it at any other angle than that fixed by the fall of the ground which, also, is the ideal for aspect and for prospect. The view is truly wonderful and I should not, I may say, have noticed the chimney if Lady Brash had not called my attention to it.

I will not take any further action until I hear from you.

Yours sincerely,

Sketches and Estimates

It would have been perhaps wiser if Spinlove had opened his letter "Dear Sir". We may assume that he was cordially greeted by the Brashes, that the common friendship with the Dalbet family thawed the ice and that the interview was intimate and not formal; but even had his client not been his senior in years and his superior in rank, Spinlove ought to have waited for him to initiate the more familiar address. Spinlove is also too garrulous: he is, of course, naturally enthusiastic at the splendour of the opportunity before him and is anxious to do himself justice and perhaps to make sure that Brash shall perceive what a discerning architect he has got; but a great part of his letter is clearly a repetition of what he has already said in conversation, and he ought to have more gumption than again to drag in the wretched chimney. He is in danger of taking a side in a matrimonial squabble, and, be it said, if he knew how his bread was buttered, probably the wrong one. It is to be hoped that his appearance and address will please. His letters certainly will not.

BRASH TO SPINLOVE

Dear Sir (*sic*),   30.1.24.

I am in receipt of your communication and am astounded at your estimated valuation. It is desirable I should finally intimate at once my conclusive inability to contemplate such a monstrously outrageous figure. May I be permitted to mention that though a matter of ten thousand pounds—the difference between the two estimated valuations you give—appears to you to be of no importance, such a sum is *of considerable importance to me*. My anticipated conception of the cost of the house is ten or twelve thousand pounds. If I consented to expend fourteen thousand on the mansion and garage, etc., that would be an outside maximum figure. I have, as you remind me, to provide for laying out garden, fencing, roads, etc. Then there is water-supply, drainage, and electric light to be included in the anticipated total of cost. Have you considered these? Your suggestion that I should expend in all nearly forty thousand pounds is, if you will permit me to say so, preposterous. I must request you to reduce your prices very considerably, for I cannot consent to entertain proposals of such dimensions as those you

15

formulate. I apprehend it is not necessary for me to indite a reply to other matters communicated in your letter, but I may mention that Lady Brash, who is temporarily residing in the neighbourhood, yesterday observed black smoke issuing from the chimney.

Yours faithfully,

We may feel sorry for Spinlove. He is not to blame and he did not deserve to be taken so heavily to task. Such things, however, frequently happen. Brash is disappointed; he is old enough to be Spinlove's father, and although he does not suppose, as many do, that an architect is a superior kind of builder who submits estimates and then builds, his ideas of the duties of an architect are evidently confused. Spinlove made a mistake in not asking Brash what he meant to spend, and he will not be likely to make the mistake again.

It will, however, be a long time before he has to ask the question, for it is usual for a private owner to bring forward, at the outset, a point so much on his mind as the cost of his project, and it is strange that Brash did not do so. No harm has, however, been done, for Brash has no intention of being unfair, and if Spinlove handles the matter wisely he will rise in Brash's confidence and esteem.

SPINLOVE TO BRASH

Dear Sir,   2.2.24.

I am sorry my letter caused you disappointment. That would not have happened had I known the sum you wished to spend, for I should then have cut the coat according to the cloth, as the saying is.

May I explain that, given certain materials and a style of building, the cost of a house is in the main determined by its size—by the measure of its cubic contents. On the enclosed sheet I give, approximately, the number and dimensions of the rooms of such a house as might be built for the fourteen thousand pounds you are prepared to lay out. You will see that the house is smaller and more plainly finished than was indicated in the original proposal. Central heating, drainage, water, and electric light services are, of course, included as before, I should mention that until a complete design has been worked out it is impossible to give you a close idea of cost; but if you will let me know what you want to spend I can scheme accordingly.

The round alternative figures I gave you were intended to cover uncertainty of the value of the decorations, fittings, and finishing you intended, which is a matter for you to decide and not for me. I need hardly say that I have no wish to persuade you to spend more than you want to spend. My hope is that I may be able to help you to lay out your money to the best advantage.

Yours faithfully,

Spinlove piqued and on the defensive is a more impressive person than Spinlove ecstatic and full of himself. He has answered Brash effectively. He has put him in the wrong and he has done it neatly, and with politeness and dignity.

BRASH TO SPINLOVE

Dear Sir, 6.2.24.

I am obliged for your letter of February 2nd. The dimensions of the apartments you indicate impress me as much too restricted. I am particularly disappointed in the dimensions of the reception rooms, and I desire at least three more bedrooms. You have included for only two bathrooms: a third is most imperative. I appreciate your theory of the dimensions of the house influencing the cost, but apprehend there must be an erroneous misconception and that a residence of the character you indicate could not possibly involve an expenditure of £14,000. If this is so I shall either have to disburse a larger sum or relinquish the ambition of building altogether. Lady Brash yesterday inspected a mansion that might, with suitable alterations, she thinks, accommodate us. Before arriving at a definite decision, however, I enclose a sketch depicting exactly the residence we anticipate we shall require. The arrangement will suit us admirably and if you will draw proper plans following my sketch we shall have something definitely depicted before us. I have not delineated the bedrooms; I leave that to you. I will also desire you to prepare some sort of a picture depicting the exterior view of the house; just a slight sketch will suffice— but Lady Brash particularly desires a *pretty* house. When the plans are drawn I comprehend that it will be admissible for you to indicate a more exactly accurate estimate. You will perceive that the dimensions I have allocated to the various apartments are in excess of those in your last communication but less than was originally desired.

Believe me,
Yours truly,

P.S.—A friend of ours has recently purchased a charming bungalow on the South Coast, the walls of which are composed of Brikko and the roof covered with Slabbo. I have not viewed the edifice myself, but Lady Brash informs me that it is extremely pretty and that residences can be erected with these materials much more inexpensively than with bricks and slates. It occurs to us that you could considerably reduce your price by availing yourself of these substances, and I also understand that their use makes it possible for walls and roofs to exactly match in colour.

It is to be noticed that Brash has climbed down. He evidently regrets his previous asperity, and asks Spinlove to believe that he is his truly. These sensitive tokens of the set of the wind are not to be ignored. It is a frank and cordial letter; the lofty diction which prefers "recently purchased" to "just bought", and so forth, is the result of success supervening on defective education, and has no significance.

SPINLOVE TO BRASH

Dear Sir,   8.2.24.

Thank you for your letter enclosing sketch. I note your wishes, but there are difficulties which will, I fear, prevent my giving effect to them. For instance, it will scarcely be possible to attempt to make any plan until the position of the house on the site, or at least its aspect, is settled. I am also sorry to say that when your plan is drawn out to scale—that is, when the various walls are arranged in the positions fixed by the dimensions you give—the house will not take the form you indicate, nor, indeed, any practicable form. For example, the front is nearly one-third as long again as the back, so that the gun-room, kitchens, etc., would form an inaccessible wing and the passage marked "private corridor" would be outside the building altogether. It is necessary, too, that all habitable rooms should have windows opening on to the outer air, and even w.c.s and larders must conform to this rule, which is enforceable by law and takes no account of the private tastes of the owner, so that the arrangements, adjoining the room marked "Den", will have to be completely remodelled. Also, I am afraid, it will be impossible to enter the house from the front door, except, of course, by going up the front stairs and down the back, which cannot be your intention. Up the back stairs and down the front is also the only way the servants can get to the door to answer the bell; moreover, the front stairs could be used to reach the bedrooms only by going out by the back door, or by one of the windows, and in at the front door. I mention these matters in order to make clear why it is impossible for me to adopt your plan, but I will make sketch designs for a house with a S.W. aspect which will give you the accommodation you show and provide, as nearly as may be, the areas you have fixed for the chief rooms.

I do not know either of the building materials you mention. There are a good many new patent materials which may be suitable for cheaply-built bungalows, but which could not be used in such a house as you intend. A uniform colour in walls and roof is a thing to be avoided rather than sought, and I think that the coincidence you refer to is accidental and due to callousness on the part of the builder. I shall hope to send you sketches in the course of the next ten days.

Believe me,

Yours truly,

This letter is a serious error of judgment. One might think that it was facetious and ironical, but the true explanation is, no doubt, that Mr. James Spinlove, A.R.I.B.A., has no sense of humour. He has regarded Brash's plan as a serious proposal; finds it a hope-

less obstacle to all solutions of the problem and, with enormous earnestness, sits down to explain why he cannot make use of it. Unfortunately, Brash's sense of humour—if he ever had any—is squashed flat under the deadweight of that self-importance which gained and supports his knighthood, so that the fat is probably in the fire. Spinlove is starting badly. I feel almost ashamed of him, for he is in a sense my protégé, *and I had no idea he could be so foolish. All he had to do was to thank Brash for his plan in a cheery note and take it for what it was worth—namely, for the information it may give of Brash's needs and prejudices. Spinlove's design need not follow the other: he will have conclusive explanations for his deviations, but probably no questions will be asked. A client's plan expresses only nebulous ideas, and the vivid actuality of the architect's design usually drives it out of remembrance. Spinlove might have made things quite safe for himself by telling Brash, when thanking him for his plan, that he proposed to prepare one himself so that the two might be compared and the best points of each combined in the final scheme. Spinlove, however, did nothing so tactful.*

BRASH TO SPINLOVE

Dear Sir,   9.2.24.

I apprehend that it is surely not necessary for me to elucidate that the very rough sketch I transmitted to you to inform you of the mansion I desire was not intended as a maturely conceived proposition. I comprehend very little of "prospect" and "aspect", and of what is "possible" and "impossible" for an architect, but I know the kind of residence I desire, and I consider that I have in various ways indicated my wishes with sufficiently lucid clearness.

The appropriate relative colours of the walls and roof of an edifice are, I consider, a matter of opinion and not of fact. I have not weighed the proposition and am amenable to guidance by your judgment, but I fail to comprehend why you should be so decisive in condemning buildings materials of which you admit you know nothing.

I await your sketches with interest,

Yours faithfully,

Sketches and Estimates

It will be noticed how much more dignified and effective Brash is when his native pepper rules. This letter shows him to be, as Dalbet described him, a real good sort. Spinlove ought to congratulate himself on getting off so lightly, and feel heartened to know the ingenuous nature of the man he has to deal with. I say ought to feel; but unawareness of his own stupidity and his lack of knowledge of men and affairs, have apparently caused this letter to throw him into consternation.

SPINLOVE TO BRASH

Dear Sir,   12.2.24.

You have, I entirely agree, given me the fullest particulars of your requirements, and my last letter was intended only to explain why the plans I am shortly sending you cannot follow the lines of the sketch you were so obliging as to give me, although they will, I trust and believe, fulfil its intentions. I very much regret that unfortunately I do not appear to have made this clear to you.

I ought also to have explained in commenting on "Brikko" and "Slabbo" that it is important, as I am sure you will agree, that the materials of which your house is built should be strong and that they should last. For this reason it is advisable to use in your house only materials which are known by experience to endure. Cheaply-built bungalows are in quite a different category, as I need, I think, scarcely point out.

The traditional association of bricks and tiles with the architecture of houses also makes it necessary to use bricks and tiles to give architectural character to your house. The substitution of unusual materials for such a purpose would create great difficulties in design, and the result would be certain to disappoint you greatly.

Yours faithfully,

It was not necessary for Spinlove to prostrate himself so completely, but the fault, if any, is on the right side. There is a respect due to years, and if Brash had any suspicion that Spinlove's offending letter was facetious he is now disabused. Brash does not appear to have replied, for we next find:

21

Sketches and Estimates

Dear Sir,   19.2.24.

I send you to-day under separate cover sketch plans and perspective view of the proposed house. The sizes of the rooms are figured, and I hope the arrangements will be clear to you. The small scale block-plan shows the position on the site. These drawings are intended only as preliminary sketches, but they will at least serve to reduce the problem to practical issues. To the best of my judgment the building shown will cost £19,500. I do not think that the cost need be higher, but I do not think it will be much less.

Yours faithfully,

These preliminary sketches, it is to be noticed, show a smaller house than Brash wants, do not follow his pet ideas of plan arrangement, and the estimate is 40 per cent more than he wants to spend. Brash also has in mind to give up the idea of building altogether and adapt an existing house. Spinlove, therefore, for whom this commission is a big opportunity, must feel considerable anxiety. Such positions frequently occur; anything may happen and no one could foretell what. A rise in stocks or a badly-cooked breakfast may settle the question one way or another. Apparently there was a rise in stocks.

Dear Mr. Spinlove,   21.2.24.

Lady Brash and myself are delighted with the plans of the house and with the charming picture delineating a view of the exterior. We are filled with admiration for the skilful ingenuity with which you have fitted everything in, and with the appropriate completeness of the arrangements. Lady Brash is particularly delighted with the cupboard in the recess in the kitchen passage and with the door shutting off the domestics' domain. There are certain insignificant matters which we desire altered : for instance, the entrance hall and staircase to be transferred farther along so as to leave an expanse of blank wall for the wistaria Lady Brash desires to plant in that situation, but these alterations I can elucidate when we meet.

Sketches and Estimates

The estimate of cost, is, I regret to intimate, a disappointment; I anticipated you would be able to reduce it after the plans were drawn out. I apprehend it will be requisite to minimize the expenditure, but we are so greatly enamoured with the design that I trust it may not be necessary to have recourse to material alterations. Would it be possible to omit the morning-room and the two projecting bays for the present so that they could be eventually added at a later date?

Can you call at Zimmon Gardens at six on Wednesday to discuss matters? Lady Brash will be disengaged at that hour. Perhaps you would be so good as to telephone to the house.

Yours faithfully,

Spinlove is clearly competent, but he is no less clearly lucky. It was quite on the cards that his design might outrage some prejudice of his client of which he could know nothing, or that in exercising his discretion, he might seriously have missed the mark, or that the plans might have been misread. If any of these things had chanced, Brash's pepper might have made him impatient and, with the added discouragement of the estimate, led him to abandon the whole project, or to consult another architect. As it happens, Spinlove has made a complete conquest. His preliminary sketches have been swallowed whole, the design is practically settled, discrepancy of cost is in a fair way to being adjusted and, from being captious and critical, Brash has become enthusiastic and appreciative. The interview evidently took place, for the next letter is dated a fortnight later.

SPINLOVE TO BRASH

Dear Sir Leslie Brash,   9.3.24.

I enclose revised sketch plans which you will see embody the whole of the alternatives except the shifting of the entrance hall and staircase, which, as I expected, cannot be moved without entirely remodelling the plan and designing the house on altogether different lines. It is unfortunate that the position of the front door and the window do not give an opportunity of training a wistaria in that particular position, but all planning is a balance of advantages, and I am afraid this one will have to go.

23

By comparing the dimensions on the revised plan with those shown on the original sketches, which I also enclose, you will see the reductions I have been able to make, and that I have also saved what space could be spared in bathrooms, passages, and so on; but nothing has been unduly pinched. I have also reduced the heights of floors as arranged, and taking everything into consideration I think the cost will be reduced from £19,500 to £17,300. To this has to be added the cost of the terrace, £1,200, which it was agreed should be included with the house, making the new estimate £18,500.

Will you please tell Lady Brash that things are so arranged that the chimney will be visible from no windows except those of the kitchen offices, gun-room, and servants' bedrooms. If you will let me know that you approve I will prepare contract drawings and documents for the purpose of securing tenders.

Yours faithfully,

BRASH TO SPINLOVE

Dear Mr. Spinlove,   14.3.24.

We appreciate the plans extremely, although we are disappointed you cannot transfer the entrance hall and staircase. I am somewhat apprehensive at the reduction in the dimensions, and anticipate we may be spoiling the ship to save a pennyworth of tar. I have therefore augmented some of them. Also I desire you will not take any chance of risks of bathrooms and passages being restricted, or the rooms too low in height. In order to meet the cost of expenditure I have decided not to erect a garage, kennels, etc., at present. I shall perhaps make a temporary wooden structure suffice to begin with, particularly as it may be desirable to first build cottages for the male outdoor staff. The terrace should be included. Will you therefore proceed with the contract and inform me immediately when the operations will commence and how long a period they will take to complete.

Yours sincerely,

SPINLOVE TO BRASH

Dear Sir Leslie Brash,   17.3.24.

Thank you for your letter. I will get on with the contract drawings at once.

24

In reply to your question, all well, the building will start in about four months' time, and take about two years to complete.

I enclose list of seven builders I propose to invite to tender. Five, as you will see, are of London; the other two are provincial firms operating in the district. All are of good standing and known to me. If there is anyone else you would like included will you please let me know.

In order to save the cost of the builder finding his own water, I propose to have the well sunk at once. As we know we shall get plenty of water at about 130 ft. it will not be actually necessary to employ a consulting engineer, but I propose nevertheless to do so both on the ground of economy and efficiency. I suggest the name of Mr. P. F. Toodlewipe, A.M.I.C.E., who is known to me.

Yours sincerely,

BRASH TO SPINLOVE

Dear Mr. Spinlove,   22.3.24.

I was dumbfounded at your communication intimating an anticipated delay of four months. I am at a loss to comprehend why this should occur. Surely now that everything is settled arrangements can be agreed with a suitable builder? Also the length of time the work will take. Two years! We are completing arrangements to take up residence next summer. Surely the operations will be terminated in fifteen months from now! Can nothing be done to expedite progress?

Certainly do as you propose as regards the well.

There is a builder at Marlford—Nibnose and Rasper—whom you might append to your list, and also a most respectable man, Mr. John Reaker, at Thaddington, who did work for a considerable period on Lord Imagwire's estate, whom I desire should tender. I fancy his son carries on the business now in partnership with a person named Mr. Smith.

Yours sincerely,

SPINLOVE TO BRASH

Dear Sir Leslie Brash,   24.3.24.

I am afraid that four months from now is as soon as you can

expect to see the builder at work. It will take me seven or eight weeks to work out the design in detail and prepare the necessary drawings and contract documents. The preparation of bills of quantities to enable builders to tender will probably take four weeks, the builder ought to have at least ten days in which to arrive at the figure of his tender, and a fortnight would be a short time in which to settle and sign the contract and for the builder to get his plant on to the site. It is true that the house might be built even in one year only, if a special point were made of it; but it would invite disaster to scramble through work of this kind, and it is doubtful if a really good builder would enter on such an undertaking. I will do all I can to expedite matters.

Thank you for names of builders. I will inquire about these firms.

Yours sincerely,

CATASTROPHE OF THE TRIAL HOLES

SPINLOVE TO MESSRS. REAKER & SMITH, BUILDERS, THADDINGTON, KENT

Dear Sirs,   28.3.24.

I understand that you have done work for many years on Lord Imagwire's estate. I want some trial holes dug in the meadow south of Honeywood Spinney on the top of Honeywood Hill. The enclosed plan shows the ground and the position of the holes, which should be 8 ft. deep. If you can undertake this work I will ask you to put it in hand at once and give me notice so that I may go down and see the ground.

If you are accustomed to building large private houses will you tell me of some you have built and give me the names of two or three architects under whose direction you have worked?

Yours faithfully,

Catastrophe of the Trial Holes

Spinlove seems to have forgotten that he is an agent of Sir Leslie Brash. In ordering this work without making clear that he acts as agent, he assumes responsibility and could, in fact, be made to pay for it.

The following letter seems to have found its way into the file instead of the wastepaper basket. It is a circular, with the name of addressee and subject added, printed by a firm which claims that its output is indistinguishable from autographs, and that it "brings business". The sort of work done by firms who depend upon this means of getting it, would not suit Spinlove, as no doubt he perfectly understands.

DOMO IDEALO LTD. TO JAMES SPINLOVE, ESQ., A.R.I.B.A.
New House for Sir Leslie Brash
Dear Sir,   2.2.24.

As a practising Architect of eminence you will be aware that, however dainty and refined the architectural design of a domestic habitation may be, the two things which will count with your client are COMFORT and EFFICIENCY, and these we are prepared to absolutely guarantee with the minimum of trouble to yourself, as our large staff of experts are always at your valued disposal.

We understand that you are the architect for the above house, and shall be glad to prepare estimates at the shortest notice for Electric Light, Heating, Water Supply, Lifts, Sanitary Work, &c., also for Carving in any material, Ornamental Plaster, Lead, Iron, and Decorative Art-craft Guild Handiwork of all descriptions.

May we call your attention to our Ultra-Violet Ozone and Water-Softening installations, without which no daintily-appointed modern gentleman's house can be considered complete. On receipt of a card or telephone message we will immediately arrange for one of our expert representatives to wait on you. Awaiting your esteemed favours.

We are dear Sir,
Yours faithfully
for DOMO IDEALO LTD.,

B. PIDGE,
Manager.

Catastrophe of the Trial Holes

SPINLOVE TO NIBNOSE & RASPER, BUILDERS, MARLFORD, KENT

Dear Sirs, 28.3.24.

Your name has been given me as builders of large country houses. If you are willing to tender for such work in the neighbourhood of Marlford I should be glad to know of buildings carried out by you and to receive the names, as references, of architects under whose directions you have worked.

> Yours faithfully,

SPINLOVE TO GEORGE BULLJOHN, ESQ., J.P. THE HAVEN, BUXFORD., NR. MARLFORD

Dear Mr. Bulljohn, 28.3.24.

Do you know anything of Nibnose and Rasper, and of Reaker and Smith, Thaddington, builders, and can you tell me what sort of standing and reputation they have? I have not seen you at the club for ages, but I hear you are sometimes there.

> Kindest regards,
> Yours sincerely,

REAKER & SMITH TO SPINLOVE

Sir, 29.3.24.

Your esteemed favour of the 28th inst. to hand and shall have attention. Our man up Honeywood way will be through with his present job Tuesday and will get on with it. We are used to working along with an architect and have just completed additions to Wheatsheaf (Public) in Main Street under Mr. Pintail, F.A.I., of Station Yard, Marlford. Mr. Reaker is away from business at present so am shorthanded.

Awaiting further esteemed favours,

> Yours to oblige,

NIBNOSE & RASPER TO SPINLOVE

Dear Sir, 31.3.24.

We are obliged for your letter and enclose list of some works executed by us with the names of the architects concerned.

Catastrophe of the Trial Holes

Mr. Claude Lambwad, F.R.I.B.A., of South Moulton Street, W.1, knows us, as we have done work for him for many years. We shall be glad to tender for the work you mention and hope to receive particulars in due course.

Yours faithfully,

BULLJOHN TO SPINLOVE

Dear Spinlove,   2.4.24.

I would not recommend you to have dealings with Reaker and Smith. Old John Reaker was widely esteemed, but the son is of a very different stamp. I may tell you that he is at this time in prison for being drunk while in charge of a motor-car. Smith has only lately come on the scenes. I hear of him as a bookmaker. Nibnose and Rasper is a most respectable firm. Whether they are up to the standard you want is not for me to say. Hope to see you again soon.

Yours sincerely,

SPINLOVE TO REAKER & SMITH

Dear Sirs,   12.4.24.

I have been expecting to hear from you. Are the trial holes ready for me to see?

Yours faithfully,

SPINLOVE TO THE SAME

Dear Sirs,   16.4.24.

I wired to you this morning. "Have holes been dug, wire Spinlove," but have received no reply. I wrote to you on the 12th asking for this information. I must expect your immediate response by wire or telephone.

Yours faithfully,

BRASH TO SPINLOVE

Dear Mr. Spinlove,   16.4.24.

I enclose a communication I have received to-night from the

farmer who is in charge of my daughter's mare, which is out at grass at Honeywood. My daughter is greatly distressed and I am also excessively annoyed and disappointed. I had no idea pits were being dug, but in any eventuality it was culpable negligence on someone's part that they were not protectively fenced. One can only be thankful that worse misfortune has not resulted. Immediate attention is necessary. I have wired to Bramble to employ a man to warn children.

Yours faithfully,

(ENCLOSURE) GEORGE BRAMBLE, COWKEEPER, TO BRASH

Sir,   15.4.24.

Your mare had an assidence up on Honeywood going on three legs near fore all tucked up and carried back very bad I never saw one that way and thorough crocked up and off feed I got her into float with rails under her and had to put on a twitch and a nice job she was a bit chafed under belly by rails but no harm and I got her slung comfortable now in cow stall and vet blistered her and tied up leg bad rench and sprained shoulder he says and dont quite know what to make there is a lot of narrow holes dug top of Honeywood I dont doubt she blundered and no wonder I did very near and deep water standing and children come in after cow slop flowers I druv off but you know what kids is and something had ought to be done or there might be a worser assidence awaiting your orders.

Yours obediently,

REAKER & SMITH TO SPINLOVE

Sir,   16.4.24.

Re wire duly to hand you did not prepay reply so write informing you same all finished twelve days ago as promised.

Awaiting further esteemed favours,

Yours to oblige,

Catastrophe of the Trial Holes

SPINLOVE TO NIBNOSE & RASPER

Dear Sirs,   17.4.24.

I write to confirm arrangements made with Mr. Rasper on telephone this morning that you will secure stout covers over trial holes dug South of Honeywood Spinney and to thank you for your message this afternoon telling me this work has been completed. I am much obliged for the particular attention you have been so good as to give to this matter.

Yours faithfully,

SPINLOVE TO BRASH

Dear Sir Leslie Brash,   17.4.24.

I need not tell you how concerned I was at the contents of your letter. The holes were securely covered to-day. I telephoned a message to this effect both to your Office and to Zimmon Gardens. I ordered the holes to be dug for the purpose of determining what draining and foundations would be necessary, but the person I employed did not keep me informed, as I asked him, of what he was doing. He should of course have covered the holes. I am more sorry than I can say at this unfortunate accident. I sincerely hope the mare will completely recover.

Believe me,

Yours sincerely,

Spinlove has been "unlucky"; but if he had had the foresight to order the holes to be covered he would have escaped this "ill-luck". As matters stand, he has not only made himself responsible for paying the cost of the work, but also for vet.'s fees and, perhaps, for the value of an expensive horse. These sorts of dangers, anxieties, and miseries always attend on the employment of builders who are not competent and conscientious; and it is scarcely possible for any architect under the strictest contract conditions to get any kind of work rightly done unless the persons he employs possess those qualities, which, it may be added, are readily found among builders scattered over the length and breadth of the land. Spinlove asks for further trouble by writing the letter which is next on the file.

31

Catastrophe of the Trial Holes

SPINLOVE TO REAKER & SMITH

Sirs,   17.4.24.

Your letter telling me the trial holes had been finished nearly a fortnight ago reached me only after I had learnt that a valuable horse belonging to the owner of the land had blundered on to one of them and been very badly injured. This as you will realize may be a serious matter for you. My instructions, which you acknowledged, were that I was to be informed directly the holes had been dug, but you neither did this nor replied to subsequent letters and telegram asking for information. Your omission to protect the holes is almost criminal. Children have been seen in the field and the pits are now half filled with water which will have to be pumped out before the bottoms can be seen. Your conduct of this matter in not completing the work and leaving me in ignorance of what was being done is inexcusable.

Yours faithfully,

The probable explanation of this tactless letter is that Spinlove feels he is in some degree responsible and seeks to defend himself by making clear to Reaker and Smith that he holds them liable. What he has, in fact, done is to warn those gentlemen and arm them against him: he has told them his side of the case. If he had merely complained that the holes were left uncovered and that he had not been notified, the ingenious Smith, always hoping for further esteemed favours, would probably have expressed regret for the omission and pleaded a misunderstanding and thus have admitted liability.

BRASH TO SPINLOVE

Dear Mr. Spinlove,   17.4.24.

I note that the holes have now been rendered secure. I apprehend, however, that it is due to myself for me to say that your extreme promptness in getting the covers fitted leaves me at a loss to comprehend why they have been supplied only after the harm is done, instead of previously. I do not consider that it was incumbent on me to direct your attention to this matter in anticipation. I extremely regret to intimate that I have a very bad account of the mare from the veterinary surgeon who is attending her.

Yours truly,

SPINLOVE TO BRASH

Dear Sir Leslie Brash,   19.4.24.

I am very sorry you have so bad an account of your mare. It was of course the clear duty of the builder who dug the holes to protect them, and in employing for this work a firm, Messrs. Reaker and Smith, which had been especially recommended by you as reliable people, I felt that they might be trusted and that your interests would be protected. I did not know that the mare was in the field when the holes were dug so that the need for covering them was perhaps not obvious.

Yours sincerely,

Spinlove appears to be losing his head.

REAKER & SMITH TO SPINLOVE

Sir,   19.4.24.

Yours to hand and re same beg to state no instructions to cover holes were given and we do work we are asked and not work we are not asked and not paid for doing or where would we be, and a nice thing to be told by an architect I must say. I am about attending to my work and no time to waste writing letters and telegrams. I said I would do the job as soon as ever the man cleared up and I done what I said and no one has any cause to complain, and if anyone goes and does a silly thing like putting a horse in a field with a lot of pit-falls to catch him well thats no fault of mine but the fault of them that ordered the pit-falls and put the horse in on top of them and if you are not satisfied I respectfully ask you to settle my account (enclo.) and we will say no more about it.

Soliciting your further esteemed favours,

Yours to oblige,

Catastrophe of the Trial Holes

Spinlove probably considers this letter extremely rude, and is much annoyed; but in point of fact the writer has no intention of being offensive or even disrespectful. He feels, reasonably enough, that he is being got at: he has no arts to hide his indignation and simply states his views. Spinlove invited such a letter and also an inflated bill. It is wise, particularly in dealing with a firm such as Reaker and Smith, to avoid rupture until the account has been delivered. Spinlove shows himself altogether too stiff in the neck in his reply. The bald address "Sirs" instead of "Dear Sirs", is inappropriate unless used in formal official correspondence in which the applicable subscription is "I am, Sir, your obedient Servant", or where, as in Smith's case, the writer feels that "Dear Sir" trespasses on familiarity. Twenty years ago things were perhaps different, but broadly speaking, no British subject has any right to address another in the tone of frigid, contemptuous resentment Spinlove adopts; and if he does so he will rightly suffer.

SPINLOVE TO REAKER & SMITH

Sirs,   22.4.24.

I have received your letter and need only say in reply that your view of the facts is untenable.

The amount of your account, returned herewith, is excessive and out of all reason. When the total has been substantially reduced and is supported by a detailed measured or day-work statement with vouchers I will consider it. The account is to be made out to Sir Leslie Brash, 19 Zimmon Gardens, S.W.3, and not to me.

Yours faithfully,

BRASH TO SPINLOVE

Dear Mr. Spinlove,   22.4.24.

In view of the trend of your communication, and although I am of opinion that your organization should have prevented the accident, I consider it desirable that I should intimate to you that as I have not hitherto put the blame for the damage to my daughter's mare upon you it was not necessary for you

34

to seek to defend yourself by fixing the responsibility on my shoulders. If, however, it had been necessary, permit me to indicate that in one sentence you asseverate it was the clear duty of the builder to cover the holes, and in the next but one that the obligation to do so did not eventuate.

I suggest to you that this subject should now be permitted to term nate, but I feel it desirable to remind you that I was not previously informed that pits were being dug and that no instructions were given to protectively cover them until after the neglect to do so had involved me—as I regret to fear—in the loss of a valuable hunter; and also to elucidate to you that I regard the proper carrying out of instructions—and not merely the appropriate issuing of them—as the duty of all persons I employ whether as architects or in other capacities. I shall be obliged if you will intimate to me that you accept this interpretation of your obligations.

> Believe me,
> Yours sincerely,

The stately creature! It is a devastating but not an unfriendly letter. On the contrary, it is evident that Brash likes Spinlove and respects his capacities. Such a letter could only be written, and tolerated, when addressed to a man young in years and experience by one mature in both. We may also imagine that Spinlove's personality is frank and boyish, and that this and his youth perhaps serve him well at this juncture; for Brash has ample grounds for feeling extremely annoyed and dissatisfied with his architect, and if that architect were not amenable to this kind of discipline his employer might well decide to be quit of him before worse disasters overtake his house-building adventure. Spinlove ought to have let Brash know that the pits were being dug; he ought to have employed a builder whom he knew to be of good standing, and he ought to have ordered the holes to be covered. If he had taken one only of these proper precautions all might have been well.

SPINLOVE TO BRASH

Dear Sir Leslie Brash,   24.4.24.
    I can only thank you for your letter and say that I accept

your view of my obligations, fully and without reserve. Permit me, however, in justification of myself to say that I had no intention of "putting the responsibility on your shoulders", but wished only to explain how it was that I did not take the necessary precautions.

Yours sincerely,

This justification of himself by Spinlove is a lame business. He has already said: (1) that it was the clear duty of the builder to protect the holes; (2) that the obligation to do so scarcely arose; (3) that responsibility lies with Brash, since the builder was employed on his recommendation; and now (4) he acknowledges that he himself did not take the precautions which he admits to have been "necessary". Spinlove's "case"—as the lawyers call it— would not have been a bad one had he held his tongue, but he has gone far to make it hopeless. However, there is not, apparently, going to be any "case" unless Reaker and Smith take action Spinlove would, this time, be right in deeming the letter which follows to be a rude one. Mr. Smith intends to be saucy and mildly sarcastic. Spinlove could only expect some such reply to his letter from such a man, and deserves no sympathy.

REAKER & SMITH TO SPINLOVE

Sir,   24.4.24.

Yours to hand, but unfortunately we have your letters to prove it so I am afraid it will come a bit thin for Mr. James Spinlove, Esq., P.R.I.B.A., R.A., K.C.B. The account must be made out to Sir Leslie Brash, must it? Well it's not, nor yet to Dempsey nor Madame Tussaud. It is going to be made out the same as it is made out to the fellow who ordered the work and has got to pay for it.

No my lord; we humbly regret account (enclo.) is not going to be substantially reduced nor yet reduced at all and have not got clerks to waste time copying out the men's day sheets, so will thank you to send cheque per return as work has now been completed four weeks.

Yours to oblige,

Catastrophe of the Trial Holes

SPINLOVE TO SNARTY BOLT & CO.

Dear Sirs,   25.4.24.

I should be glad if you would make an appointment for your representative to call and see me here on the subject of a heating lay-out.

Yours faithfully,

There are letters of a similar kind to various other contracting specialists from which we may deduce that Spinlove is up to his chin in the contract drawings.

SPINLOVE TO BRASH

Dear Sir Leslie Brash,   28.4.24.

Reaker and Smith have sent me their account for digging trial holes, £37 2s. 6d. This, in my opinion, is nearly twice as much as the work is worth. They also ask for immediate payment, have refused to make any reduction, and refused also to give details showing how the charge is arrived at. I think they feel they have put themselves in our black books and have nothing more to lose, and that they mean to make the most of the claim. They have written in such terms that I cannot continue negotiations. I should mention that after I had entrusted them with this work I made confidential inquiries, and had a very bad account of both Mr. Reaker and Mr. Smith. I am afraid it will be necessary to let your solicitors take charge of the matter. I know of no circumstances that could justify any such claim.

I enclose Messrs. Nibnose and Rasper's account for covering the holes and pumping out water so that the bottoms could be seen. I think £4 5s. a moderate charge for this work.

Yours sincerely,

It is most unfortunate that Spinlove should bring solicitors on the scenes at this early stage and in such a trivial matter. With his enormous advantage in education and social standing he should have no difficulty in coming to terms with Smith if he swallowed his humiliation, taught himself to be amused at Smith's letter, and realized that he should not have written that to which it is a reply. It is, however, a failing of our friend Spinlove to be inordinately stiff in the neck, and, as we have already observed, his sense of humour is far to seek. If he approached Smith with diplomatic overtures designed to save his own bacon he might well fail; but if he sincerely tried to do the man justice by putting himself in his place and regarding him as a human being reacting to vanity and self-preservation in the same way as himself, the thing would probably be settled in ten minutes, leaving good feeling instead of bitterness on both sides. Whether such action is in this case worth while is, however, another matter. It would probably best fit Spinlove's idea and serve his ends if he sent Smith say, £25, with a gesture signifying he could go to the devil, and later on charged Brash fifteen or twenty as a disbursement. That, however, is not Spinlove's way of handling the matter. I respect Spinlove, but that does not prevent my observing him to be a devoted ass. He has no lightness of touch. He goes boring down into the dregs of every misery. We may see Brash squirming in his chair as he writes his reply, which is in autograph.

BRASH TO SPINLOVE

Dear Mr. Spinlove,   30.4.24.

I consider that I have been involved in a sufficiently excessive expenditure over these wretched trial holes (the mare was shot yesterday) without being defrauded by overcharges. It is unfortunate that you did not ascertain the character of the firm *before* you employed them instead of *after*. I certainly have no intention of submitting to the extortion of these people, and if, as you intimate, their charge is preposterous—and it certainly seems outrageous to me—and, for some reason I do not understand, you are unable to negotiate with them, I apprehend my solicitors must take up the matter and I will instruct them to communicate with you. It is regrettable that at the very first outset, and in such a small matter, I should be involved in so many annoyances and vexations.

Yours truly,

Preparation for Tenders

Dear Sir Leslie Brash,   2.5.24.

I am more sorry than I can say to hear of the loss of your mare and for my unlucky part in the matter. I made inquiries of the standing of Reaker and Smith for the purpose of finding out whether they were suitable people to invite to tender, as you suggested they should do. It did not occur to me, after your recommendation, that they were not to be trusted to dig the trial holes. Messrs. Russ, Topper, Mainprice, Cornish and MacFee rang up to-day—I mean the firm did—and I have made an appointment to see them with correspondence, etc., on Wednesday at 2.30.

Yours sincerely,

There is a hiatus of six weeks. Drawing-boards and T-squares have been well employed, we gather, during that time.

PREPARATION FOR TENDERS

SPINLOVE TO BEDDY & TINGE, QUANTITY SURVEYORS

Dear Sirs,   14.6.24.

As arranged with Mr. Tinge I send you contract drawings Nos. 1 to 6 inclusive, and six sheets of rough $\frac{1}{2}$ in. and other details. I also send draft specification. The drawings have not been traced and will be completed, as usual, after the quantities are taken off. Will you please, as usual, complete specification to agree exactly with the bills. I shall be glad to see you and settle any matters not made clear.

Will you also be so good as to make a preliminary estimate of cost and let me know the figure?

I understood from Mr. Tinge that you could have the bills ready in four or five weeks' time. Will you please confirm this?

Yours truly,

Preparation for Tenders

Spinlove's arrangements are good. He has evidently "been there before". He secures that the bills shall include for no more and no less than he intends, and that the drawings and specifications shall show or describe the position of work measured. If particular care is not taken in these matters, work may be shown in the bills the position of which is not determined in the specifications—e.g. dowels—with the result that it is not included in the building, although paid for; or, on the other hand, the architect may intend a certain class of work and the bills not cover for it. He is wise to get an estimate before the bills are prepared and to let Beddy and Tinge know that time is an object. Quantity surveyors commonly work against time, and the architect who does not make a point of date of delivery will be likely to have to wait on those who do.

The next letter has been duplicated to seven firms of builders by Spinlove.

SPINLOVE TO VARIOUS BUILDERS

Dear Sirs,   14.6.24.

I shall be glad to know whether you will be willing to tender for a brick mansion, fourteen bedrooms, on a site at Thaddington, near Marlford.

In the event of your being willing to do so you may expect to receive bills of quantities and form of tender in about five weeks' time.

Yours faithfully,

Spinlove's object in writing thus is to secure that the firms he wishes to tender will be prepared to take up the work of pricing the bills when the time comes. If bills are sent out without such warning there is a chance that some builders may be so busy as to be unable to prepare a competitive tender within the time allotted. A builder will always send in a tender, because he feels that not to do so will prejudice his chance of being invited on a future occasion; but unless he has an opportunity of giving close attention to the business, his tender will be no serious bid and of no use to Spinlove nor to anyone else.

To save himself the trouble of arriving at a figure which will be too high for acceptance and yet presentable as a tender he will, if opportunity serves, obtain such a figure from another builder who is making a bona fide *offer.*

RUSS & CO., SOLICITORS, TO SPINLOVE

Brash v. *Reaker and Smith*

Dear Sir,   16.6.24.

Messrs. Reaker and Smith have now offered to accept the sum of twenty-seven pounds (£27. 0. 0.) in full settlement of their account. We think the matter should be so agreed and propose to advise Sir Leslie Brash to that effect unless you have any objections to raise.

Yours faithfully,

SPINLOVE TO RUSS & CO., SOLICITORS

Brash v. *Reaker & Smith*

Dear Sirs,   17.6.24.

In reply to your letter I cannot agree that £27 0. 0. is a reasonable charge for digging the trial holes. I have referred the measurements to my quantity surveyor, who estimates £23 10s. 0d. as an outside figure.

Yours faithfully,

Spinlove's tenacity is worthy of a better cause. He is evidently soured against Smith and cannot endure that he should get more than strict measure.

BRASH TO SPINLOVE

Dear Mr. Spinlove,   20.6.24.

I have a communication from Mr. Russ intimating that Reaker and Smith are prepared to settle for £27, and as I am given to understand your own estimate is £23 10s., I have instructed him to signify acceptance of that offer. Will you oblige me with the sketch plans? You may remember that I intimated this request some time ago and you promised to transmit them. They have not, however, so far eventuated.

Yours sincerely,

Preparation for Tenders

Spinlove's reluctance to return the sketch plans is perhaps the wisdom of the once bitten. The contract drawings can only be made after the sketch plans have been approved, and the reopening of questions already settled, which ruminations over the sketch plans by the client is apt to provoke, is a disaster.

BEDDY & TINGE, QUANTITY SURVEYORS, TO SPINLOVE

Dear Sir,   20.6.24.

Drawings and specifications received and instructions noted. We cube front house at 2s. 8d., and offices and servants' quarters at 2s. 0d. The terrace will cost about £1,500. Total £20,140. We will endeavour to have bills ready in five weeks' time.

Yours faithfully,

B. and T. it will be noted, waste no words. Their speciality is facts. There here follow letters from all seven builders signifying readiness to tender. Then we find:

SPINLOVE TO BRASH

Dear Sir Leslie Brash,   21.6.24.

I enclose the sketch plans with apologies for not having sent them before. The drawings and specification are with the quantity surveyors and the tender forms will go out in five weeks' time. All builders have agreed to tender.

I note that you are proposing to settle Reaker and Smith's account for £27, but I should mention that my estimate of £23 10s. is an *outside figure*. My idea of the proper charge is £19 15s.

Yours sincerely,

What object Spinlove had in writing the last paragraph Spinlove himself could scarcely say. His grudge against Smith is probably accountable. Our James has the rattle-brained pertinacity of a blue-bottle, and his victim will feel the same wild, helpless irritation. The matter of the trial holes is well over and

42

Preparation for Tenders

Spinlove should be thankful it is so. The whole history is a first-rate example, in miniature, of the way in which unlucky chances, favoured by faulty organization and lack of conscientious foresight, may lead from insignificant causes to disastrous catastrophes. If the owner's liability in this matter had been a thousand or ten thousand pounds instead of a hundred, we may be sure the architect would not have been left scatheless.

SPINLOVE TO BEDDY & TINGE

Dear Sirs,   23.6.24.

I am sorry your estimate is so high. The owner expects £18,500, and I am anxious not to disappoint him. I must try and knock off £1,500. On enclosed sheet I have made a list of suggestions to this end, and I shall be glad to go into the matter further with you.

Yours truly,

Spinlove's wisdom in getting down to estimates before the quantities are taken off is now proved. It is a sad business to have to cut down costs after tenders are in, with attendant supplementary bills and specification, and notes in red ink on the drawings and other elements of confusion and future misunderstanding.

BEDDY & TINGE TO SPINLOVE

Dear Sir,   19.7.24.

Receive herewith copy of bills and form of tender sent to-day to seven builders as instructed. Also drawings and specifications completed with notes of modifications agreed.

Yours truly,

LADY BRASH TO SPINLOVE

Dear Mr. Spinlove,   29.7.24.

I met an acquaintance to-day who told me that the kitchen window ought to be on the left side of the range for the light and architects always put it on the other side but I want mine to be on the *right* side. What lovely weather we are having!! Sir Leslie is fishing in Cornwall till next week.

Yours sincerely,

The Tenders go Wrong

Dear Lady Brash, 30.7.24.

Thank you for your letter. You will be glad to know that the kitchen window *does* come on the right side. Yes, the weather, as you say, has been beautiful, but I am sorry to notice that it is clouding over this morning. I hope Sir Leslie will enjoy his visit to Cornwall. I know of no part of the country where I would rather spend a holiday.

Yours sincerely,

Spinlove knows how to purr loudly, but there was an ambiguity in Lady Brash's letter which he appears to have overlooked. However, here are the tenders at last.

THE TENDERS GO WRONG

Dear Sirs, 1.8.24.

I have to thank you for your tender for £18,221, and to say that I am prepared to recommend it for acceptance. You may expect to hear from me in a day or two.

Complete list of Tenders received is as follows:

	£	s.	d.	
Carloop Building Co.	25,000	0	0	18 months
Bintoch Bros.	24,429	10	9	18 months
Paul & Kirsh, Ltd.	21,050	0	0	18 months
Toller, Bunsen & Topp ..	19,500	0	0	18 months
George Robble	19,237	15	0	2 years
John Grigblay	18,970	0	0	16 months
Nibnose & Rasper	18,221	7	8	20 months

Yours faithfully,

The Tenders go Wrong

Omitting the first two, which are not bona fide *tenders, but mere formal compliances, these tenders are a fairly close group except for the big difference of £750 between the lowest and that next it, where small differences only are to be expected. It seems that Spinlove has not realized the significance of this disparity.*

The following letter is marked as having been sent to all unsuccessful firms.

SPINLOVE TO UNSUCCESSFUL BUILDERS

Dear Sir,   1.8.24.

I have to thank you for your tender, but regret I am unable to recommend it for acceptance. The complete list of tenders received is as follows: [*List as above.*]

Yours faithfully,

Spinlove is right in notifying results to all firms as it is important to builders, for many reasons, to know at once what their obligations are. It would have been better, however, had he omitted the names of firms from the list, for as he will be likely to invite them to tender on a future occasion, he is opening the door to collusion.

SPINLOVE TO BRASH

Dear Sir Leslie Brash,   1.8.24.

I opened tenders to-day, and enclose list. I am glad to feel that the result will be satisfactory to you. You will see that Nibnose and Rasper's price is well within the figure I named. I recommend the acceptance of this tender. Twenty months is a reasonable time for carrying out the work.

I am sorry John Grigblay is not the lowest for he has a reputation for this kind of work, but I have good accounts of Nibnose and Rasper from architects for whom they have done work, and I was favourably impressed when I called at their premises one day when I was in Marlford. Have I your authority to accept their tender?

Yours sincerely,

The Tenders go Wrong

BRASH TO SPINLOVE

Dear Mr. Spinlove,   2.8.24.

I am deeply gratified at the contents of your letter intimating the result of the tenders. It is, I can assure you, a great satisfaction to Lady Brash and myself after waiting so long a period to know that the estimate is not to be exceeded. Most certainly act upon your recommendation and accept Messrs. Nibnose and Rasper's tender, but only on the express stipulation that they complete the work within the period of sixteen months, for, as another firm undertakes to perform the erection within that limit of time, there is no excuse for Messrs' Nibnose and Rasper not entering upon a similar engagement. I anticipate that there will be certain legal Contract documents for signature.

Since I am in credit on the tender in the sum of £300, I contemplate augmenting the dimensions of the reception rooms which I still consider somewhat restricted in area. I will determine these and communicate particulars in the course of a few days. The erection of the mansion will, I assume, now commence immediately.

Yours sincerely,

As it is impossible to know whether Spinlove first read this letter or the telegram that is filed next it, it is impossible to imagine his feelings on that second day of August 1924. We shall be safe, however, in giving him our sympathy.

(TELEGRAM) NIBNOSE & RASPER TO SPINLOVE

2.8.24.

Regret must withdraw tender writing Nibrasp.

NIBNOSE & RASPER TO SPINLOVE

Dear Sir,   2.8.24.

We much regret we were obliged to wire to you to-day withdrawing our tender, as per enclosed confirmation. On receipt of your letter, for which we thank you, we noticed the large difference between the amount of our tender and the next

46

The Tenders go Wrong

lowest price, and on checking over our prices we found an error of several hundred pounds. We may say that such a thing has not happened in our experience, and was due to an irregularity in the bills. The tiler's bill is paged 1, 2, 3, 2, 3, 4, and the clerk in collecting the castings of each page to arrive at the total did not observe the repetition of pages 2 and 3, and omitted two pages, which was not noticed in the check as they were stuck together by a blot of ink.

The correct total of our pricings is £18,953 4s. 7d., and we shall be obliged if you will substitute this figure for that entered on our tender, as the mistake arose through error in the particulars supplied to us, and although we would have corrected it had we noticed, we feel that we were led into the error which would not have occurred had the bills been correctly paged.

We shall be glad to send the bills to you or to your quantity surveyor for examination so that our statement may be checked.

Yours obediently,

Spinlove has again been unlucky, but his ill-luck is again attributable to his lack of perspicacity. He should have noted the incongruity of Nibnose and Rasper's tender; told them that before recommending their tender the priced bills were to be sent to the quantity surveyor for examination; and said nothing of the other tenders received.

The state of affairs now is that as Nibnose and Rasper know the amount of the tender they have to beat they can increase their bid to one very little less than the next one above. This, it appears, is what they may actually have done. Bills are usually priced out in pencil and the rates could be readily reviewed and amended to give a more judicious total. Opinions would differ on the point whether, in the matter of business, this would be a dishonest act. The old-established building firms, in which the pride and tradition of craftsmanship still linger, are, with scarcely an exception, honourable and fair-dealing; but the field of business is very much a field of battle and has its own code, and when one side surprises a weakness in the defences of the other it can only be assumed, in the course of business, that use will be made of that advantage. This revised tender is, however, a new tender; and as it has not

47

been delivered before the hour fixed for the receipt of tenders it is, strictly speaking, inadmissible. On the other hand, the error in the original tender arose from irregularity in the particulars supplied and "Nibrasp" is entitled to some consideration.

Spinlove, also, has notified Grigblay and others that their tenders are not accepted, and any or all of them may have other irons hot in the fire or have given the go-by to options and quotations upon which their tenders were based, and thus will be unwilling to renew their tenders except at an increased price; and as each now knows who his rivals are, all can get together and arrange a lowest tender in collusion, so that the devices to secure bona fide competitive tenders are now, in a great measure, stultified. It should be understood that this kind of collusion is not illegal.

Another aspect of the case is whether Spinlove's notification to "Nibrasp" that he had recommended their tender for acceptance, constitutes actual acceptance, and therefore debars "Nibrasp" from withdrawing; but as the tender relieves the proprietor from obligation to "accept the lowest or any tender" we may assume the tender has not been accepted and that the "Nibrasp" withdrawal is good. In any case it would be a foolish policy to compel him to build at a price which was known to be disastrous for him: a house is not a sewer or a gasometer, and the ready collaboration of the builder is necessary for its success. Spinlove's predicament is, therefore, an awkward one; and he has also the painful duty of swallowing his own complacency and deflating the exuberances he has roused in the bosom of his client.

SPINLOVE TO BRASH

Dear Sir Leslie Brash,   4.8.24.

I am extremely sorry to have to tell you that with your letter of Saturday I found a telegram from Nibnose and Rasper withdrawing their tender; and this morning I have received a letter from them stating that they made a mistake in casting up their total, and substituting a tender of £18,953 4s. 7d. Such a thing is quite new in my experience. This revised tender is only £27 less than Grigblay's and I am very sorry to say, more than my estimate has prepared you for. I should mention, however,

The Tenders go Wrong

that the tenders include the sum of £300 for contingencies—that is a sum to cover unforeseen work which may, only, be wanted—so that the actual tender for the work can be considered to be £18,653 4s. 7d., which is only £153 4s. 4d. more than my own estimate. I am extremely sorry this has happened and am much disappointed. Perhaps it would be well if I saw you to-morrow. I can come over at any hour that suits you if you would be so good as to ring up and let me know.

Yours sincerely,

As Spinlove was before far too self-congratulatory, so he is here altogether too apologetic. Although the uninitiated may suppose that an architect, by looking at the plan of a house, can name the lowest sum for which unknown builders on an unknown day and under unknown conditions will bargain to build it, Spinlove's estimate of £18,500 was, in fact, not so wide of the mark as such estimates go. He was probably too ready to hope for the best in arranging modifications with the quantity surveyor, but he is less than 2½ per cent below the tendered price. Brash has nothing to complain of, and Spinlove should not, as he does, invite him to think that he has. Spinlove ought to have found an early opportunity of letting Brash understand that an architect can, at best, make only a shrewd guess at the cost of a building; and that even builders, with exact particulars before them of the measured amount of labour and materials involved in the work, arrive at results varying by 20 and even 30 per cent and, when all is done, often find themselves on the wrong side of the account. Spinlove, although his earnestness is exemplary, is worrying and wearying himself to no useful purpose by identifying himself so closely with his client's monetary anxieties. He should regard himself strictly as an agent conducting another's business; his own particular business being to get the house well, economically, and beautifully built. He should have written in some such terms as these: "Dear Sir Leslie Brash—Nibnose and Rasper have withdrawn their tender on the grounds of an error in their calculations, and have substituted an amended tender for £18,953 4s. 7d. Will you let me know what you wish me to do. Perhaps it would be better if I saw you. . . ."
If he had so written he would have exonerated instead of blamed

49

himself, and put the plain question before Brash instead of confounding him with a confusion of issues. Such a letter, it is true, would appear to Brash curt and offhand in contrast with those he is used to receiving from his architect, and is to be regarded as the sort of letter Spinlove ought to be able to write without appearing curt and offhand. The meeting, we gather, duly took place, for we next read:

SPINLOVE TO WILLIAM WYCHETE, ESQ., PP.R.I.B.A.

Dear Mr. Wychete, 5.8.24.

You have been so kind in letting me ask your advice that I hope you will not mind my writing to you, as I am in a fix. On the enclosed sheet I have set out the position of affairs. The question is what ought I to do? Sir Leslie Brash, my client, is fixed in his decision to accept the second lowest tender, that of John Grigblay, because Grigblay is the better builder. He says he has the right to accept any tender, and he can do what he likes. I can make no impression on him. If you could tell me what line I ought to take I should be very much obliged to you.

Yours sincerely,

WYCHETE TO SPINLOVE

My dear Spinlove, 7.8.24.

Your scrape interests me. Your client is morally bound to accept the lowest tender: that is clearly understood when particular builders are invited to tender, for if their tenders are not wanted there is no just reason for troubling them to prepare them. You can do no more than tell your friend this. He is, however, within his rights in not accepting the lowest or any, although this right is intended only as a safeguard.

I do not think Nibnose and Rasper's revised tender is admissible. It was sent in after the amounts of the other tenders were published, and for all we know their actual prices may originally have been *higher* than Grigblay's. If you accept it Grigblay would have grounds for feeling aggrieved. You could write to N. and R. and say that as they withdrew their original tender their substituted tender is a new tender and was received too late for you to consider it; but I think the best course would be to tell them that the owner has instructed you to say that he cannot accept. Grigblay will certainly come to terms; you will have secured a good builder; will be free of responsibility for the choice, and relieved of the necessity for deciding a difficult point and finding reasons for your decision. You ought to be glad your client has taken the matter into his own hands.

Best Wishes from,

Yours sincerely,

SPINLOVE TO BRASH

Dear Sir Leslie Brash,   8.8.24.

I saw Mr. Grigblay to-day. He is willing to renew his tender, and I am meeting him to-morrow at the quantity surveyor's to see what reductions can be made in the matters I proposed to you. I will write to you to-morrow or call in the afternoon.

Yours sincerely,

SPINLOVE TO NIBNOSE & RASPER

Dear Sirs,   8.8.24.

I am instructed by the owner, Sir Leslie Brash, to thank you for your tender of August 2, but to say that he regrets he is unable to accept it.

Yours faithfully,

NIBNOSE & RASPER TO SPINLOVE

Dear Sir,   9.8.24.

We were naturally astonished to get your letter informing us that our tender is not accepted. We may say that we are unused to being treated in that style and we are quite as capable of making a good job as Grigblay or any other on your list. If we had known our tender was only going to be made use of as a check upon the prices of other firms we should not have accepted your invitation, and we may say that we are not

51

anxious to tender again with any such purpose. We do not know what the meaning of all this business is nor why Grigblay is given a preference over us when we were invited to tender and our firm was well known long before Mr. Grigblay came on the scenes, but we may say that we consider that we have been treated in a very offhand and inconsiderate manner.

Yours obediently,

SPINLOVE TO NIBNOSE & RASPER

Dear Sirs,   11.8.24.

Permit me to assure you that in inviting you to tender I did so with the intention that you should be given the contract if you offered the lowest price. The decision not to accept your tender did not originate with me nor did I favour it. I can only say that I regret very much what has happened, and that I hope you will tender to me in the future and be successful in securing the contract, for I should have confidence in entrusting work to you. Believe me,

Yours truly,

Spinlove is distinguishing himself. Wychete's advice has been well observed by him. Without it he would characteristically have elaborated the matter of the substituted tender and involved himself in a wrangle. As it is, he has written a letter which is obviously sincere and which will go far to soothe the "Nibrasp" chagrin—although not so fully, it appears, as to produce an acknowledgment—and he has not, for once, said too much.

SPINLOVE TO BRASH

Dear Sir Leslie Brash,   11.8.24.

I send you herewith memorandum of agreement in duplicate signed by Grigblay. If you will sign both with witness where marked and return to me I will let Grigblay have his copy and get yours stamped. I enclose copy of the schedule of variations you saw, showing the reductions by which the total of £18,440 is arrived at.

Grigblay signed drawings and specification to-day. He will

begin getting his plant on the site on Wednesday and on Friday I am going on to the site. Can you come down on that day and approve the marks fixing the position of the house?

Yours sincerely,

GRIGBLAY, AND BRASH, GET TO WORK

SPINLOVE TO EWART HOOCHKOFT & CO., LTD.

Dear Sirs,   15.8.24.

I shall be glad if you will send me two or three samples, with prices, of your medium, red, broken-coloured, $2\frac{1}{2}$ in. sand-faced slop facing bricks such as I saw at last year's Building Trades' Exhibition. The samples should show extremes of variety in colour, texture, etc.

Yours faithfully,

GRIGBLAY TO SPINLOVE

Dear Sir,   22.8.24.

Our foreman, Bloggs, who is setting out house, has informed us that dimensions on plan do not work out correct. Shall be glad if you will give immediate instructions so that we can get on with the digging.

Yours faithfully,

We are to gather that Brash duly approved the position of the house on the ground, and that the builder has since been engaged in setting out the position of walls preparatory to laying their foundations.

Grigblay may be a good builder and a competent organizer, but he appears from this letter to be a man who means to get the job carried through and no nonsense about it. Spinlove would be justified in feeling a little uneasy. A really first-rate builder would be likely to show solicitude and say what the difficulty in question was. Grigblay may have had unfortunate experience at the hands of architects in the past and, having met Spinlove, may have sized him up. He does not intend to put up with flabbiness. As a successful builder he knows his job and he expects the architect to know his.

BRASH TO SPINLOVE

Dear Mr. Spinlove,   23.8.24.

Lady Brash and myself have been considering the plans and have decided, after mature reflection, that we desire the drawing-room inverted the other way round—that is, turned at an angle of 90 deg. to its present orientation. There is still time to make the emendation, and as the dimensions will remain the same there will be no inflation in the expenditure. The alteration would permit the loggia to extend the whole extent of the length of the apartment instead of across its width, and it would then be possible for my daughter to play ping-pong there on wet afternoons.

Will you please instruct the builder accordingly.

Yours sincerely,

The foregoing letter evidently crossed the following one from Spinlove, as the dates are the same.

SPINLOVE TO BRASH

Dear Sir Leslie Brash,   23.8.24.

I think I ought to warn you of extras. Everything necessary for the completion of the building, with fittings and decorations, is included in the contract, and I can promise that there shall be no extras so far as I am concerned; but if you make changes in the work it will be impossible for me to avoid them creeping in.

Another matter I ought to mention is the importance of your making any request through me and never on any occasion saying anything to the builder's people that can be interpreted as an order; otherwise it will be impossible for me to keep control and extras are sure to arise.

I mention these matters because I am most anxious to avoid exrtas, and I can only do so with your co-operation.

Yours faithfully,

All Spinlove says is perfectly true, and he might have drawn a harrowing picture of the confusion, disasters, cross-purposes, and ill-temper that interferences by the owner produce. At the same time it is most unusual for the architect to give the matter the weight of a formal warning that has almost the character of a threat. Spinlove might with better diplomacy have explained the point in conversation and perhaps confirmed in a brief sentence when writing. The hint is usually welcomed by the client, and observed. The letter which follows is one such as Spinlove ought to have written, but apparently did not.

SPINLOVE TO GRIGBLAY
(*Supposititious*)

Dear Sir,   23.8.24.

I write to remind you that the contract lays down that no claim for any extras shall rank unless that claim is made at the time the work is ordered and acknowledged by me as an extra.

I, on my part, agree to notify you of any omissions as the work proceeds.

Yours faithfully,

The object of this letter would be to make the builder understand that the stipulation in the contract as to extras must be observed. There are always some variations, and it is understood that omissions are set against extras unless the contrary is recorded at the time; and if the builder is to notify the architect of extras for which he claims payment it is only fair that the architect should similarly notify the builder of omissions in respect of which he claims credits.

Builders are shy of claiming extras while the work is in progress; to do so has an appearance of refractoriness. If, however, work is done which the architect knows *to have been an extra,* **he is bound in honour to allow it to rank in the final statement**

55

of account, and the fact that that extra was not claimed and acknowledged at the time it was ordered, and that it has, nevertheless, been allowed, makes the architect a party to the irregularity and opens the door for the builder to claim other unrecorded extras.

As the architect has acquiesced in the one case it is very difficult for him to refuse to consider other claims on their merits. The result is that the stipulations of the contract are stultified, and the statement of account becomes not a plain question of fact, but of argument and wrangling of which the builder always has the best, for he has kept records of extras whilst the omissions, which might be set against them, have been forgotten.

For this reason it is well for the architect to notify the builder of extra work involved in his details, as well as of omissions. The builder has then no grounds for making claims at settlement which have not been agreed, and if he does so the architect can, with perfect fairness, refuse to consider them.

Our friend Spinlove, however, seems to have other ways of safeguarding extras. We shall perhaps see later on what his methods are and how far they succeed.

SPINLOVE TO GRIGBLAY

Dear Sir,   23.8.24.

I am at a loss to understand your foreman's difficulty. The dimensions on the plan were all checked up, and as you do not say what the discrepancy is I am unable to arrange matters. It is impossible for me to go on to the site until next Tuesday. Will you please wire to your foreman and ask him what it is he wants to know?

Yours faithfully,

BRASH TO SPINLOVE

Dear Mr. Spinlove,   25.8.24.

I can assure you that I am the last person to order extras of any description, and you may place reliance in my refraining from doing so.

I note that you desire all communications with the builder

should be transmitted through yourself. This may, I apprehend, prove somewhat an inconvenient arrangement, but I commend your purpose and will keep it in mind.

Yours sincerely,

SPINLOVE TO BRASH

Dear Sir Leslie Brash,   25.8.24.

Your letter was a shock to me because the alterations you propose involve a radical change in the design, a new set of contract drawings and, I am afraid, a supplementary bill of quantities to determine the amount of the variation in cost, if any.

There are many objections and difficulties in the way of your proposal, and you will notice that it would not be possible to get from the hall to the drawing-room without turning the stairs round and making them begin on the other side of the hall. This would involve making other modifications in the plans and spoil the effect aimed at and which I have, I think, been fortunate in achieving.

I may also point out to you that the pump-house chimney would, as a result of the alteration, be visible from the end of the drawing-room and from the bedroom over, as the trees will not screen it from that point of view.

The alterations would also hold up the work for many weeks and, all being well, the digging for foundations may be expected to begin in a few days. I hope, therefore, you will reconsider your suggestion.

I am sure, when you are aware of all that is involved in the change, you will prefer to leave things as they are. I will take no further action till I hear from you.

Yours sincerely,

Spinlove's adroitness in himself making profit out of the pump-house chimney is a master stroke. There is some advantage after all in having no sense of humour, for no one who had any would have dared such impudence.

Grigblay, and Brash, get to Work

SPINLOVE TO HOOCHKOFT

Dear Sirs,   26.8.24.

I like the samples of the bricks and the price is satisfactory.
The very light-coloured brick seems soft and under-burnt, the
red and purple brindled bricks will give all the variation in
colour necessary. I have directed the builder, Mr. John
Grigblay, to place the order with you.

Yours faithfully,

SPINLOVE TO GRIGBLAY

Dear Sir,   26.8.24.

Please order from Messrs. Hoochkoft & Co., facings of their
multi-broken coloured red 2½ in. sand-faced slops to sample
already approved by me, price 147s. per 1,000 on rail.

Yours faithfully,

*Spinlove is looking well after his bricks, but it would have been
wise, as he does not know them and has not ordered from a
merchant known to him, to have seen the bricks in bulk at the
brickyard.*

GRIGBLAY TO SPINLOVE

Dear Sir,   27.8.24.

I enclose letter received from foreman Bloggs to-day. Shall
be glad of instructions.

Yours faithfully,

(ENCLOSURE) BLOGGS TO GRIGBLAY

Sir,   26.8.24.

In reply to your wire re dimensions along main back front
is figured 138 ft. 10 in., total of dimensions 138 ft. 6¼ in., error
+ 3¾ in. Where am I going to make it? Drawing-room right
for window and fireplace cannot find where + is.

Yours humbly,

Grigblay, and Brash, get to Work

Dear Sir,   28.8.24.

In reply to your letter enclosing your foreman's note, the discrepancy will work itself out. I really do not understand why this trivial matter has been given such importance and progress delayed.

Yours faithfully,

Spinlove's experience must, indeed, be limited for him to write such a letter as this. He ought to be the first to know that the dimensions on a plan, like a bank ledger, must balance. Any error may be the difference between greater errors, but in any case errors of $3\frac{3}{4}$ in. do not readily "work themselves out". $3\frac{3}{4}$ in. off the width of a narrow backstair makes all the difference between one that is narrow and one that is too narrow. $3\frac{3}{4}$ in. cannot be spared off a doorway, and the want of $3\frac{3}{4}$ in. may entail omission of a window, and single inches in the width of a moulding may mar the design of an important feature.

In the next place Spinlove is discouraging the builder from precision in observing instructions, whereas he ought to take every opportunity to make the builder understand that exact precision and minute conscientiousness are expected of him. It would suit the builder to go ahead and settle things for himself, and this letter will encourage him to shrug his shoulders and do so. It is, further, the special duty of the builder, under the terms of the contract, to call attention to all discrepancies, and it is folly on Spinlove's part to deter him.

BRASH TO SPINLOVE

Dear Mr. Spinlove,   29.8.24.

I am at a loss to comprehend what the difficulties are in altering the plan, but as it appears to involve bringing the pump-house chimney into visuality, Lady Brash has decided against the proposition. As you know, we greatly admire the plans; we observe, however, that the kitchen window is on the right-hand of the range. Lady Brash informs me that you intimated you would have it located on the other side. I must ask you not to overlook this important matter—it is merely necessary, you will perceive, to put the fireplace at the reverse end of the kitchen.

Yours sincerely,

SPINLOVE TO BRASH

Dear Sir Leslie Brash,   30.8.24.

I have looked at Lady Brash's letter to which you refer and find that it asks that the kitchen window should be arranged on the *right* side of the range, and this is what is shown on the plans.

I am very glad you have decided not to go on with the alteration to the drawing-room. I may point out——

Spinlove, with his fatal instinct for saying a great deal too much, here goes on to elaborate a number of reasons why it would be impossible or objectionable to put the drawing-room "the other way round". He even goes so far as to say "perhaps your daughter may not care so much for ping-pong by the time the house is finished". This is not only entirely unnecessary, but will be extremely irritating for Brash to be troubled to read, and as Spinlove is already engaged in another tussle with Brash on the subject of plan alterations, it is unfortunate he should write a letter that will only stiffen the obstinacy of the man he wishes to placate.

BRASH TO SPINLOVE

Dear Mr. Spinlove,   1.9.24.

I deeply regret that I must venture to differ from you in considering that the right-hand side of the range is the right side for the window. The left is the correct side for perfectly obvious reasons, although architects, as I am informed, always put the window on the right-hand side. Lady Brash wishes the window on the left, which is the right side, and I must request you to make the necessary emendation, which, as I have intimated to you, can be done by merely shifting the range to the other end of the apartment.

Yours sincerely,

Grigblay, and Brash, get to Work

Dear Sir Leslie Brash,   3.9.24.

I have again read Lady Brash's letter and find that in one place the term "right side" is used in the sense of correct side, but I read it to mean the right-*hand* side.

It is quite true that it is best for the window to be on the left hand of the range, but this cannot always be managed without sacrificing more important considerations. If the range is put at the opposite end of the kitchen, as you suggest, the door from servery will have to be moved farther down the passage and the scullery and larder will be remote from the range instead of close at hand.

The range in the new position will require a chimney stack all to itself, and this will go very awkwardly in the external view of the house; and although the back bedroom can have its fireplace moved to the stack at its other end, the small bedroom will have no fireplace at all unless the stack for the present range is carried up for this purpose only. If so, you will have two chimneys each carrying only one flue, and unless they are extravagantly built they will be weedy and unsightly.

As now arranged the kitchen has two large windows in the long side, and, as the walls and ceiling are to be painted with white enamel, the place will be flooded with light and there will be no shadows at the range. This I can promise you.

The plan provides for a very short course from kitchen to servery, and everything is compact and falls together well. It would, I assure you, be a great mistake to make the changes you propose and you would certainly regret it. Any such alterations will involve delay, and I hope to get the work on the trenches well forward by the end of the week. Unless, therefore, I hear from you to the contrary, I shall assume that the range is to be as shown on the plan.

Yours faithfully,

The last sentence assumes too much and is wanting in tact. It would be likely to provoke opposition. It would have been wiser if Spinlove had expressed himself as hoping he would be allowed to build according to the plan.

Grigblay, and Brash, get to Work

Dear Sir,   3.9.24.

When I was on the site yesterday I instructed your foreman
to amend his adjustment of the error in the dimensions. In
looking further into the matter, however, I find that I must
alter the instructions I then gave him. The enclosed plan shows
the dimensions to be followed. Please change the figures on
your plan accordingly.

There seems to be a certain amount of surface water about
the site and·I shall be glad if you will arrange to pump out the
trenches.

Yours faithfully,

*Spinlove, it will be seen, is muddling along. He has discovered
that the small error of 3¾ in. is not such an unimportant matter as
he supposed. However, although he has had to give three contradictory orders in order to get matters put right, we may assume
that he has definitely settled the matter at last and will not have
to devise some ugly botch later on.*

*He has no right to call upon the builder to instal pumps. All
he can do is to require the builder to keep the trenches free from
water. It may suit the builder better to drain, as it is a sloping
site; or perhaps to bale out from sumps may meet the case.*

Dear Mr. Spinlove,   4.9.24.

I must request you to emendate the arrangements so that
windows come on the left-hand side of the range. I do not
object to the small bedroom having no fireplace.

Yours sincerely,

*This is thoroughly bad judgment on Brash's part. Spinlove
ought to have been able to persuade him to a right decision and
it is probably entirely due to his irritating methods that he has not
succeeded in doing so. Perhaps, too, Lady Brash is fretful. The
unhappy Spinlove, however, with characteristic tenacity, does
not admit defeat.*

Grigblay, and Brash, get to Work

Dear Sir Leslie Brash,   5.9.24.

   I was very sorry to read the contents of your letter. I think I ought to see you before altering the plans. I will ring up to-morrow if you will be so good as to leave word what time will suit you.

                                        Yours faithfully,

Dear Sir,   5.9.24.

   Revision of set-out figures received. We have told Bloggs to get on with digging. We will see trenches are kept clear of water; the site seems dry enough.

                                        Yours faithfully,

   The following letter indicates that Spinlove's last effort to persuade Brash to accept his kitchen arrangements was useless. It also supplies an instance of how an architect may be too ready to find alterations in his plans impracticable.

   No doubt Spinlove had thoroughly explored alternatives, and it was only the torment of being compelled to revise his cherished schemes which led him to find that he had overlooked one possibility. This sometimes happens, and it also sometimes happens that the revised scheme is an improvement on the original arrangement. One gathers that it may be so in this case.

Dear Sir Leslie Brash,   8.9.24.

   Since I saw you I have spent some time on the revision of the plan and I am glad to say that I have hit on an arrangement which meets the case excellently, as I think you will agree. I enclose sketch. You will see that by rearranging scullery, servery and den, etc., the kitchen can be lighted from the east instead of from the north, which I think an improvement; and that the length of the corridor to the back door, now a little nearer to the north front, is shortened. The bedroom arrangements, you will see, are improved, as both bedrooms have an east window, and you will note that one chimney stack serves all.

This chimney stack comes to place well on the ridge of the roof of the small gable formed by the projection of the den on the south, and this small gable makes an attractive feature on the south elevation.

Yours faithfully,

Spinlove, as usual, is fulsome in pointing out the beauty of his own devices and scarcely leaves Brash any opportunity for discovering any merits in them. He is, in fact, challenging Brash to make objections; but his very frank surrender, which is perfectly sincere and born of his wish to give Brash what it is best for him to have, will be likely to establish him more firmly in favour. Brash, we have noted, has been of late more than usually portentous and stiff, and not without reason.

BRASH TO SPINLOVE

Dear Mr. Spinlove, 10.9.24.

Both Lady Brash and myself entirely approve of the amended plan as the window is shown on the left of the range. Will you please instruct the builder to make the emendations?

May we have the pleasure of expecting you at lunch at 1.30 on Saturday? There are several matters which Lady Brash and myself would like to discuss with you.

Yours sincerely,

THE DISTRICT SURVEYOR INTERVENES

GRIGBLAY TO SPINLOVE

Dear Sir, 16.9.24.

Bloggs reports that Mr. Potch, the rural district council surveyor, called on site and took great exception to work being begun before plans approved. Shall be glad if you will communicate or he may make things awkward.

Yours obediently,

Dear Sir,   17.9.24.

It has been reported to me that you visited the site of the new house at Honeywood and commented on the trenches having been cut out before approval of plans. Please accept my apologies for the oversight.

May I point out that it is more than six weeks since I submitted plans and application form, but that I have heard nothing from you, although I have twice written calling your attention to the matter.

Yours faithfully,

Dear Mr. Spinlove,   17.9.24.

We were motoring in the vicinity of Marlford to-day and diverged on to the site. Both Lady Brash and myself were dumbfounded at the limited extent of the dimensions of the rooms as indicated by the trenches. We comprehended that the dimensions were restricted, but what we observed to-day alarmed us. Are you quite sure that the trenches are correct? The foreman assured us that they were exact, but have they been checked and certified? I cannot comprehend how these inconsiderable squares and oblongs can represent the apartments in which we have to reside. Please communicate by telephone between 2.30 and 3 at the office.

Yours sincerely,

The Brashes have suffered the usual shock with which the owner of a house views its plan entrenched on the ground. The adequate dining-room of 22ft. × 16ft. appears before him as but a plot of grass four paces by six—for the width of the trenches eats up a foot or two along each wall—and nothing but a tape measure will establish his peace of mind. Spinlove no doubt poured assurances into the telephone next day.

SURVEYOR, R.D.C., TO SPINLOVE

Sir,   19.9.24.

In reply to your letter my council takes strong objection to the high-handed action of beginning operations in contravention of by-laws before plans have been approved.

I would recommend you to attend the next meeting of the Plans Committee which is at 8 o'clock at Marlford School House on Tuesday next, to make your explanation of your irregular behaviour.

Any work you may have done will be at your own risk.

The members of my council need holidays, the same as others do, and there have been no meetings of the Plans Committee since July 28, as you could have learned if you had troubled to inquire.

Yours faithfully,
V. POTCH.

The explanation of this extraordinary letter is that Marlford is a small provincial town with its own local architects, surveyors, auctioneers, agents and traders; and these men hob-nob together and play into each others' hands and are jealous of any who do not belong to the place taking money out of it. We have also seen that Nibnose and Rasper, who belong to the place, have a grievance against Spinlove which, in such a community, would become general knowledge; and if neither member of the firm is on the council their friends are sure to be.

It is also possible that Mr. Potch practises privately as an architect independently of his official duties, and that it is in his interest to make things difficult for all architects who trespass upon his local preserves, so that it may be generally perceived that any who employ Potch as their architect will have no trouble with interference by the district council, but that if they employ anyone else they probably will have.

Potch's proposal that Spinlove should attend at Marlford at

The District Surveyor Intervenes

8 p.m. is part of his system of inflicting annoyances upon his rivals. If Spinlove was so foolish as to act on the suggestion the surveyor would perhaps forget to mention that he was in waiting, or persuade his committee to decline to see him.

Mr. Potch has impudently ignored a fact of which Spinlove appears to be ignorant, namely that the Public Health Act ordains that approval or disapproval of intended work shall be signified by a local authority within one month of the deposit of plans.

SPINLOVE TO CLERK, MARLFORD R.D.C.

Sir,   20.9.24.

I enclose copy of my letter to your council's surveyor and of his reply, and shall be obliged if you will ask your council for an explanation of that reply.

I do not propose to attend the meeting of your Plans Committee on Tuesday.

I have to point out that I complied with your by-laws in submitting application form and plans nearly eight weeks ago, and that if I am called upon to stop the work your council will have to accept responsibility for breaking the contract.

Yours faithfully,

Spinlove has, apparently, "been there before". He wisely addresses himself to the clerk: he could scarcely reply to Potch's letter, and if he did so the council would probably never see the correspondence, but would have only the surveyor's hostile report.

THE CLERK, MARLFORD R.D.C., TO SPINLOVE

Dear Sir,   24.9.24.

Your letter and enclosures were laid before the Plans Committee on Tuesday and the surveyor was instructed to write you.

My committee instructs me to say that the dates of their meetings are fixed to suit general convenience and can be obtained on application, and that they have instructed the surveyor to stop work being commenced before approval of plans as much trouble is caused.

Yours faithfully,

The District Surveyor Intervenes

Sir,   24.9.24.

I have to inform you that the Plans Committee of my council are prepared to recommend plans of Honeywood subject to alterations, see below. Plans and form returned under separate cover.

Attic to have vertical height at wall 5ft. 6 in., and average height of ceiling over floor area of 9 ft. 6 in.

Window area to be not less than one-tenth floor area.

Independent vent, as per by-laws.

Walls of house to be increased in thickness down to ground to comply with by-laws for house of three floors.

Yours faithfully,

Sir,   25.9.24.

There is no attic. The third floor is roof space and is clearly marked *boxroom*.

I return plans and application form and shall be glad to receive notice of approval.

Yours faithfully,

Sir,   27.9.24.

I am obliged to you for pointing out that an attic occupies roof space. Unfortunately, my committee are not in the habit of regarding habitable attic rooms as roof space because the architect calls them boxrooms on the plans.

The plans and application form herewith.

Yours faithfully,

Sir,   29.9.24.

I have amended plans by writing "*roof space*" instead of "boxroom", as you ask. The concrete will be laid in trenches immediately. Plans and form are returned herewith.

The District Surveyor Intervenes

The parcel containing your letter and the plans was not stamped. I enclose the label with excess stamp and shall be glad to receive refund of 1s. 6d.

Yours faithfully,

Potch's quibbling attempt to force Spinlove to alter his drawing, and his neglect to stamp the parcel, are all part of his method of obstructing and bullying those who, in his private practice, he regards as rivals. If he could infuriate Spinlove into some indiscreet act of protest or retaliation which could be adversely commented on at the council meeting and reported in the local paper, which loyally supports local interest, Potch would consider his trouble well rewarded.

One cannot but commend the characteristic tenacity of Spinlove as exhibited in his letter that follows.

SPINLOVE TO CLERK, MARLFORD R.D.C.

Dear Sir,   6.10.24.

A week ago I had to ask your surveyor to refund 1s. 6d. excess postage paid by me on parcel of plans sent unstamped. I enclosed label showing the excess stamp. I have had no reply except a form of approval of plans. I shall be glad to receive the money.

Yours faithfully,

CLERK, MARLFORD R.D.C., TO SPINLOVE

Dear Sir,   8.10.24.

In reply to your letter, Mr. Potch states that you did not enclose excess stamp, and also states that postage on parcel is recorded in his stamp book. It appears, therefore, that there must be some mistake or else the stamps came off in the post.

Yours faithfully,

SPINLOVE TO BULLJOHN

Dear Mr. Bulljohn,   9.10.24.

I know you to be a local magnate and I am writing to ask

your help in what seems to me to be a public scandal, for if I submit to the obstructions of the Marlford Council I may get into serious difficulties in the building of this house at Honeywood.

I enclose copies of correspondence with the clerk and surveyor. I pinned the excess stamp on to the letter myself. I have no doubt the parcel was intentionally posted without stamps just as the reply to my request for refund was purposely ignored.

You will notice also the tone of the other letters. If this sort of thing goes on I shall have to make a strong protest to the council, but probably a word to the right person will act as a warning.

I am informed by the builder that Mr. Potch is notorious, and that he has a private practice so that it is to his interest to make difficulties for everyone who does not employ him as architect.

I should be much obliged if you could drop a hint in the right direction.

Yours sincerely,

BULLJOHN TO SPINLOVE

Dear Spinlove,   10.10.24.

Yes, it is all very bad. There have been lots of complaints, but the fellow has many friends on the council and among the local tradespeople. However, I see the chairman sometimes—a very decent man—and I will give him a hint. I am keeping the papers you enclosed.

Ever yours sincerely,

POTCH TO SPINLOVE

Sir,   15.10.24.

I am glad to inform you that I am directed by my council to present you the enclosed postal order for the value of one shilling and sixpence. I regret that the requirements of the auditors of His Majesty's Local Government Board make it necessary for me to trouble you for a receipt, but no stamp is required as sum is less than £2.

I have the honour to be, Sir,
Your obedient servant,

Spinlove's action has not soothed the savage beast, but that was scarcely, in any case, to be hoped, for such men are swayed only by cupidity and funk, and Mr. Potch may be depended upon to make things as awkward for Spinlove as opportunity safely allows.

BRASH TO SPINLOVE

Dear Mr. Spinlove,   10.10.24.

I made a détour to-day and diverged to Honeywood for a brief period after the workmen had vacated the site. It will be necessary for you to immediately return to the makers the bricks, of which a vast quantity are already on the site.

It was clearly demonstrated, I must remind you, that the mansion was to be constructed of *red* bricks. Have you, may I inquire, seen what the builder is purposing to use? They are yellow, green, and all colours, and seem to be partly composed of cinders. I observed many to be broken and am at a loss to comprehend how Mr Grigblay could suppose that I would tolerate such abominable rubbish. Has it not been explained to him that this is to be a gentleman's residence? I must request you to give this matter your immediate attention.

Yours sincerely,

SPINLOVE TO BRASH

Dear Sir Leslie Brash,   11.10.24.

The bricks you saw are not the outside or "facing bricks", but the rough bricks of which the inner thickness of the walls, and where covered with plaster, will be formed. None of the facing bricks has yet been delivered, but I have chosen them. They are, of course, red bricks and are of the best make. No wonder you objected to the bricks you saw if you supposed they were for the outside face.

Yours sincerely,

THE AFFAIR OF THE SPRING

Dear Mr. Spinlove,   13.10.24.

I enclose copy of a communication I have received from the solicitors of the proprietor of the estate on the other side of the road at the bottom of my property, and from whom I acquired Honeywood.

I have conferred with my own solicitors, who approved the conveyance of the land, and these gentlemen confirm that the spring must not be interfered with.

I trust that there will be no trouble anent this. I understood from you that the well was to be sunk previously to the other work being commenced, so that the builder could supply himself with water.

Yours sincerely,

(ENCLOSURE) SPOONBILL & WELLSTAFT, SOLICITORS, TO SIR LESLIE BRASH

Dear Sir,   10.10.24.

Mr. Gregory Witspanner, who is the tenant of Honeywood Farm, adjoining the property lately conveyed to you by our client, Mr. Rallingbourne, has written to our client complaining that the water supply to Honeywood Farm, which flows from a spring in Honeywood Spinney and along the watercourse on the land conveyed to you, has been recently, and now is, badly discoloured with clay, marl, vegetable soil or other foul matter, causing pollution of the water flowing from the said spring on to the said land in Mr. Witspanner's tenancy.

Our client understands that building operations are being carried out on your property and supposes that the pollution is due to the action of the men employed by you in those operations.

We have to remind you that it was expressly laid down in the conveyance to you of Honeywood Spinney that our client's user in the water flowing from the said spring should be maintained unimpaired and that there should be no interference with the flow of pure spring water on to his Honeywood Farm property as heretofore.

We have to call upon you to take immediate steps effectively to abate the pollution and shall be glad to hear that the matter has your attention.

Yours faithfully,

In other words, "the spring at Honeywood is being fouled contrary to the terms of the conveyance. Stop it!"

SPINLOVE TO BRASH

Dear Sir Leslie Brash,   14.10.24.

I have written to Grigblay and told him the spring must not be fouled. I will let you know what can be done. I shall be on the site on Friday. I had intended getting the well sunk, but when I noticed the spring I deemed it not necessary to take that step.

Yours sincerely,

SPINLOVE TO GRIGBLAY

Dear Sir,   14.10.24.

The owner of the property lying below Honeywood has written complaining that the water delivered on to his land from the spring in Honeywood Spinney is being fouled and requires that pollution and interference with the flow shall cease. He has a right to the flow of the spring water on to his land. I must ask you, therefore, immediately to arrange for another source of water supply.

Yours faithfully,

Spinlove is here altogether too aloof and disinterested. He ought to identify himself with this misfortune to the builder and at least make a gesture of readiness to help him, if possible. How is the builder to find water? The position is serious.

The Affair of the Spring

Dear Sir,   16.10.24.

It will be a serious matter for us if we are not to draw water from the spring. Where else are we to find water? When we went to the site before completing our tender we naturally assumed that we could make use of the spring as there was no stipulation in the contract that we should not make use of it. We can only suggest that the well should be sunk immediately and that we should be allowed to draw from it. This will involve a considerable delay, and we shall have to ask for an extension of the contract date corresponding to the time it takes to find water. In the meantime we have told Bloggs to use all possible care not to foul spring.

Yours faithfully,

Dear Sir,   17.10.24.

The contract stipulates that the builder is to make his own arrangements for the supply of water. You would be at liberty to use the spring if it were available, but, unfortunately, it is not. I will give orders for the well-sinking to be put in hand as soon as possible; in the meantime it will be necessary for you to make temporary arrangements of some kind, as Sir Leslie Brash would never consent to let the work stand while the well is being sunk.

Yours faithfully,

If Spinlove thinks that he can settle the matter in this fashion he is very much mistaken. Does he suppose that the builder is to carry water up hill on to the site? The question is, how is water to be found? The circumstances are awkward.

Dear Sir,   17.10.24.

Since we last wrote, Mr. Grigblay has been on site and arranged for Bloggs to dig out ditch and form a weir, and lay

74

a 1 in. pipe from above weir to 1,000-gallon tank to be sunk into ground further down slope. This amount of water will not affect the flow from the spring and we shall not go near ditch or foul spring in the future. We shall be glad to have your approval of this proposal.

We have now got cellar excavated and shall be glad if you will approve same. The ground is dry and compact marly clay, and, as we should like to get concrete in and walls up before chance of rain, we shall be glad of your approval at once.

Yours faithfully,

SPINLOVE TO GRIGBLAY

Dear Sir,   18.10.24.

I am sorry I cannot accept your proposal to form weir and draw water from spring as Sir Leslie Brash has no right to interfere with the flow. I will, however, communicate with Sir Leslie Brash and ask him to refer the point to his solicitors.

Yours faithfully,

GRIGBLAY TO SPINLOVE

Dear Sir,   20.10.24.

I rang up to-day and asked you to put off writing to Sir Leslie Brash *re* spring. If permission is asked of solicitors it may very well be refused, as there is no inducement why it should be granted. The amount of water I shall take from the spring is nothing at all and no one will be any the wiser or know what is being done, as all pollution will cease. There will be no objection to the work proposed, as all will be removed at completion and no harm done.

Yours faithfully,

Grigblay is perfectly sound in his judgment in this matter, nor is there anything sly or deceitful in his proposal. All that the adjoining owner requires is that the spring shall not be polluted and that his right to the flow shall not be interfered with.

The Affair of the Spring

Dear Sir,   21.10.24.

If you care to carry out the arrangement you propose at the spring at your own risk and to indemnify Sir Leslie Brash from all liability, I will not object, although I cannot approve of or consent to the spring being made use of.

Yours faithfully,

Spinlove is taking a great deal too much upon himself here. He is, as accredited agent to Brash, engaging him in words which, to say the least, are ambiguous. Supposing that in some way Grigblay's interference with the spring violates a covenant of the conveyance and involves Brash in some penalty or forfeiture, is it to be imagined that Spinlove's letter will fix liability on Grigblay? This is not likely. It is difficult to know what Spinlove's letter stands for if it is not a formal consent to Grigblay's proposal by the owner's accredited agent. It appears, too, that Grigblay never acknowledged that letter, so that he would be entitled to say, "Yes, the architect said he would hold me responsible, but I never agreed to accept responsibility for more than having to dismantle the arrangements."

It would have been better for Spinlove to have written to Grigblay saying he had no power to authorize him to interfere with the spring and leave him to interpret that letter by such a hint as is sometimes conveyed by a wink.

Dear Sir,   22.10.24.

I confirm authority for you to get on with concreting of cellar. You will note that the cellar damp course is to be carried up outside walls to the level of the normal damp course; this cellar damp course will come below the bottom of the concrete floor and above the bottom of the hard core.

I was glad to see such good progress had been made and to note that the concrete seems quite satisfactory. I have, however, to take exception to the facing-bricks, one load of which has been delivered. In ordering these from the makers I expressly excluded the bright red bricks, which are soft and probably under-burnt. I yesterday selected and marked three samples covering the whole range of variations in colour, etc., which your foreman has set aside in his office. The soft bright red bricks must be thrown out and no more must be delivered.

Will you please let me know in good time what detailed drawings you want?

Yours faithfully,

BRASH TO SPINLOVE

Dear Mr. Spinlove,   21.10.24.

I am in receipt of a strongly-worded communication from Mr. Rallingbourne's solicitors stating that the pollution of the spring continues and is worse than formerly, and requiring me immediately to have the state of affairs ameliorated and even hinting at proceedings. The occupier of the farm asseverates he cannot water his livestock and has to draw from a well.

This is all extremely regrettable and alarming, as I desire to maintain amicable relations with Mr. Rallingbourne, who will be my adjoining neighbour and is a most influential gentleman. It is now eight days since I desired you to give attention to this subject and yet nothing has eventuated.

Yours faithfully,

SPINLOVE TO BRASH

Dear Sir Leslie Brash,   22.10.24.

The matter of the spring has been attended to and there will be no pollution in future. The necessary work, unfortunately, involved muddying the water for a few hours.

Yours faithfully,

TROUBLE WITH BRICKS

GRIGBLAY TO SPINLOVE

Dear Sir,   23.10.24.

We note your instructions *re* facing-bricks. We may say we

ordered bricks as selected by you according to your instructions, but have now taken up the matter with the brickyard.

Yours faithfully,

Spinlove, it will be remembered, dealt directly with the brick manufacturer in selecting bricks and merely told Grigblay to order bricks as selected, without defining, with samples or otherwise, what bricks exactly he was to receive. Grigblay accordingly did not know what bricks to expect and was not in a position to approve or disapprove of what was sent. Spinlove ought to have carried out his negotiations with the brickmaker through Grigblay and made Grigblay responsible for the bricks being up to sample.

GRIGBLAY TO SPINLOVE

Dear Sir,   25.10.24.

With regard to the common bricks specified and seen and approved by you, Bloggs reports that some built into the foundation walls have blown already. We have had no experience of these bricks, not having used them before, and understand they come from Belgium; but Bloggs says that quite a few have lime in them and will blow, and for our own satisfaction we would prefer not to use them on the face of plastered walls. The price is very low, but we should be willing to substitute Strettons for this purpose.

We shall be glad to have your approval.

Yours faithfully,

Grigblay means by this that the clay of which the bricks are made has not been thoroughly ground so that there are lumps of lime in it. These become quicklime when the bricks are kilned, and when such bits of quicklime occur near the surface of the brick the lime swells when the brick is wetted and a flake is lifted from the surface. For a very few such bricks to blow and push the plaster away from the walls, perhaps after papering and painting is completed, is a terrible disaster, and the defect may go on appearing months after the house is finished.

Trouble with Bricks

Dear Sir,   27.10.24.

I am much obliged for your letter. I had a good report of
these bricks which pleased me when I saw them. I do not like
Strettons for facing plaster walls. What other proposal can
you make?

                                                Yours faithfully,

*Spinlove is right. Stretton bricks have a smooth, greasy face
and square edges and show a narrow joint, so that even when the
joints are carefully raked the key for the plaster is not good. A
rough-surfaced, irregular brick is what a builder likes for plastering upon, and there is nothing better for this purpose than the
London stock.*

Dear Sir,   28.10.24.

Our proposal was for grooved Strettons, although the cost
to us would be a little higher than the bricks specified. We
understand you have no objection to these and have ordered
as we shall require them at once for cellar.

                                                Yours faithfully,

*The bricks referred to have grooves formed by pressing rubber
ridges into the brick; the rubber expands with the pressure and
contracts on its withdrawal, so that the groove is slightly dove-
tailed in consequence and forms an excellent key for plaster.*

*Grigblay is a little inclined to take charge of matters and tell
Spinlove what he ought to do, but his quickness to notice the
defect in the specified bricks is one of the advantages which an
architect gains by employing a good builder.*

Dear Sir,   29.10.24.

I was on the site yesterday and found that your foreman had
not carried out my instructions to throw out the soft facing-
bricks. I have to ask you to see that this is done.

Trouble with Bricks

Another trolly load of these bricks arrived while I was on the site, and it seemed to me that it contained as large a quantity of the objectionable bricks as the earlier consignment. These must be picked out.

Yours faithfully,

GRIGBLAY TO SPINLOVE

Dear Sir,   30.10.24.

We have noted your instructions *re* facings and will see that no unsuitable bricks are used, as the bricklayer will have instructions to throw them out. It is not necessary to handle the whole lot over first. We have written again to the brickyard calling attention to the matter.

We enclose list of detailed drawings as per your request. Bloggs points out that the 14 in. return where Den breaks forward (see revised plan No. 8) will not give room for gable knee to match other gables (see ½ in. detail No. 6) as indicated on ⅛ in. scale elevation. It is too late to alter now, but call your attention to same.

Yours faithfully,

It will be recalled that this projecting gable marking the Den was one particular of the kitchen range modification. Here is an instance of the mishaps that are too apt to follow revision of the design. Spinlove, in making his design as a whole, would have kept this point in mind, but pecking at it against time he has overlooked the condition imposed by his ½ in. detail of the gable knees. Some sort of contrivance or botch will have to be made to meet the case. It may perhaps lead to an interesting variation; on the other hand it perhaps will not, and in any case the matter is an annoyance to the architect, as his letter in reply makes clear.

SPINLOVE TO GRIGBLAY

Dear Sir,   31.10.24.

I am sorry to learn of the mistake with the Den gable. You say it is "too late to alter now", but I have to point out to you that you are responsible for the building according to the true intent and meaning of the drawings and for referring all discrepancies to me. I am not in this case going to require you to take down the wall and build 1 ft. 10½ in. break, but I must reserve to myself the right to require strict observance of this condition of the contract. The list of details you enclose does not help me much as they are general and cover the whole building. What I ask is that I may be kept informed beforehand of details that may be immediately wanted.

Yours faithfully,

This will not do! Spinlove is unfair and he is even foolish. The condition he quotes is a saving clause. It determines that the builder is responsible for the correct building of the house, but it does not make him responsible for the architect's definite instructions any more than it does for the design. Spinlove directed a break of 14 in. it seems, and he ought to be grateful to the builder for warning him of what lies ahead, and not discourage him, as he has done, from looking beyond what is strictly his business. The dimension was a definite instruction; the detail of the particular gable knee is supposititious. The tone of Spinlove's letter is wrong; he ought to make the best of the matter to the builder, and not the worst. Disparagement is always an error; expostulation or even reprimand may be necessary, and a builder will not be put out of countenance even if he feels grieved; but disparagement serves no good end whatever and destroys that atmosphere of common purpose on which good results depend.

GRIGBLAY TO SPINLOVE

Dear Sir,   1.11.24.

We note your remarks and have to say that we quite understand what we have to do and are giving this work our best attention; but when an architect sends us a figured dimension to work to we work to it unless it disagrees with other figured dimensions, which please note and see conditions of contract, page 2.

With reference to our foreman's question *re* finish of Den gable knee, of which we have not yet received details, we are instructing him not to take any such action again. The details which we immediately require are those which vary from contract drawing and specifications now in our hands, as you may deem it necessary for us to have and as per our list.

Yours faithfully,

This is a very stiff letter for a builder to write to an architect. Grigblay is naturally annoyed. His letter states the case fairly and entirely demolishes Spinlove. No contract can be carried out at all if the letter of the conditions only is to be observed. A common spirit of good intention and fair play and good sense is necessary.

SPINLOVE TO BRASH

Dear Sir Leslie Brash, 6.11.24.

Before I arrange for the well to be sunk, would it not be worth while to consider whether the spring cannot be made use of? I understand that you are under covenant not to pollute or interfere with the flow, but you could lay on to a storage tank without infringing either condition. Two thousand gallons a day, which would be more than you would use for all purposes, would in no measurable way interfere with the flow. I took the opportunity when last on site to observe the flow where it discharges into the stream below Honeywood Farm, and it seemed as strong as at the source. so that the owner seems to have little use for the water. If the spring were tapped as I propose, the cost of well-sinking would be saved and also most of the cost of installing and running a pump, for the fall of the ground makes it an easy matter to put in an efficient ram. The waste water from this would be returned to the spring. I assume the spring water to be fit for drinking purposes, etc., but it ought to be reported upon by an analyst. I will take no steps until I hear from you.

Yours sincerely,

Spinlove, it will be noticed, has put himself to some trouble to master the facts and devise a scheme that shall give Brash a better service and save his pocket. Such action is not merely the prerogative of the architect, but a privilege which brings dignity to his office and adds joy to his activities. To do a thing well for the sake of so doing it, and not for the money it brings, is what distinguishes the professional from the commercial code. It is because the commercial man is conscious of this that he bleats continuously: "I wish to serve you," and protests that his performances are "genuine", and "real", and "bona fide", and "super". I make this comment because there are signs that the spirit of disinterested initiative here displayed by Spinlove is in some degree discredited by the architects of a new generation. It will learn better when its own children revolt against the sophistication which numbs the sense of true life values for their parents, and puts the architect in a hopeless rivalry with the shopkeeper.

BRASH TO SPINLOVE

Dear Mr. Spinlove,   8.11.24.

I am extremely gratified at your communication anent water supply. I have transmitted a copy of your letter to my legal advisers who approved the conveyance in my behalf and who will no doubt be able to inform me what the correct interpretation of "pollution" and "interference" is to be understood to signify. I will communicate with you when I have received this information. In the interim please desist from all operations in regard to water supply.

Yours sincerely,

MORE DIFFICULTIES

GRIGBLAY TO SPINLOVE

Dear Sir,   8.11.24.

We are sorry to say that Bloggs reports difficulty with damp course. He has carried up cellar to near level of ground, but in fixing level of damp course at bottom of cellar wall he did not allow for main damp course also running round, so that joint is 1½ in. too high at ground-floor level. What we propose to do is to take down a couple of courses and level over wall below ground to give the correct joint level. Shall be glad of your approval.

Yours faithfully,

The fact that Grigblay has confessed to this blunder and referred his proposal for making good to Spinlove is a sign that he has a particular sense of his obligations. The foreman of some builders would have levelled over with cut bricks in cement, and when the architect objected to the botch would have made excuses and belittled the matter, confident that as the wall was sound and the work finished and out of sight, the architect would not call upon him to demolish it.

SPINLOVE TO GRIGBLAY

Dear Sir,   10.11.24.

Your foreman had no grounds for assuming that the main damp course would not run round the top of cellar walls, and if he did suppose so he should have realized that the width of the two courses of slates in cement had to be made up somehow to allow the joints of facings to run through. I am not prepared to accept your proposal to level up. It will be necessary to pull down, say, fifteen courses and save the 1½ in. out of the joints in rebuilding.

Yours faithfully,

Spinlove is right in pointing out that the foreman made a stupid mistake, but his letter is unsympathetic; so long as a builder does his best the architect ought to try to help him out of difficulties. There is no weight on the walls, and the half course would be out of sight in the thickness of the floor or perceived only by an expert eye below the ceiling of the unplastered cellar. On the other hand it is a good thing at the beginning of a job for an architect to be exacting in his demands on the builder; for if he passes over small irregularities at the outset, the builder may assume that the architect is easy-going and some later deviation from exactness may lead to dreadful difficulties and makeshifts. It will take perhaps two hours to pull down the wall and a day to rebuild, and the cost to the builder will be perhaps £7. The foreman will "know all about it", and he and the builder will be warned to be wary. On the whole, Spinlove's decision is probably the best one, but he can write polite, and even ingratiating letters to his client, and he should know better than to write crusty and domineering ones to the builder.

GRIGBLAY TO SPINLOVE

Dear Sir,   12.11.24.

We enclose letter we have received from Messrs. Hoochkoft *re* facings. Please return with your instructions.

Yours faithfully,

(ENCLOSURE) HOOCHKOFT TO GRIGBLAY

Sir,   8.11.24.

We do not understand the complaint of the architect. The bricks we are sending are same as approved by him. If we are required to pick over we shall have to charge 35s. per thousand extra. There is nothing wrong with the bricks.

Yours faithfully,

SPINLOVE TO GRIGBLAY

Dear Sir,   14.11.24.

I return Hoochkoft's letter, of which I have kept copy, and enclose copy of my letter to the firm.

Yours faithfully,

(ENCLOSURE) SPINLOVE TO HOOCHKOFT

Dear Sirs,   14.11.24.

Mr. Grigblay has shown me your letter to him of 8.11.24. My objection to the bricks you have delivered on the site is that they include a quantity of the soft bright red bricks which

I expressly said I could not use at the time I ordered the bricks.

Yours faithfully,

Dear Mr. Spinlove,   14.11.24.

I have been in correspondence with my solicitors, Messrs. Russ, Topper, Mainprice, Cornish and McFee, and have further discussed with them the proposition of obtaining water from the effluent of spring, but they are unable to advise me what interpretation should be given to the covenant limiting my use of the water. They approved the conveyance in my behalf so that I should have expected them to be able to tell me what the words mean, but this they seem unable to do. I am given to understand that only a judge can say what the words mean and that probably different judges would have different views as to their meaning. I am now, at my solicitors' suggestion, obtaining the opinion of an eminent K.C. as to what opinion a judge would be likely to give on the matter. When I have this information I shall know better how I stand. I inform you of these minutiæ in order that you may comprehend that a considerable period must elapse before anything can be definitely determined.

Yours sincerely,

The way Brash sets forth this matter makes it appear ludicrous. The predicament of his solicitors is in fact grotesque—the more so as there are five of them—though Brash does not perceive it. We do not know what the terms of the clause in question are, and should be little the wiser if we did, but it may be that Brash is under covenant not to "interfere" with the flow of the spring, and that the question is what exactly constitutes "interference" having regard to the terms of the conveyance as a whole and the physical circumstances of the case? We lately saw Spinlove light-heartedly committing Brash in ambiguous words, and now we find skilled lawyers all at sea as to the meaning of their own carefully-weighed phrases. A great part of the business of lawyers is to determine the meaning of words used by other lawyers. The law is what is known as "a lucrative profession."

More Difficulties

HOOCHKOFT TO SPINLOVE

Dear Sir,   15.11.24.

We have respectfully to point out that you accepted our quotation for bricks *ex kiln*. It is true you said you did not care for the bright-red bricks and we are accordingly extra firing the bricks for your order, but we cannot guarantee that there will not be a small number of bright reds unless we send you picked, for which our price is 182s. per thousand instead of 147s.

Yours faithfully,

Spinlove's letter accepting quotation for facing bricks was as follows: "I like the samples of the bricks and the price is satis-factory. The very bright-coloured bricks seem soft and under-burnt; the red and purple brindled bricks will give me all the variation in colour necessary. I have directed the builder, Mr. John Grigblay, to place the order with you." This is a sloppy letter. Spinlove means to say that he accepts the tender on the understanding that the bright, under-burnt bricks are excluded, but he does not say it. He first approves of the samples and the price, and then expresses a preference, only, for the better-burnt and darker bricks—that, at any rate, is an interpretation which the "shrewd, hard-headed business man" Samuel Smiles taught us to admire, before we taught ourselves to recognize the com-mercial sharper, would put upon the letter if it helped him to a half-sovereign. In some firms the taking advantage of verbal ambiguities and the dealing in them themselves, is part of a daily routine. It is best for an architect to buy only from merchants and manufacturers of established reputation; but whether he does so or not it is his duty to be exact and precise in his directions, or he may mislead an honest man to his disadvantage by the same loose phrases by which he places himself at the mercy of a dis-honest one. Hoochkoft's talk of extra firing is nonsense; if all the bricks were thoroughly burnt some would be over-burnt and there would be waste. Hoochkoft seems to have got our friend Spinlove on toast.

More Difficulties

SPINLOVE TO HOOCHKOFT

Dear Sirs,   17.11.24.

My order was for facing bricks to sample, but omitting the soft bright-reds. It was for you to amend your price if necessary, but you did not do so, but took the order on the tendered price. I cannot use the soft bricks and no more must be sent on to site.

Yours faithfully,

HOOCHKOFT TO SPINLOVE

Dear Sir,   19.11.24.

We respectfully regret that we cannot agree that the price we quoted and which you accepted was for picked. We are doing our best to reduce the number of bright-reds and do not know what you have to complain of, but we cannot supply picked at same price as *ex kiln* as quoted, but to meet you will offer you special rate of 175s. per thousand picked.

Yours faithfully,

SPINLOVE TO GRIGBLAY

Dear Sir,   20.11.24.

I enclose copy of my correspondence with Hoochkoft. Can you arrange to take over the bricks thrown out and credit them? The extra cost of the picked bricks will be about £70, as nearly as I can judge.

Yours faithfully,

GRIGBLAY TO SPINLOVE

Dear Sir,   22.11.24.

Another lorry of facings has been delivered with about the same number of soft reds as before. We were willing to throw out from the first load, but you will realize this is going to be a serious matter for us if we are to pick over the whole facings. We estimate 15 per cent will have to be thrown out. The only offer we can make is to credit the throwouts against the cost of picking and use them in the back walling. We await your instructions.

Yours faithfully,

Grigblay's proposal is fair, but the bargain would, no doubt, favour him. The result would be that Brash would pay 175s. a thousand for perhaps 7,000 extra useless bricks. It seems, therefore, that when Spinlove said he would engage not to run into extras he flattered himself, for his difficulty with the brickyard is entirely his own fault. It will be remembered, however, that Spinlove has included the sum of £300 as a provision for contingencies upon which he can draw without involving Brash in an extra; but I do not recall that he explained to Brash that this £300 provision was to cover the contingency of the architect making mistakes, although it is available for this purpose as all architects are thankful to know. This is not unfair. A small margin for error is the due of the most exact human machinery.

SPINLOVE TO HOOCHKOFT

Dear Sirs,   24.11.24.

A third load of your facing bricks similar to those to which I have objected has been delivered. I have told Mr. Grigblay not to allow any more to be brought on to the site, and I must ask you to send only bricks equal to approved sample as ordered.

Yours faithfully,

SPINLOVE TO GRIGBLAY

Dear Sir,   24.11.24.

I am obliged for your letter but the bricks were ordered to approved sample. If I accept your proposal it appears there will be an extra of about £120. I enclose copy of my letter to Hoochkoft of to-day. Please refuse to allow any further consignments including defective facings to come on to site.

Yours faithfully,

Spinlove has not realized the consequences of this prohibition.

More Difficulties

GRIGBLAY TO SPINLOVE

Dear Sir,   25.11.24.

May we remind you that we have some face work now built on part of the south front and that we shall have to close down the work if we send back facings. We have been urging delivery. It will also be impossible to match the bricks from another yard, and it seems necessary to come to some arrangement with Hoochkoft at once.

Yours faithfully,

HOOCHKOFT TO SPINLOVE

Dear Sir,   26.11.24.

We can only repeat that we did not quote for picked and that the bricks we have sent you are as per your order.

We gather from your letter informing us that no more un-picked will be accepted that you wish us to send picked facings in future.

Yours faithfully,

SPINLOVE TO HOOCHKOFT

Dear Sirs,   28.11.24.

It is no concern of mine what steps you take to supply facings similar to samples approved by me, but further con-signments containing the soft bright-reds will not be received on the site. If, therefore, you cannot supply to sample without picking, the bricks must be picked.

Yours faithfully,

Spinlove has now dropped into the trap in which Hoochkoft, with skill acquired by long practice, has manœuvred to catch him. Spinlove's contention is that it was part of the bargain that the soft reds should not be included. Hoochkoft has identified this with "picking", for which he has quoted a higher price; Spinlove, by here adopting the term "picking", gives Hoochkoft an oppor-tunity for charging for "picked facings".

It should be added that the tone of Spinlove's letter is too aggressive—a common fault with him. Such a letter will not, in fact, disturb the equanimity of Hoochkoft, who, in common with his kind, has the hide of a rhinoceros; but it is undignified, and not the sort of letter a professional man should write. It may also be remarked that power largely subsists in self-control; any exhibition of feeling is a mark of weakness.

GRIGBLAY TO SPINLOVE

Dear Sir,   2.12.24.

Bloggs informs us that yesterday another lorry load of facings arrived. They are much as previous lots, but as Messrs. Hoochkoft would not have received your letter before loading up, we did not send them back. We shall have to stop work if the facings don't come regular.

We notice that your brick detail of front entrance, drawing No. 10, omits mat-sinking and shows the front step 1¼ in. above finished level of ground floor as fixed by bench mark to your approval. As the ⅛ in. scale plan shows a mat-sinking we set out the brick joint on the floor level, so that the top steps should line up with brick joint. If we raise step 1¼ in. it will mean cutting the bricks to build in step, which we think you will not care for. Have we your authority to drop the bench mark and the ground floor level 1¼ in.?

                                                        Yours faithfully,

We may gather from the above that the horizontal brick joints have been set out to a bench mark approved on the site by Spinlove as the level of the ground floor. The ⅛ in. scale drawings show a sinking for the mat at the front entrance, but Spinlove in his ½ in. detail of the entrance has eliminated the mat-sinking, which harbours dirt, and has, as an alternative, raised the top front step 1¼ in. above the level of the floor. Grigblay points out that to build in the step in this position will involve unsightly cutting of the bricks and proposes to make the top of the step agree with the bench mark and brick joint, and to lower the floor 1¼ in. below bench mark. That Grigblay should write on such a matter shows him to be a good and careful builder.

More Difficulties

Dear Sir,   1.12.24.

We note your instructions re facings, which shall have our best attention.

We are, dear Sir,
Yours faithfully,

This letter is so worded as to support a claim for picked bricks at the increased price, while it gives Spinlove to understand that the objectionable bricks are to be eliminated at the rate originally quoted. Sly deceit of this kind is practised by many business firms, but an experienced architect readily protects himself by exact methods and precision in the use of words, and he soon learns to distrust ambiguous phrases and to spy out the treacherous purpose hidden in them. Spinlove seems to have no suspicion, although the affable subscription to this letter might well have warned him.

Dear Sir,   4.12.24.

Thank you for your letter. Please drop the floor $1\frac{1}{4}$ in. as you propose. The finished ground floor will now be $1\frac{1}{4}$ in. below bench mark from which all vertical heights are figured.

Hoochkoft has now agreed to pick out the soft bright-red bricks to which I have objected, and further consignments containing them are not to be unloaded, but must be sent back.

Yours faithfully,

Dear Sir,   14.12.24.

I was on the site yesterday and saw the last delivery of facings, which are quite satisfactory, but they will show up a little darker in tone than the facings you have already built. Luckily there is not much of this and I have arranged with your foreman that he shall mix what remains of the old with the new, and see that the redder and brighter faces of the new bricks are shown in the next few courses so that there will be a gradation of tone from new work to old.

I was glad to notice that the bricklayers have now got into the way of pressing the mortar out of the joints and cutting off with the edge of the trowel as specified; but they are apt, from force of habit, to press the mortar home with the flat, which they *must not do*. I spoke to your foreman on this matter. He seems to have trouble with one or two of the men, and I told him he would have to get rid of them if they did not do what they were told.

> Yours faithfully,

The matter of finish to the brick jointing is of great importance, as Spinlove has evidently learnt. He seems, however, to think that the only occasion for a letter is to find fault. Bloggs appears to be doing his best under troublesome conditions, and the architect ought at least to hint appreciation.

BRASH ON BRICKS

BRASH TO SPINLOVE

Dear Sir,   19.12.24.

I visited my Honeywood property to-day and was aghast to view the house. I was given to understand that it was to be a *red* brick mansion, but the bricks are of all colours and they are not smooth, but rough, with wide rough spaces; in fact, thoroughly cheap bricks. I rubbed one of them and *it came off* on my finger. I never saw worse house building in my life; not like a gentleman's house, but appertaining to the similitude of a barn. The bricks I desired and which I assumed would be embodied in the fabric are the pretty pinky-red smooth bricks with straight white lines and all matching and not diversified in tint.

There is nothing more elegant and charming than these smooth, neat pink bricks, but the bricks I see are brown instead of red, and exhibit a dirty appearance and are not of one tint, but discoloured and *spotty* and *uneven* instead of being smooth. Is it really too late to put the matter right? Cannot the walls be coloured in some way and the spaces made straight and white and not so rough and broad? I have seen such work being performed in London, I think.

I am afraid to contemplate what Lady Brash will say when she views the edifice on her return from Buxton next week.

I have just arranged to rent a furnished house, "Roselawn", Thaddington, where we shall reside during the spring and summer so that Lady Brash and myself may be on the spot.

I must request your attention to the question of the bricks which is most urgent.

Yours sincerely,

One may feel sorry for Brash. No doubt he will learn to like his "uneven, dirty coloured, spotty" house, but the disappointment is probably a heavy one. The "operation" he refers to seems to be raddling and tuck pointing. The penultimate paragraph will not be the tidings of great joy to his architect that he seems to imagine.

SPINLOVE TO BRASH

Dear Sir Leslie Brash,   22.12.24.

I am sorry you are disappointed with the facing bricks, but it is difficult to judge the effect of the finished house from a near view of the small piece of walling now built. The bricks are, I assure you, good quality, hand-made red bricks, and the variations in colour will not give a spotty effect as you fear, but a deep, soft colour, instead of the rather thin, hard, insipid tone of uniformly-tinted smooth bricks.

The pinky-red uniform smooth brickwork with fine white joints you speak of would be quite unsuited to the architecture of your house: it belongs to a quite different style of building. You will realize this if you have seen, for instance, Spronton Whytgates, and the Orangery at Kensington Palace. The former represents something of the brickwork effect aimed at in your house; the latter shows the kind you have in mind. I can

assure you it would not only be a disastrous anomaly and confusion of ideas to build your house in the style of the Orangery,
but almost impossible to do so. I have given close attention to
the appearance of the brickwork and I feel sure you will like
the effect when the walls begin to display themselves.

Wishing you the compliments of the season,

Yours sincerely,

*Spinlove has not chosen the best of all happy moments for
wishing Brash a merry Christmas by tagging the message to a
letter telling him he does not know what he is talking about. It
was certainly an awkward one to have to write, for there is no
ground of common intelligence upon which to approach Brash;
it would have been better, instead of saying: "You are an ignorant donkey. Wishing you a happy Christmas. . . ." if Spinlove
had written: "The bricks are all right. I will explain when I see
you."*

BRASH TO SPINLOVE

Dear Mr. Spinlove,   23.12.24.

You may be quite correct in what you say from your own
personal attitude of view, but you must permit me to inform you
that I *admire* the pinky-red smooth bricks with straight white
space lines, which you appear to hold in such contempt. Our
diversity of tastes differ in this matter, which I much regret.
I desire to add that I visited Kensington Gardens and viewed the
Orangery yesterday and I entirely fail to visualize the least re-
semblance between that building and your design for my
mansion. No two edifices could be more dissimilar in their
diversity, and I am astounded that you should express the
contrary view.

Reciprocating your seasonable good wishes,

Yours sincerely,

*The explanation of this letter probably is that Brash was so
irritated by Spinlove's that he did not read it with any care.*

Brash on Bricks

Dear Sir Leslie Brash,   24.12.24.

You have misread my letter. I did not instance the Orangery as having anything in common with my design for your house, but as *not* having any; and I do not dislike the bricks you say you admire, but delight to use them in a design to which they are appropriate. If I had known that you particularly wanted your house faced with them I would gladly have made a design to suit, but nothing was said to suggest this. I feel confident that when you see the house taking shape you will be pleased, and not find the walling too rough or lacking in warm red colour.

Thank you for good wishes.

Yours sincerely,

Dear Mr. Spinlove,   28.12.24.

Lady Brash has returned home and has perused your letters on the subject of the bricks and is sure that if they are similar to those at Sponton Witgate (*sic*) they will be extremely pretty. I should mention that Lady Brash has the pleasure of acquaintance with the Rt. Hon. Lady Issit (*sic*) whose husband the Vicount (*sic*), as you are probably aware, is the owner of the house, which Lady Brash has heard much of. I apprehend that your judgment in selecting the bricks was quite correct, although they happen to be an innovation to me.

Yours sincerely,

Spinlove has struck it lucky: but poor old Brash! As Lady Brash does not know her acquaintance's name (Issy) nor the name of her house, and Brash cannot spell her husband's title, we may imagine that the great lady once opened a bazaar at which Lady Brash was a stallholder; and that the reason Lady Brash never wears a ring in her nose is that on that memorable day the Viscountess did not do so. How deep, therefore, will be the dear woman's gratification in possessing a house whose bricks are similar to those used in her friend's famous mansion. I make these comments to elucidate what I gather to be the inner meaning of Brash's letter. Whether Spinlove caught its significance depends upon how far he is sensitive to the manifestations of social snobbery.

GRIGBLAY TO SPINLOVE

Dear Sir,   27.12.24.

We are now several courses above datum all round and have a good deal of material prepared and shall be glad of a certificate for £2,000.

Yours faithfully.

A BOX OF CIGARS

SPINLOVE TO HOOCHKOFT

Dear Sir,   29.12.24.

On my return to the office to-day I found a parcel containing a box of fifty cigars. I am led to think that these have been sent by you, as your trade card with the season's greetings was found on the floor.

I appreciate your friendly intentions, but you will understand that it is impossible for me to accept presents from those with whom I do business in my professional capacity.

If you will confirm that you sent the parcel I will return it to you.

Yours faithfully,

Spinlove is right in returning the parcel and in the reason he gives for doing so; and, as he lays claim to no superior virtues, he will wound no susceptibilities—if Hoochkoft should harbour any, which is unlikely. It occasionally happens that a builder or specialist or merchant, yielding to a feeling of good fellowship or personal regard or gratitude for some friendly act, will, as an individual, send an architect the kind of gift that passes between convivial friends at Christmas, but all such ingenuousness has been rendered suspect by commercial enterprise, which is ready to falsify the purest motives of humanity at sixpence a time, and which fouls everything it touches. To accept gifts from firms is impossible; and an architect who accepts from individuals must expect to lose the respect of the giver as he deserves to do, for he has in like degree lost his own self-respect.

There are practising architects who are contemptuous of those who refuse gifts, and laugh scornfully at the idea of a couple of boxes of cigars or a case of champagne weighing with them when, as arbiters, they have to determine the measure due from and to the giver, and to interpret the contract against his interests. The scornful tone of that laugh is the reaction from the laugher's contempt for himself in accepting; and if his impartiality in meting out justice is not, in fact, swayed, it is because his nature is insensitive to obligations that do not involve self-interest. The gifts are offered as an investment by those whose business it is to get full return for their investments, and they are accepted by those who desire possession and whose greed outweighs their self-respect.

HOOCHKOFT TO SPINLOVE

Dear Sir,   31.12.24.

We thank you for your kind appreciation and trust that you will not put yourself to the inconvenience of returning the small customary token we venture to send at this time of the year to our more valued customers, with whom we trust we may be permitted to include your good self.

With our respectful compliments for your good health and prosperity in the coming year,

We are, Dear Sir,
Yours faithfully,

Hoochkoft sent this greasy letter in view of the fact that they have deceived Spinlove and intend to press the claim for picked bricks which they know he will resist. The reference to the architect as a customer is a deceptive gloss. Spinlove is the agent of Brash, who is the customer—a very different matter—though Spinlove's habit of ordering goods without stating that he does so on behalf of his client would lead us to believe that he is not fully aware of the distinction. There is no reason why Brash, as a customer, should not accept Hoochkoft's cigars, but this he will never have a chance of doing. It is never the principal to whom the gift is offered, but his agent; it is not the lady of the house to whom the grocer sends the drum of candied fruits, but her cook.

SPINLOVE TO HOOCHKOFT

Box of cigars posted to-day under separate cover.

for J. SPINLOVE,
R. S. PINTLE.

A distinguished architect tells me that when any gift is sent to him he accepts it with a grateful letter of appreciation and thanks, and an expression of his very deep regret that his doing so will make it impossible for him to place any orders with the giver in future. If his example were widely copied the practice would soon end.

SPINLOVE TO GRIGBLAY

Dear Sir, 1.1.25.

In reply to your letter asking for certificate, will you let me know how you arrive at your estimate of £2,000?

Yours faithfully,

GRIGBLAY TO SPINLOVE

Dear Sir, 5.1.25.

We enclose estimate for certificate, as requested. If not convenient please draw certificate for such less amount as you may think proper.

Yours faithfully,

SPINLOVE TO TINGE, QUANTITY SURVEYOR

Dear Mr. Tinge, 7.1.25.

The builder has applied for certificate for £2,000. I enclose

A Box of Cigars

his estimate. The walls are up an average of two courses above ground floor all round—there are about 10,000 common and 3,000 facing bricks on site and ground-floor window frames are practically made. His claim for materials prepared and on site seems excessive, and the inclusion of £400 out of preliminary and general provisions does not appear justified. Will you please examine the figures?

Yours truly,

TINGE TO SPINLOVE

Dear Sir,   10.1.25.

Value of work done and materials prepared or on site £2,250, less 20 per cent retention, £1,800.

Estimate returned herewith.

Yours faithfully,

SPINLOVE TO GRIGBLAY

Dear Sir,   12.1.25.

I have examined your estimate, but am unable to agree that you are entitled to a certificate of £2,000; and as the contract stipulates that certificates shall be for not less than £2,000, you are not entitled to any certificate.

Yours faithfully,

Spinlove has no business to write these graceless letters to the builder, which will wound his self-respect and make bad blood. The tone is that of Scotland Yard addressing a ticket-of-leave man. No doubt Grigblay is "trying it on", but there is no harm in asking, for some architects are easy-going and, knowing their man, are willing to stretch a point to oblige him, for the architect usually has the right to draw a certificate for less than the minimum named if he thinks fit. A builder has to pay his merchant or lose the 2½ per cent discount usually allowed for settlement within three months, and if he is to make full use of his capital, as most of them do, he must get his money in promptly or borrow at interest, in which case his profits will vanish.

Spinlove ought to identify himself with the builder's interests

100

as well as with his client's, and the sort of letter he ought to have written is somewhat as follows: "As I was not able to follow the details of your estimate I referred it to Mr. Tinge, who arrives at a figure, less retention, of £1,800. I should be glad to certify for this amount, but you will see that the contract stipulates a minimum of £2,000. I am afraid, therefore, that the matter must stand over for a few weeks."

No builder could object to such a letter as this. The quantity surveyor is an impartial authority; the terms of the contract are inviolable. Spinlove is right in keeping to the letter of the contract, however, and Grigblay will not be likely again to lay himself open to a similar repulse.

LADY BRASH TO SPINLOVE

Dear Mr. Spinlove,   15.1.25.

I am writing as Sir Leslie is shooting with a friend at Westerham. I went down to-day and was horrified to find them *soaking it with water!!!* I spoke to one of them, but I am afraid he did not pay much attention, so will you please be so good as to have it *stopped* as I particularly want it *dry?* All my family are subject to rheumatism, so you may imagine my feelings to-day when I saw *water being poured over them!!!*

How very cold the wind has been lately!!

Yours sincerely,

It is a pity Lady Brash's regard for her family does not extend to another kind of relatives—grammatical!

SPINLOVE TO LADY BRASH

Dear Lady Brash,   17.1.25.

Your house will, I can promise, be a thoroughly warm and a perfectly dry one. Bricks are always wetted so that the mortar will set hard. The walls will become quite dry in due time.

Yes, as you say, the wind has been very chilly. I hope Sir Leslie has had good sport.

Yours sincerely,

In point of fact it is difficult to get bricklayers to use enough water with absorbent bricks which, if not kept very wet, suck up moisture out of the mortar and give it no opportunity of setting properly. The bricklayer's hand gets softened by being constantly wet, and the sand on the handle of the trowel cuts his skin.

CARRYING ON

SPINLOVE TO GRIGBLAY

Dear Sir,   22.1.25.

When I was at your yard yesterday I had to condemn five cills, seven jambs, and two mullions on account of sap or shakes; I notice also a certain amount of sap in the timber coming from the sawmill. Will you please see that none is included in the worked-up stuff?

Yours faithfully,

GRIGBLAY TO SPINLOVE

Dear Sir,   22.1.25

Our shop foreman tells us that you objected to some of the oak prepared for window frames. We may say that this is one of the best lots of oak we have seen for a great many years; it is ten years old, Sussex white, grown on the chalk, and not weald oak, and we defy anyone to show you finer timber as it is not to be had and there is very little as good as this anywhere. These slow-growing trees do not come very straight, so we are bound to get a little sound sap wood running in and out in places, and if we threw out all that showed a trace we should have to throw out more than half. Some of your jambs are near 9 ft. long. We will carefully select and keep any sappy angles on the back face; we will also creosote or tar the backs and underside of cills if you wish.

Yours faithfully,

Carrying On

It was easy for Spinlove to specify "the timber to be well seasoned, free from sap, large loose or dead knots, waney edges" —and all the rest of it. The point is, how is he to interpret words which describe the general characteristics of timber and which mean a different thing to different persons and have a different value according to the purpose for which the wood is to be used? In what degree is the timber to be free from those particular defects? To apply the rule literally and rigidly would drive any builder into flat revolt, and no arbitrator would support the interpretation. A bit of sap running in and out on the back angle of cill or jamb is of no account, and large live knots are characteristic of English oak as also are shakes, which cannot be objected to when they are superficial and the wood is well seasoned. If Spinlove has no stomach for the robust, rugged integrity of English oak he ought to have used Austrian or Danzig or Japanese.

Grigblay's letter strongly suggests that the stuff he is cutting is first class, and that Spinlove's objections are due to ignorance. The fact is that the established form of specification with its impracticable stipulations is not the best for securing first-rate work; a more discerning and indulgent description, which shows that the person specifying knows what he can get and means to have it, is the right thing, and enables a builder to understand what he is actually expected to provide. For instance, what exactly does "well seasoned" mean? How long seasoned and in what form? Seven years felled and three years in plank can be had, and the builder will provide it, or its equivalent, if he has allowed for it in his tender.

SPINLOVE TO GRIGBLAY

Dear Sir,   27.1.25.

I raise no objection to the general quality of the oak, but the specification is definite in ruling out sap, shakes, etc., and I must require you to conform to it.

Yours faithfully,

James is riding for a fall.

Carrying On

Dear Sir,   3.2.25.

Our shop foreman has now selected and got out the whole of the planks we propose to use for window and door frames for your inspection, and we shall be glad to have your approval of same before they go to the mill.

We may say that the planks we are selecting from have been in store for more than four years.

In the event of your not approving same perhaps you will let us know where we are to get it.

Yours faithfully,

This is a distinctly stiff letter for a builder to write to the architect. It is clear that Grigblay has no great respect for Spinlove's practical knowledge or experience and has no great regard for him personally. Spinlove, one imagines, is helpless: how is he to tell Grigblay what he wants or where it is to be got when he does not know? He ought, however, since he has approved of the general quality of the oak, to refuse to approve it in detail in plank, for the suitability of the components of the window frames to be cut from the planks will depend entirely upon the skill and judgment of the joiner in laying out the work and scheming to avoid defects. If Spinlove accepts definite planks he will prejudice his position if, in avoiding waste defective timber is worked up into jambs and cills.

GRIGBLAY TO SPINLOVE

Dear Sir,   12.2.25.

We shall be obliged if you will now favour us with certificate for £2,000.

We are sorry to say the frost has got into the upper course of brickwork and some of the pointing has been caught. We have the green work well covered, but the papers say frost is to continue, so we have stopped bricklayers. Bloggs has set out the main drain to sewage outfall and we should like to get on with this if you will approve same. We notice there is a provision of £350 for septic tank and filter beds and shall be glad to have your instructions.

We are awaiting details of brick window-cills; there is a lot of bed and back cutting to these and we should like to put bricklayers to work on it.

Yours faithfully,

Dear Sir, 16.2.25.

I enclose certificate No. 1 for £2,000. I was on the site yesterday and agreed set out of main drain. The branch drains I will deal with later on. The exact level of the outfall will be fixed by the anaerobic tank; I will send you particulars of the work covered by the provision for this as soon as possible. I enclose detail No. 21 of brick window-cills and weatherings; the lengths of these cills, you will note, vary, so that in order to keep joint widths constant, i.e. $\frac{1}{2}$ in., and the bricks equal in width, it will be necessary in some cases to reduce the bricks by cutting or rubbing so that exact regularity is maintained.

You will note that the cills and all weathered members are to be bedded, jointed, and pointed in cement waterproofed with Puddlyt. This must be carefully attended to as the bricks are absorbent and not to be relied on to keep out water.

Yours faithfully,

Dear Sir, 17.2.25.

We are obliged for detail No. 21 showing brick cills, etc., and note your other instructions. With regard to gauging the brick cills we shall be glad to have your authority for the extra as same is not included in the contract. Are we to understand that the same rule applies to brick heads and to the brick gable copings, etc.?

Yours faithfully,

Dear Sir, 18.2.25.

You are right in understanding that the whole of the brick

cills, heads, and weatherings are to be cut to show equal widths and uniform $\frac{1}{2}$ in. joints. I do not agree that you are entitled to an extra for this work, which is required under the general condition that all work shall be of the best quality.

Yours faithfully,

We shall hear more of this!

BRASH TO SPINLOVE

Dear Mr. Spinlove,   18.2.25.

At long last, after this interminable period, I have received counsel's opinion on the proposal you suggested for making use of the spring; I append a copy as its perusal may interest you. I have conferred with my legal adviser on the appropriate action to be taken and I desire you will be so good as to wait upon Messrs. Russ, when you have made your arrangements, and inform those gentlemen of the work contemplated, as they anticipate they may wish to take counsel's opinion again, for I consider it advisable to make things secure and not to incur any liability of a law suit or to be compelled to dismantle the arrangements after they are instituted.

I should mention that it is not desired that attention should be attracted to the operations, and I apprehend that when the work is completed there will be nothing visible to see. Perhaps it would be desirable to direct the work to be performed during the night.

I am considerably indebted to you for propounding the suggestion for utilizing the spring. Will you please arrange for the necessary sample of water to be procured for analysis, if this precaution has not yet been safeguarded. I am informed that the receptacle should be thoroughly cleansed before the water is enclosed, to avoid contamination.

Yours sincerely,

(ENCLOSURE) OPINION

Re Rallingbourne v. *Sir Leslie Brash*

1. The Defendant is not entitled to use the spring in Honey-

wood Spinney of which he is the owner for any purpose that will interfere with the natural pure flow of the stream on to the Plaintiff's land injuriously to the Plaintiff and in addition is bound to maintain such pure natural flow.

2. Any building or works extending into the stream is *prima facie* an encroachment upon Plaintiff's rights and is a cause of action in respect to the possible consequences to the pure natural flow without the necessity for Plaintiff proving actual injurious interference or proving the probability of any particular specified damage by such interference the onus being upon the Defendant to show that no act or omission to perform any act by or in his behalf or with or without his knowledge by any person in his employ or otherwise does in fact amount to interference with the pure natural flow and also that the said acts or omissions have not and cannot in the nature of things have any perceptible injurious effect upon the natural flow of the stream. *cf.* Bickett *v.* Morris L.R. 1 Ap.47 L. Blackburn. Orr-Ewing *v.* Colquhoun L.R. 2 Ap. ca. 853.

3. Having regard to the facts in this case I am clearly of opinion that the Defendant will be able to show that his installation of a ram as proposed can in no perceptible degree obstruct pollute or diminish the pure natural flow of the stream on to the Plaintiff's land and that therefore an action for breach of covenants cannot be successfully maintained. *cf.* Per Cur Rhodes *v.* Airedale Commiss: L.R. 1 C.P.D. 392 45. L.I.C. P. 341.

(Sg) GEOFFREY CHAWLEGGER,
2 Midden Court,
Inner Temple.

So help you!

GRIGBLAY TO SPINLOVE

Dear Sir,   19.2.25.

We regret that we cannot agree to gauge brick cills and weatherings. No gauged work is described in the specification or measured in the quantities, and our price does not cover for it.

We may say that in all our experience we have never been called upon to gauge in work of this character. We are accustomed to turn out brickwork which will equal the best done anywhere and to the satisfaction of leading architects, and we will pick the bricks and keep the joints as near to ½ in. as no matter, and we believe that this will meet with your satisfaction. If anything more is required, payment for extra time and waste must be allowed us.

Yours faithfully,

This is a perfectly right and reasonable view of the matter.

SPINLOVE TO GRIGBLAY

Dear Sir,   21.2.25.

It is you who have introduced the description "gauged brick work". I have not asked for it. I am not concerned with what is included in the quantities; the bills are not part of the contract and any question arising out of them must be settled between Mr. Tinge and yourselves.

Yours faithfully,

Spinlove is right in what he says of the quantities, which have no place in the contract except as a schedule of prices fixing rates at which any variation shall be valued, but he is perfectly wrong in every other particular. His letter is lamentable in its arrogant disregard of the builder's point of view, and his requirements are childish. What he asks for is, in point of fact, not gauged work— for gauged work is a particular process employed with particular bricks—but his demand is akin to it, and a special clause in the specification could alone entitle him to make the demand.

GRIGBLAY TO SPINLOVE

Dear Sir,   23.2.25.

We beg to say that we are perfectly aware the bills are not part of the contract, but if your requirements for gauging the cills, etc., were included in your specification Mr. Tinge would have measured the item, and the fact that he has not done so supports our contention that the work is not included in the contract. We have given special instructions to Bloggs *re* this work and have no doubt that it will give you satisfaction, but we cannot handle the cills as gauged work without being allowed the extra price, which we are willing to agree with Mr. Tinge.

Yours faithfully,

SPINLOVE TO TINGE

Dear Mr. Tinge,   24.2.25.

I enclose copies of correspondence with Grigblay on the subject of brick cills and weatherings. Surely the general requirement of "work to be of the best description" and "to the architect's satisfaction", includes this necessary cutting and jointing?

Yours faithfully,

TINGE TO SPINLOVE

Dear Sir,   26.2.25.

We did not measure any gauged work nor describe any special labours in cills of the kind you describe, as such work was not asked for in your specification nor shown in the drawings.

Yours faithfully,

We probably admire Tinge's pithy style more than Spinlove, who wants to have his view of Grigblay's obligations. That, however, has nothing to do with Tinge; it is a point for the decision of that tremendous person widely known as "the Harshtec". Spinlove evidently did not know how to reply to Grigblay, for there is no letter on the file. He has obviously allowed his mind to be obscured by his drawing-board, which has presented to him a problem that, in practice, does not exist. Spinlove (who cannot lay bricks) has been trying to show a bricklayer (who can) how to lay them by representing bricks and their joints as equal rectangular blocks with straight edges ranged out with dividers. The resources of the craftsman are out of mind for the draughtsman; the problems presented by set-square and dividers do not exist for the craftsman.

A SANITARY EXPERT APPEARS

Dear Sirs,   28.2.25.

I enclose layout of drains for house near Marlford, with contours, and shall be glad if you will let me have a scheme for sewage disposal. Before you do so, however, I should like you to see the subsoil and discuss things with you, preferably on the site. Will Tuesday next suit you? I shall be travelling by the 2.5 from Charing Cross on that day.

Yours faithfully,

Dear Sir,   2.3.25.

We duly received your esteemed communication, with plan, and we will have pleasure in arranging for our Mr. Peter Schwarb to place himself at your entire personal disposal and visit the site in your good company on Tuesday next, as per your letter.

As one of our fleet of motors is available on that day we shall be favoured if we may be allowed to place it at your personal disposal, and would arrange for Mr. Schwarb to call for you at one o'clock at your office, or any other place or hour convenient to your good self, for the purpose of personally escorting you to and from the site.

We are, dear Sir,
Your obedient servants,

Wreek & Co. evidently believe in "personal charm as a commercial asset", and by "personal charm" they appear to understand a fawning sycophancy directed to establish in the charmed one a sense of obligation which shall make it difficult for him to reject their proposal, question their price, or condemn their performance. To experience three hours boxed up in a motor with Mr. Schwarb's unflinching personal charm—sublimed, perhaps,

110

with a touch of scent—will probably settle Spinlove's hash, or, on the other hand, perhaps it will not. The needs of personal charm have, we may guess, led Mr. Schwarb to scheme to join Spinlove at lunch and pay for both; and, at a hint, it would probably find him ready to carry the architect upstairs on his back and put him to bed.

SPINLOVE TO WREEK & CO.

Dear Sirs.   3.3.25.

As I understand you are motoring down to Marlford on Tuesday I shall be glad to accept a seat in your car. I will expect it after lunch at 1.30.

Yours faithfully,

One cannot here altogether regret the graceless style Spinlove adopts to those under his direction, but although the insincerity of Wreek's obsequious letter smells strongly, there is no reason why Spinlove should not thank them on the frank assumption that the intention is to save their own, and his, time.

SPINLOVE TO THUMPER & CO.

Dear Sirs,   7.3.25.

I write to confirm arrangements made with your manager by telephone to-day for your representative to call here at 1.25 on Tuesday to go with me by road to site near Marlford for the purpose of taking particulars for ram. There is a level and staff on the site.

Yours faithfully,

Spinlove's action in inviting the representative of another firm of kindred activities to take a seat in the car put at his disposal with such unctuous blandishments by Wreek & Co. is the last thing that Wreek & Co. would expect or desire. Thumper's man will greatly dilute the personal charm of Wreek's Mr. Schwarb, and we have to picture James Spinlove beset as by rival beauties, each trying to ingratiate herself and displace the other in his favour.

A Sanitary Expert Appears

SPINLOVE TO THUMPER & CO.

Dear Sirs,   11.3.25.

I am obliged for your report with specification and tender for water supply. You say nothing of the guarantee of rate of discharge from the ram, which was promised.

I will write to you further when I have inquired into the rights of the adjoining owner.

Will you please send down and take sample of water and send it to Sir Geoffrey Whittle for analysis. I am writing to him.

Yours faithfully,

SPINLOVE TO SIR GEOFFREY WHITTLE, F.R.S., M.I.C.E.

Dear Sir,   11.3.25.

I have instructed Messrs. Uriah Thumper & Co. to send you sample of water from spring rising in Honeywood Spinney on high ground at the top of Honeywood Hill, four miles north of Marlford, Kent. The water is wanted for domestic use and is to be pumped by ram to storage tank under roof of house.

I shall be glad if you will make your report cover the question of ram-lining, pipes, and tank.

Yours faithfully,

Spinlove seems to have had experience of water supply, judging from the exactness of his arrangements. He directs the sample to be taken by those who will take it at the source and in a clean flask of ample size, which they will seal and mark. A sample taken from a limey bucket thrust into a ditch below a dead crow and put into an imperfectly washed embrocation bottle, the cork of which has been moistened in the mouth of a labourer who is chewing tobacco, often gives unsatisfactory and perplexing analysis.

Spinlove is evidently aware that pure spring water is not pure, but is a highly diluted chemical; and that pure soft water, i.e. rainwater, will dissolve lead by oxidation. Spring water contains carbonic acid in quantities that sometimes rusts iron so fiercely that galvanized pipes are no protection against stained, iron-

112

smelling water; and there are acids dissolved from heather roots and peat beds which act disastrously in a similar way in hot water service pipes; and various other dangers. These awkward conditions can be met, but they must be first known. Freedom from organic pollution and fitness for drinking has obviously also to be proved. Water analysis is a special subject and the expedients demanded by the analysis are also a matter of special knowledge and practical experience.

GRIGBLAY TO SPINLOVE

Dear Sir,   12.3.25.

We are sorry to have to mention the matter, but Sir Leslie Brash has not yet honoured your certificate of 16.2.25 for £2,000. We wrote him on March 1 calling his attention to same, but have received no reply. If you will mention the matter to him we shall be grateful.

Yours faithfully,

When an architect has drawn a certificate the owner is bound to honour it within a certain time defined in the contract, and usually thirty days. The architect has a duty to the builder of drawing certificates when due, and to the client of seeing that the amounts certified are, in fact, due. Spinlove ought, however, to have notified Brash that he had drawn a certificate and in a letter somewhat as follows: "The contractor has applied for payment on account. I find that he is entitled to the sum of £2,000, and I have to-day sent him a certificate for that amount." Such a letter warns the owner and gives him the assurance, otherwise only implied, that the certificate duly conforms to the requirements of the contract.

SPINLOVE TO BRASH

Dear Sir Leslie Brash,   14.3.25.

Mr. Grigblay happened to mention to me that he thought you might not perhaps understand that the payment of instalments is due on presentation of each certificate. I think you will like me to let you know this.

The work, as you will see, is going ahead now. A few days were lost by frost, but progress is good and I think Grigblay is well up to time.

With kind regards,
Yours sincerely,

This letter of Spinlove's is so extremely circumspect and tactful as to suggest he thinks Brash is trying to avoid payment. It would have been better had he written: "Grigblay seems to want a cheque rather badly. Perhaps I ought to have explained to you that it is customary to honour certificates on presentation."

We may remember that Brash is by profession an expert economist, and he has perhaps calculated that if he holds back each certificate (and there will be ten of them) for three weeks he will gain the interest on £2,000 for six months. Brash, apparently, is what is known as a "bad payer". Spinlove, however, is a much younger man than Brash and his sensitiveness is natural. He has probably never had to write such a letter before and will perhaps never have to do so again.

BRASH TO SPINLOVE

Dear Mr. Spinlove,   16.3.25.

I certainly did not comprehend that the builder was to be paid cash immediately. The contract, I may remind you, stipulates that certificates are to be honoured within thirty days, of which twenty-eight have only so far elapsed. I have not, I may inform you, overlooked the matter, and it is unnecessary for Mr. Grigblay to suppose that I shall not complete my obligations, but at the time you drew the certificate there was very little to be perceived of the building.

I shall be visiting the site again shortly and am gratified to know that the progress made meets with your satisfaction.

Yours sincerely,

SPINLOVE TO BRASH

Dear Sir Leslie Brash,   17.3.25.

The stipulation in the contract for payment within thirty

days of date fixes the *outside limit*. I enclose copy of the clause from the conditions, from which you will see that the builder is entitled to be paid at once, and this is the established custom.

You will understand, of course, that at the date each certificate is drawn you have security in the work done to the value of 20 per cent more than the amount certified. This first certificate included for all the digging and foundations.

Yours faithfully,

SPINLOVE TO TINGE, QUANTITY SURVEYOR

Dear Mr. Tinge,   18.3.25.

I enclose letter, plan, specification, and drawing of sewage disposal together with Wreek & Co.'s tender. You will see they have connected two of the baths and six of the lavatory wastes to a separate tank, as they say that the considerable flow from baths, which are all used at one time when the house is fully occupied, will flood out the anaerobic tank and put the filter out of operation. If they make the anaerobic tank big enough to deal with this flow it will not operate satisfactorily with the normal flow. This second tank will involve an extra, I am afraid, but their estimate of £525 greatly exceeds the provision you fixed. Will you please examine their estimate and report.

Yours faithfully,

TINGE TO SPINLOVE

Dear Sir,   23.3.25.

Wreek & Co.'s price is at least 30 per cent too high; they could also do much less extravagant work. I see no object in bronze bushes to tip, or of grid over the filter; the white glazed outfall channel and fireclay detritus chamber could quite well be replaced by concrete and brick; stone cover to septic tank is all that is wanted.

Why not let Grigblay do the building work under their direction at scheduled rates? The cost ought to be about half of that proposed.

Yours faithfully

A Sanitary Expert Appears

Personal charm seems to extend to the flattery of suggesting that an architect of Spinlove's distinction and social eminence will require a kingly sewage outfall.

SPINLOVE TO WREEK & CO.

Dear Sirs,   24.3.25.

I have carefully considered your estimate, but your proposal is too extravagant and your prices too high, and I will ask you to send me an amended competitive estimate omitting bronze bushes to tipper, and the grid over filter and substituting brick and concrete for outfall channel and detritus chamber, and excluding building work, which I will arrange for the general contractor to carry out under your direction.

I am not able to invite you to tender for ram and water supply, as you ask. That matter is already arranged for.

Yours faithfully,

Mr. Schwarb has evidently seized the opportunity suggested by meeting Thumper's man in the motor, to follow the first precept of commercial enterprise and "do the other fellow in the eye".

WREEK & CO. TO SPINLOVE

Dear Sir,   27.3.25.

We are gratified to know that our proposal for sewage disposal installation meets with your esteemed satisfaction and only regret that you are not in a position to spend the sum necessary to secure that your client's drains shall be of the finish now in favour with the leading architects and included in the modern equipment of the great houses recently built.

We may mention that refined and dainty sanitary works are becoming the rule rather than the exception among the nobility and gentry, and we should like to feel that you and your good client will not in the future have to regret that his septic tank and filter will not compare favourably with those possessed by his more distinguished friends and neighbours. We may say that many gentlemen who are our clients take pride in their sewage plant, which they frequently view, as they would their conservatory, and introduce to the notice of their friends.

In order to give your client this satisfaction, and out of consideration for your good self and with a wish to make our super high grade Antystynk plant better known, we will make you the special offer of 12½ per cent reduction on our previous estimate. In case, however, your client cannot afford our super high grade Antystynk, we enclose specification and estimate for our lower grade plant, such as we instal at police stations, factories, etc. We regret that we always keep the building work in our own hands. We may mention that we absolutely guarantee our effluent, the purity of which is well known. Our Mr. Sinclair Vennom, the celebrated septic tank expert, who lately retired from our board of directors owing to ill-health, frequently demonstrated the fact by drinking a wineglass of it.

Yours faithfully,

The flunkeyism displayed in this letter is the same as that with which certain shops shame the parvenu into buying the most expensive goods by suggesting that if he does not he is ignorant of the correct thing and a stranger to the best circles. Their Mr. Sinclair Vennom seems to have demonstrated the purity of the famous effluent once too often; but as Brash's enthusiasm for his sewage plant is not likely to lead him to similar exuberances the effluent may be considered satisfactory.

SPINLOVE TO WREEK & CO.

Dear Sirs,   1.4.25.

I have to acknowledge your amended tender. Your proposal is satisfactory, but your price is not, and I shall be glad if you will see what you can do to reduce it before I invite proposals from other firms.

Yours faithfully,

As different firms of specialists use different methods and different materials, plant, and workmanship, competitive tenders, in the strict sense, are not possible. All the architect can do is to compare the proposals and prices of reputable firms, and choose what best suits the case. Apparently Wreek & Co. do good work, or Spinlove would not take so much trouble to get an acceptable tender from them.

BRASH TO SPINLOVE

Dear Mr. Spinlove, 1.4.25.

I have to-day transmitted cheque to Mr. Grigblay. I was certainly much gratified by the advance progress has made, which I observed when I viewed the operations yesterday.

Yours sincerely,

This letter gives the impression that Brash would not have honoured the certificate had not the appearance of walls above ground satisfied his ideas of "progress". To the uninitiated there is always dismay at the early stages, delight when the walls rise rapidly, as they do, and final despair at the interminable operations of interior work and finishings.

WREEK & CO. TO SPINLOVE

Dear Sir, 4.4.25.

In reference to your esteemed request, we have carefully reconsidered our proposal and enclosed revised estimate.

By using less expensive bricks and making other immaterial alterations we are able to reduce our price to a figure which we trust will be acceptable to your good self. The price we are quoting is made specially low in order that we may have the satisfaction of not disappointing you.

We are, dear Sir,

Yours faithfully,

The indications are that Wreeks have stood out for a price much higher than the value of the work justifies, as specialists of high reputation are able to do. Their substitution of a "less expensive brick", etc., is to "save the face", as the Chinese say; the real consideration is that if they do not cut down their figure they will lose the job. Spinlove appears to have understood the game they were playing.

SPINLOVE TO WREEK

Dear Sirs,   7.4.25.

I write to accept your amended estimate of £375 for sewage disposal plant. The outfall drain is now in hand, and I shall be glad if you will make arrangements with Mr. Grigblay and get the work started at an early date.

Yours faithfully,

THE THICK OF THE FIGHT

SPINLOVE TO RUSS & CO.

Dear Sirs,   9.4.25.

By Sir Leslie Brash's instructions I enclose complete particulars of water supply from spring. I am to await your approval of these proposals before putting the work in hand.

Yours faithfully,

RUSS & CO. TO SPINLOVE

Dear Sir,   14.4.25.

We return particulars for drawing water from spring at Honeywood. We see no objection to these proposals so long as the pure natural flow of the spring is not interfered with injuriously to the owner's interest by any act or omission in the carrying out of the works or in subsequently withdrawing and pumping the water.

Yours faithfully,

The charge for this letter will be, we may suppose, 13s. 4d.

SPINLOVE TO RUSS & CO.

Dear Sirs,   15.4.25.

I have duly received your letter and enclosures, but you have
119

not answered the question I had to refer to you. I am aware of the stipulation you describe. and what I want to know is whether my proposals infringe those stipulations.

Yours faithfully,

Spinlove's unappeasable tenacity is here very much to the point. Brash's solicitors have burked the question partly because of their habit, as lawyers, of using extreme caution, and partly because they cannot say whether the installation and operation of the ram may, or may not, impress the House of Lords as an infringement of the covenants, the House of Lords being the only decisive tribunal for the interpretation of these covenants.

RUSS & CO. TO SPINLOVE

Dear Sir,   17.4.25.

In reply to your letter on the subject of Honeywood spring, we see no objection to the proposal providing that the restrictions of the covenant of conveyance are not infringed.

Yours faithfully,

"Say 6s. 8d."

SPINLOVE TO BRASH

Dear Sir Leslie Brash,   18.4.25.

In accordance with your instructions I referred proposal for installing ram to Messrs. Russ & Co. and enclose copy of correspondence. Will you please let me know what action I should now take?

Yours faithfully,

Spinlove is handling this matter creditably. For this occasion at least we may say that no flies are settling on him.

BRASH TO SPINLOVE

Dear Mr. Spinlove,   22.4.25.

I conferred with Mr. Russ to-day and he signified to me that he perceives no objection to the contemplated ram proposal if carefully executed; and he advises me that the chance of the probability of Mr. Rallingbourne taking action is extremely remote, and that if he were so ill-advised as to do so he would certainly not succeed. Will you, therefore be so obliging as to ensure that the work shall be carried out *at night* with as little ostentation as possible.

Yours faithfully,

It will be noted that Mr. Russ can give an opinion in conversation that he will not embody in a letter. This is perfectly understandable: the risk of being proceeded against is one for Brash's shoulders alone; Russ can only accept official responsibility for advising what those risks are. The temper of the adjoining owner; his health and sanity; his attitude towards his rights in general; whether he is easy-going and generously-minded, or jealous of his rights and grasping; and also the actual nature of his interest in the property, which may be entailed or held in trust; all are vital considerations of which Russ knows nothing. His judgment, however, as a man of the world, which he puts at the disposal of his client in conversation, is entirely a different matter.

SPINLOVE TO GRIGBLAY

Dear Sir,   25.4.25.

I enclose Thumper's estimate, specification, etc., of work in connection with ram and piping to house. The cover of chamber enclosing the spring should be kept a few inches below surface of ground and well banked in and covered over and turfed so as to be inconspicuous.

Will you please carry out your work at the spring head *at night*. To be done day-work and set against provision for pump.

Yours faithfully,

GRIGBLAY TO SPINLOVE
(*Personal*)

Sir,   27.4.2.5

I have seen your letter on the subject of spring head and

venture to write to you privately as I gather that your instructions to do the work at night is to keep it secret.

You will pardon me pointing out, with all respect for your superior judgment, that to have men up in Honeywood all night with lights visible from road and for miles round to the south and west, is not the best way to keep it secret. Down there they wouldn't have any excitements if they did not all look sharp after other people's business, and the whole country will be in a buzz. Some of my men are sure to mix it up with a drop of beer at the public, and we shall have the New River Company and the London Water Board and Thames Conservancy round to have a look at us, and "Mystery of Honeywood Spinney" on the evening papers.

Bloggs does not allow any on the site, and there is no one about would be the wiser if you let us do the work all in the ordinary course and get it finished out of hand. You will pardon me addressing you, but I thought best after I got home to-night as it will save a bit of trouble.

Yours faithfully,

This friendly letter reveals Grigblay to us as he is under his skin. He writes privately as he could not well question the order to work at night officially, since the reason is no business of his. He has already prevented Spinlove from hanging up the whole work while the solicitors negotiated permission for the builder to use the spring, and he has again come to the rescue. The letter displays the honest good-nature and practical wisdom of the writer; and we recognize in his kindly, dry, ironical humour the salt of sterling British national character. Spinlove ought long ago to have established friendly personal relations with such a man.

SPINLOVE TO GRIGBLAY

(*Private*)

Dear Mr. Grigblay, 28.4.25.

I am very much obliged for your letter. Of course you are perfectly right. Please act as you suggest.

I was on the site yesterday and I wish to tell you that I am entirely satisfied with the brick window cills that I saw. Please work the flat arch heads and weatherings in the same way. I appreciate the attention your foreman has given to this matter and also the way he has managed the gradation from the first lots of facings to those now being sent. This has been done extremely well; no one would notice the change unless his attention was called to it.

Yours truly,

This is a private unofficial letter, and it would not be amiss if Spinlove used it as a model for his official letters to the builder in place of those he is so ill-advised—and ill-mannered—as frequently to write. It is clear he understands that Grigblay takes a pride in his work and wishes to please the architect, and he ought always to keep it in mind.

BRASH TO SPINLOVE

Roselawn,
Thaddington.
Dear Mr. Spinlove,   2.5.25.

You will perceive from the above address that we have now gone into residence here until the autumn. I visited the site last evening and am gratified to observe that progress is advancing, but there are several matters which I do not quite comprehend. Could you meet us on Saturday? I shall be travelling by the 12.27 from Cannon Street and we might go down together in concert and visit the site after luncheon.

Yours sincerely,

P.S.—Lady Brash requests me to say that our daughter is expecting some young friends to tennis in the afternoon, and it is desired that you will bring your bat, etc., if you like disporting yourself in that pastime.

We may conclude that Brash has never played lawn tennis.

SPINLOVE TO BRASH

Dear Sir Leslie Brash,   4.5.25.

As the builder's people will have left in the afternoon and

The Thick of the Fight

I want to see the foreman, I will go down early on Saturday and come to the house at 1 o'clock.

Yours sincerely,

P.S.—Will you be so obliging as to inform Lady Brash that I shall be charmed to comply with her invitation to tennis.

I detect a touch of east wind here. Spinlove's postscript—as recorded on the carbon file copy of his letter—is in autograph, as was that to which it replies, and as we know Spinlove well enough to judge that he would not so answer an invitation from a lady without being aware of a gaucherie, we may gather that he has deliberately retaliated on Brash by accepting in the same form and through the same channel as the invitation. His adoption of Brash's stilted diction and condescending tone cannot possibly be accidental; in fact, we appear to have surprised a bit of the Old Adam in our friend James. It seems clear that he has come to resent the condescending self-sufficiency of Brash (discernible to us only in his letters) and has reasons for being wide awake to social slights. Lady Brash would have written her own invitation had she not felt it incompatible with her social eminence to so condescend to her architect—that, at any rate, is my sense of the matter—and, if I am correct, Spinlove has shown a very proper spirit, although, without knowing what lies in the background, it is impossible either to commend or condemn his manner of showing it.

SPINLOVE TO GRIGBLAY

Dear Sir,   8.5.25.

I was on the site on Saturday and was greatly concerned to notice that two of the brighter of the red bricks in the facings are *already beginning to decay*. The surface is coming away in a powdery dust near the edges of the brick. I expressly prohibited the inclusion of these red. under-burnt bricks in facings; you promised that you would throw them out, and I selected and handed to your foreman samples of the bricks which only were to be used.

It is really inexcusable that, after my particular and exact

124

The Thick of the Fight

directions to the contrary, these soft bricks have been built into faces. Your foreman is going over the work and marking the doubtful bricks, and when I have checked over I must ask you to cut out and replace them with the bricks sent under the new arrangement with Hoochkoft.

It is a great disappointment to me that the frost spoilt so much of the jointing. It is a pity this work was not protected, as the top of the wall was, with sacking. It will be impossible to match the cut-off joint by pointing, so that the whole of the facings will now have to be raked and pointed. I have asked your foreman to have different samples of pointing done so that I can decide which to adopt.

I also had to call your foreman's attention to the clearing of the battens in the hollow walls.

Yours faithfully,

The battens referred to are those which are hung in the 2 in. space of hollow walls and carried up with the brickwork to prevent mortar falling into the space and collecting at the bottom, where it might conduct damp from the outer to the inner wall and block the ventilation inlets which, by allowing air to circulate, keep the space dry. These battens have to be pulled out and cleared of accumulations of mortar at frequent intervals if they are to serve their purpose thoroughly.

GRIGBLAY TO SPINLOVE

Dear Sir, 9.5.25.

Referring to your remarks *re* decay of facings, we cannot accept responsibility for same. If this matter had been left to us we should never have accepted such bricks as Hoochkoft first sent, but it was not in our hands as we acted on your orders and were told you had approved the bricks. We picked over the bricks to oblige you without charge, and Bloggs worked to your instructions and you saw what he was doing. It does not seem likely there can be many of the defective bricks and we will arrange to cut out and replace, but shall have to charge men's time for same and shall be glad of order for extra.

The frost getting at joints is no fault of ours, as faces cannot be protected. We were obliged to take off top course and re-build, as you know, although that work was protected.

Yours faithfully,

Grigblay is not to blame for frost attacking the green mortar joints; and he is not only entitled to disclaim responsibility for the decaying bricks, but is obliged to do so, for if he agreed, as part of his obligations under the contract, to remedy the defect in only one or two bricks, he would be accepting liability for the soundness of the whole of the facings.

SPINLOVE TO GRIGBLAY

Dear Sir,   12.5.25.

As you are well aware I have all along objected to the red soft bricks and expressly forbidden their use. I actually selected samples of what I *did* approve, and your foreman had these to guide him. I asked you to pick over the bricks, but you said the bricklayers would throw out the soft bricks as they came to hand. This has not been done and I must call upon you to make good.

Yours faithfully,

Spinlove, we know, is responsible for the bricks supplied. But for his vigilance 15 per cent or more of the whole of the facings would be defective; he would not be able to avoid direct responsibility to Brash, and it is very doubtful if he could by any means fix liability on Hoochkoft. Again we see how a small lapse from formal exactness in organization may lead to disastrous consequences.

Under-burnt facings have been known to decay before the roof of a new house was on, so that the whole had to be pulled down and rebuilt with the architect unable to fix responsibility on any-one because the samples he had approved had not been marked and could not be identified.

GRIGBLAY TO SPINLOVE

Dear Sir,   16.5.25.

We have to say that we accept no responsibility for defective bricks for reasons given. We note that the bricks delivered under the new arrangement with Hoochkoft meet your approval.

Bloggs tells us that bricklayers threw out all bricks that did not agree with samples. He did not keep samples after work completed as no reason to. He writes that about forty bricks had ought to come out.

Yours faithfully,

It will be noticed that in his first paragraph Grigblay repeats that he accepts no responsibility for the facing bricks, and then records that Spinlove has approved present deliveries. He does this in order to consolidate his position—so to speak—and put on record that he has always disclaimed responsibility.

GRIGBLAY TO SPINLOVE

Dear Sir,   19.5.25.
We shall be glad if you will pass us a further certificate for £2,500.

Yours faithfully,

SPINLOVE TO BRASH

Dear Sir Leslie Brash,   25.5.25.
The builder has asked for a further payment on account, and I have to-day sent him certificate No. 2 for £2,500.

Would it be convenient to you, I wonder, to let me have, say, £400 on account of my own fees?

Yours faithfully,

It would have been just as well if Spinlove had not asked for any fees at this time.

In dealing with business firms, public companies, corporations, Government offices, and so forth, it is well for an architect to send in claims for fees on account according to the letter of the custom (see R.I.B.A. scale of charges), for it is no one's business to ask the architect whether he wants any fees, and later on he may be called on to explain why the claim was not made earlier. The case is different, however, when the architect's employer is a private person. There is an etiquette which directs that, when employed by the nobility and gentry, the architect waits until invited to send in an account. This etiquette, which is linked with the past, flatters the architect by dissociating him from commercial activities, and it is a pity for the architect to discourage the sentiment.

In a certain high social plane it would be a gaucherie for the architect to ask for his fees; it would not so particularly mark a man in sore straits for money, as one who did not know what was what.

GRIGBLAY TO SPINLOVE

Dear Sir,   28.5.25.

Bloggs reports that he finds that the heads of window-frames come $1\frac{1}{2}$ in. too high to allow top of brick-on-edge head to line with horizontal joint of facings. The frames are made as figured on your detail No. 11, but we think you overlooked that ground floor is now $1\frac{1}{4}$ in. below bench mark datum from which the height of brick cills was figured. We might have saved it out of the joints, but we are up twenty courses now. Shall be glad of your early instructions.

Yours faithfully,

SPINLOVE TO GRIGBLAY

Dear Sir,   30.5.25.

I am annoyed to hear of the mistake with the frames. If the detail had been checked with the actual work this would not have happened. I shall be going on to the site next Tuesday and will see what can be done.

Yours faithfully,

It is difficult to see what exactly has happened, but the mistake has arisen from Spinlove having confused the ground-floor line with the bench datum with which it was originally identified. The builder is here at fault. All joiner's details are—or should be—sent on to the site so that they may be checked and figured up to agree with the actual work. It is likely that Spinlove's blunder trapped Bloggs; and it is also likely that the detail of the brick cills was prepared after the detail of the window-frames which had to be made early for building in. There are plenty of openings for slips and mistakes, but the builder who allows any joinery to be prepared which will not fit the building is to blame.

SPINLOVE TO BRASH

Dear Sir Leslie Brash,   30.5.25.

I have received report of the analyst, Sir Geoffrey Whittle, and enclose his account. The report is quite satisfactory, but it will be necessary to use specially lined pipes and lead tanks; and a water softener, at least for drinking and special purposes, is recommended. I should like to discuss this with you at an early opportunity. I shall be on the site on Tuesday.

Yours sincerely,

P.S.—Since dictating the above I rang you up and have now received your message and will arrange to meet you on site at 5.30 on Tuesday and stay to dinner. I will bring analyst's report with me.

SPINLOVE TO GRIGBLAY

Dear Sir,   3.6.25.

I was on site yesterday and arranged with your foreman to adjust error in height of window-frames by building a 6½ in. brick-on-end flat arch in place of 4½ in. brick-on-edge, so that the top of flat arch will now come one course higher than originally intended and shown on ½ in. detail.

I approved the bricks in facings marked by your foreman as to be cut out. I agree to an extra (day-work) for this work.

I also approved sample of pointing. A flat joint makes the joint appear too wide, and the irregularity of the bricks makes it untidy. The mortar is, therefore, to be slightly pressed back into the joint with a rounded piece of wood. This is to be done *as the work proceeds*. Facings already built to be raked and pointed to match.

The work looks very well and Sir Leslie Brash, you will be

glad to hear, expressed himself as delighted with all that has been done and with the progress being made.

Yours faithfully,

There is a healthy change of tone in this letter. "The band has come." Probably the Brashes, now first able to see the house taking understandable shape, are appreciative, and Spinlove's heart is lightened. It will be noticed that he has admitted his responsibility for the faulty bricks by allowing Grigblay an extra for replacing, and has found a satisfactory way of getting over the undue height of window-frames without the loud lamentations and complaints we have learnt to expect from him.

SPINLOVE TO THUMPER & CO.

Dear Sirs,   5.6.25.

I enclose analyst's report and recommendations, and shall be glad to receive an amended specification and estimate for ram installation and piping to storage tank, all in accordance with the recommendations of the report. I should also be glad to receive proposal from you, later on, for water softener. This is to serve one bath and bib cocks in pantry and scullery and H.M. closet.

Yours faithfully,

THE LAST OF THE SPRING

GRIGBLAY TO SPINLOVE
(*Private*)

Sir,   11.6.25.

Rather an awkward thing happened to-day, but no harm done, I believe, and lucky for us. Just before I got on to site Mr. Witspanner, tenant of Honeywood farm, came on to our ground and wanted to know whether we had right to hay in meadow below, and then he noticed our water tank. "Hullo,

130

you've a nice lot of water," he says. "Yes, and we wants a nice lot, too," Bloggs told him. "That's my water," he says, "and you've no right to take it." Well, I suppose Bloggs gave him a bit back, and off he goes saying he'd complain to Mr. Rallingbourne.

When I drove up he was just getting over the gate at the bottom, but Bloggs sent a whistle after, and he saw me and waited while I went down. Well, to make a short story, I took him to the hotel, and it's like this. He will not interfere with us taking the water, but he wants that bit of grass which is not of much account, anyway, after horses have been on it, so the business can be put right if Sir Leslie Brash will agree. But I was asking him about his landlord, Mr. Rallingbourne, and he says he's the sort that has got to be cock of his own dunghill. If you're polite, and not unreasonable, and don't presume, he will agree to near anything, but if he thinks you're trying to better him or steal an advantage he gets all his hackles up and nothing will move him. He does not care for money; it's bossing up he values.

Now, Witspanner knows we are using the water and if the ram is put in your client will be at his mercy, and he's a sour-tempered fellow and no mistake. What I suggest is that Sir Leslie should get Rallingbourne's consent to the ram by offering to pipe the spring on to his land. More water is lost travelling the ditch than the ram will pump.

With apologies for troubling you.

Yours faithfully,

The remarkable lucidity and completeness of Grigblay's presentment of the position will be noticed. Not only do we get the facts, but Bloggs, Witspanner, and Rallingbourne stand before us as actual persons, and we have an intimate and minute understanding of the state of affairs. Brash could not do it; the whole forces of Russ & Co. could not attempt it, nor could Spinlove. Grigblay has no educated knowledge of the use of words; but he has humour, practical insight, and the habit of single-minded frankness.

The Last of the Spring

Dear Sir Leslie Brash,   12.6.25.

The letter of which the enclosed is a copy is marked private, but I have Mr. Grigblay's permission to show it to you. It seems important to open negotiations with Mr. Witspanner at once and get in touch with Mr. Rallingbourne. I estimate cost of piping ditch, which is 320 yds. long, at £20.

                                        Yours faithfully,

Oh, do you, Mr. Spinlove!

This estimate is wildly at sea. One can only suppose that Spinlove has light-heartedly mixed up yards with feet and made no allowance for consolidating and levelling ditch and filling in with earth, wheeled or carted, and making good to ram waste and spring-head. Assuming that a 4 in. pipe will serve, a reasonable estimate is from £60 to £100.

Spinlove has here airily tossed a trifle from his richly-stored bins of knowledge to Brash as he might throw a scrap from his plate to a dog; but Brash will make the figure the basis of his negotiations with Rallingbourne. Facile, off-hand estimates ought not to be given. Spinlove would do well to notice the stolid ignorance of Bloggs, who, in common with every other foreman, never has any idea of the value of any kind of work and, when rallied, merely grins wisely. Spinlove's lapse is here quite inexcusable; he has not been confronted by a sudden demand for an estimate, but offers it gratuitously; he does not describe his figure as a rough approximation and he has not paused to visualize the work involved or even to scrutinize his absurd figure.

BRASH TO SPINLOVE

Dear Mr. Spinlove,   15.6.25.

I thank you for your communication transmitting copy of Mr. Grigblay's letter. Will you please convey to him my sensible appreciations of his action. I have indited a letter to Mr. Witspanner, which I have entrusted to a gentleman who will call and negotiate with him, and I will open the subject with

Mr. Russ to-morrow on the lines suggested in Mr. Grigblay's proposal.

Yours sincerely,

SPINLOVE TO BRASH

Dear Sir Leslie Brash,   17.6.25.

I have received the enclosed from Grigblay. Perhaps you, or your solicitors, will write to Grigblay direct, as there appears to be no time to lose.

Yours sincerely,

(ENCLOSURE) GRIGBLAY TO SPINLOVE
(*Personal*)

Sir,   16.6.25.

Bloggs writes that Witspanner was on site to-day and wants 5s. a thousand gallons for all water used past and future. We do not hold with this, but would rather pay than be stopped, though we are using a thousand gallons a day or more while the hot weather lasts. We do not want, however, to prejudice your client's position, so write to ask instructions. Bloggs held him off for a day or two, but he means to have the money so we shall have to agree to something.

Yours faithfully,

This impudent claim by Witspanner is, frankly, blackmail. It is rather a highly-coloured instance of the subtle undercurrents that constitute business, with a big B, in which concessions are made in one matter on the tacit understanding that mischievous interferences will be withheld in another. Witspanner has no property in the spring; and even if Grigblay diverted the whole of it, his claim would be against his landlord, Rallingbourne, and not against Grigblay or Brash. The price he is asking is such as he might charge if he were pumping as well as supplying the water.

It is to be noticed that if Grigblay had not adopted a false position by drawing the water secretly, he could not thus be victimized by Witspanner.

The Last of the Spring

Dear Spinlove [*sic*],   20.6.25.

I am happy to intimate that all future anxiety anent the spring is finally eliminated.

My secretary interviewed Mr. Witspanner, and offered the hay for nothing if he would desist from objecting to our use of spring, but he said the crop would not be worth taking and desires me to pay him for mowing and carrying. He has also a claim against Grigblay for the water he has used.

This evening I met Mr. Rallingbourne, quite unexpectedly, at the house of friends by whom Lady Brash and myself were being entertained at a dinner-party. I found an opportunity of informing him that the builder was using water from the spring. I found him a most affable gentleman. He intimated he had no objection so long as Witspanner had sufficient flowing to him. I then asked if he would complete an arrangement for me to utilize the water, and acquainted him what our proposal was. He said he anticipated there would be no objection, but desired to appoint a surveyor to report, and, of course, some agreement will have to be executed. He made a memorandum of your address, and I will request you to represent me and meet this surveyor.

I desire to record my appreciation of the great assistance you have been in enabling me to secure the spring for my use, and which would never have eventuated but for your initiation of the proposal.

> Believe me,
> Yours sincerely,

This letter is in autograph, written at night and after a very pleasant dinner-party. The champagne is not out of Brash's veins and the glow of a social triumph newly fills them. These facts account for the unusual warmth and intimacy of the letter, and for the generosity of its concluding acknowledgment, but Spinlove is entitled to gratitude. He could not have been more concerned for Brash to benefit by the spring if the house had been his own.

Spinlove's Special Roof

Dear Sir,   22.6.25.

On receipt of your telephone message yesterday telling us that rights to spring were agreed and not to deal with Witspanner, we wired to Bloggs to warn him. We enclose his letter received to-day, which you may like to see.

Yours faithfully,

(ENCLOSURE) BLOGGS TO GRIGBLAY

Sir,   21.6.25.

Your wire received and noted. Two o'clock Witspanner clomb over fence so I thought better use a bit of tack. What are you bargin in for I says dont you see the notice board. What do I care for you and your blinking notice boards he says, when are you going to pay me for my water he says. Blinking yourself I says you can go to blazes out of here you lousy tup I says or I'll chuck you out. After that he began to get a bit saucy and I admit we add a few words till Alf Cheese chipped in and offered him a thick ear and I thought it would come to a scrap, but the men wouldnt have it and he cleared off saying as how he was going to talk to Mr. Rallingbourne on the telephone.

Yours humbly,

SPINLOVE'S SPECIAL ROOF

SPINLOVE TO GRIGBLAY

Dear Sir,   7.7.25.

I yesterday saw first delivery of roofing tiles, which are quite satisfactory, but I noticed no tile-and-half tiles for verges. The tiles are cogged, as well as prepared for nailing and, as on further consideration I do not think it necessary to nail the whole as specified, will you please nail every fourth course on south and west slopes only, and verges and eaves throughout. I have noted this as an omission.

Will you also let me know how you intend to mix the three different colours so as to give the "broken colour" tiling specified? Patches of uniform colour must not show, nor must there be any appearance of arrangement.

I asked your foreman to build a yard run of eaves and verges with one of the kneeler oversails, all as shown on drawing No. 27, for my approval. I also directed that rafters should *not* be lined up on plate and at ridge, but allowed to range a little unequally so that the finished surface of tiling will show undulations; and directed that the tiling battens should not run truly parallel, but vary ¼ in. each way, and the battens themselves be bent or "sprung" as necessary, so that gauge of tiles will *not* show in rigid parallel courses. Please give these matters particular attention.

Yours faithfully,

We may sympathize with Spinlove's solicitude and applaud his vision—although Grigblay is unlikely to do either—without necessarily commending the principles of the game he would be at. All architects who have the right salt acquire affections—or affectations—which they afterwards discard in favour of others, and we have no right to decide that Spinlove is either precious or silly because the immediate colour of his architectural creed may not be also ours. Spinlove has, clearly, lifted the idea bodily from a book, for it would scarcely have jumped into his head in such complete detail; and he has never tried to get the thing done before or he would not suppose carpenters and tilers to be ready, at a word, to do haphazard and crookedly the particular work which it is the pride of their skill and experience to perform by a rule of perfect exactness. He would also have known, had he before experimented in this way, that his demands upon the builder in these matters are intolerable.

GRIGBLAY TO SPINLOVE

Dear Sir,   8.7.25.

We note your instructions *re* nailing tiles. The tile-and-half bonnet and ridge tiles are on order. With regard to mixing tiles, specification calls for "broken colour tiling", from which we understood they would be supplied ready for hanging as they came to hand. The tilers will want more money, but we will have the three different kinds sent up in equal quantities and the tilers can be trusted to use them haphazard, as you wish, but we must ask you to set off this against omission of nailing.

We have directed our foreman to build sample eaves, etc., as you ask, though we were not prepared for this; and with regard to the other matters you mention, will do our best to meet your wishes, but we must point out that this is special work not covered by the contract, and we may have to claim an extra for it.

Yours faithfully,

If Spinlove had not launched out with his prescription for a sham medieval roof, Grigblay would not have been likely to comment on his other exactions. That comment is made, on principle, to remind his young friend, the architect, that a builder pays for his compliances in hard cash, and that favours should be sought and not demanded. In the circumstances, Grigblay is not unreasonable, and he evidently foresees that the stolid inertia of the carpenters and tilers will put the extinguisher on Spinlove's crotchety roof. He knows that they will listen respectfully to his directions for battening and tiling, while perhaps sharing a few winks behind his back, and then carry on much as usual. On a later day it will appear that the architect has not been understood; and if he is tenacious in his purpose, he will be asked questions he cannot answer and will be left to surrender the position either before provoking a mutiny, or after doing so. All this Grigblay perfectly understands. It is possible to build such a roof as Spinlove has set his heart on, but only with foresight and after careful preparation and with selected workmen.

SPINLOVE TO GRIGBLAY

Dear Sir,   9.7.25.

I agree to the omission on nailing tiles being set against the extra work you say I have asked for, but the method of roofing I described must be included. I do not agree that it is "special

137

work". The whole of the work, I may remind you, has to be done "to the architect's satisfaction".

Yours faithfully,

Spinlove has once already tried to bludgeon Grigblay with this God-given power conferred upon him by the contract, and his second attempt will probably be as futile as was the first, for Grigblay's claim is sound: the field of the architect's satisfaction is, of course, limited to the work described in the contract.

GRIGBLAY TO SPINLOVE

Dear Sir,   10.7.25.

We regret we cannot accept your view that the special work in roofing you have called upon us to do is included in the contract, and we must respectfully ask you to note that we can undertake it only on the clear understanding that it is an extra. We will ask you to give directions to the carpenters and tilers on the spot, so that your exact wishes may be understood as these are not clear, and to note that we cannot accept responsibility for the soundness of this method of work, which is new to us. When we know exactly what is required we will give you estimate of the extra value of carpenters' work, and subsequently of the tiling.

Yours faithfully,

This stiff letter is not remarkable if we consider the extremely provocative one to which it replies. We notice Grigblay's assumption of authority. We have before observed this, and found the explanation in Grigblay's sense of Spinlove's practical inefficiency. If Spinlove had the gumption to treat Grigblay as a colleague, the interchange of such unpleasant letters would be avoided. Another builder might well have taken Spinlove's orders; made a dreadful botch of the roof, and brought in a heavy claim for extra at settlement; and Spinlove ought to be grateful to Grigblay for his plain speaking.

BRASH TO SPINLOVE

Dear Mr. Spinlove,   7.7.25.

I enclose specification anent inserting pipes in ditch from

Mr. Rallingbourne's surveyor. I understand you have signified your approval of the proposition and shall be obliged if you will direct Mr. Grigblay to proceed with the operations.

Lady Brash and myself are much gratified with the advance in progress and anticipate eventually moving into the house considerably in advance of the expiration of the contract period, as the chimneys are now completed and the roof commenced and little remains but the interior work. I inquired of Mr. Bloggs as to the signification of the flag I observed to be affixed to a staff on one of the chimneys, and as I ascertained that many of the workmen were addicted to total abstinence from alcoholic liquor, we arranged for a picnic tea to be served to them on Friday. Our hospitality, I gather, was greatly appreciated, and the event will, I trust, serve still further to expedite progress.

All our friends join with us in admiring the fine appearance the edifice is assuming. The effect promises a very pretty and charming residence when complete.

I beg the pleasure to enclose cheque for £250 on account of your fees.

> Believe me,
> Yours sincerely,

P.S.—I am requested to remind you that your anticipated presence for lawn-tennis is expected on next Saturday prox. Jump in to eats and toe the line at 2 before the patters scrum starts, Woggles and Biff will be here. Snooty tried the tea-tray toboggan stunt backwards and is nursing her bumps, poor dear.

The last lines are in a hurried, bulgy hand so different from the body of the letter, that we may decide Sir Leslie Brash did not write them.

The pleasure Brash begs will find Spinlove begging. On May 25 Spinlove applied for £400 on account of fees, and now, after an interval of six weeks, Brash sends his architect £250 as a mark of approval and by way of encouragement. It will probably be a very long time, indeed, before Spinlove again has such an experience; but if he continues long in practice he will learn that the reaction of the private client to claims for architect's fees—knit up, as it is, with personal relations and respective social standings and financial circumstances—is as varied as any other of the characteristics of which every individual is compacted. Broadly speaking, an architect who is reasonably competent and conscientious may, saving disasters, expect not only to have his bill paid in full, but to be thanked for his services; yet he may not always be paid as and when he expects. There are also sensitively honourable men and women who confuse the architect with the commercial agent, and who are taken aback at being charged for services which they have not made use of—such as advice, sketch plans, or even contract particulars; and there are others who feel that they should not be called upon to pay for advice which has misled them, e.g. where contract particulars have been authorized under the architect's estimate and no tender near to his figure is obtainable. There are also men and women who are not sensitively honourable and who resist on principle all obligations, and will make unjust quibbling objections to the amount of both builders' and architects' accounts in confidence that the matter will be settled to their own advantage without recourse to lawyers. It is impossible to instance all the different kinds of treatment an architect may receive from private clients in the article of fees; they cover every degree of meanness and of generosity which human nature knows. It is a fact that will appear odd only to those whose experience of men and affairs is slight, that trouble over payment of fees is most to be expected when the scale or amount of them has been particularly and exactly agreed beforehand. The sort of man who bargains with his architect on the point of fees is precisely the sort who boggles at paying anything, and who will seek to interpret the understanding unfairly against the architect. This is the "shrewd, hard-headed" principle which is better admired at a distance than near at hand, although most architects obtain a close view of it sooner or later.

SPINLOVE TO BRASH

Dear Sir Leslie Brash,   8.7.25.

Thank you for cheque, I enclose form of receipt.

There is a misunderstanding for which I may possibly be

responsible. I gather from the amount of your cheque (£250) that you suppose I asked for payment on account of £400 fees, whereas I asked for £400 on account.

Please do not trouble to rectify. It will prevent all chance of confusion in future if I follow the established business custom and invoice architect's charges as they fall due for payment. I will take an early opportunity to get things straightened out on this footing.

Yours sincerely,

Spinlove is always at his best when his resentment is awakened and he forgets himself. He was evidently hurt, and composed his letter with the care which the task of being decorously venomous deserves. He pays Brash the compliment of assuming that the thing Brash has done is so unthinkable that a clear impossibility can alone be the explanation. Unless Brash has forgotten how to blush—and in view of his self-conscious aspirations to the genteel this is not unlikely—we may imagine him as growing pink when he reads his architect's letter. He will probably be thankful to avail himself of the fantastic excuse offered him, and it is difficult to see how, in the future, he is to avoid completing with reluctant cheque book the "formal business arrangement" which the solicitous Spinlove, entirely for his client's convenience, has promised to adopt. We need not, however, be hard on Brash: he means well. He sent his cheque, in fact, on an impulse of generous appreciation; but his activities have left him aware of little but his own importance and his own gain, and he knows no better than to behave in this way. Spinlove has taken a strong line, but, from what we know of Brash, it is justified and will be unlikely to do any harm. He was not merely entitled to make protest, but it was so necessary for him to do so as to be almost a duty.

SPINLOVE TO BRASH

Dear Sir Leslie Brash,   9.7.25.

It gave me great pleasure to know that you are so well satisfied with the work that has been done, but I think I ought to tell you that you must not expect to get into the house *before* the contract date. There has been delay from frost and bad weather and also that arising from alterations in the plans, and this lost time will unavoidably delay completion. The interior represents the greater part of the work, but I am satisfied with the progress Grigblay is making.

I enclose list of grates and sanitary fittings. Will you let me know, when I see you, whether you would like to choose any of these? The prices are those included for in the contract.

Yours sincerely,

BRASH TO SPINLOVE

Dear Mr. Spinlove,   13.7.25.

I was extremely disappointed to conclude from your last communication that our residence will not be completed till subsequently to the expiration of the contract date. I clearly comprehended that the contractor was under penalty to complete the house *previously* to the day designated. Surely the vagaries of our climate are an eventuality which the contractor must risk, and an alteration does not necessarily involve elaboration! I desire to be informed when the house will be completed for occupation so that we may make necessary arrangements.

I am obliged for the list of grates and conveniences. I will purchase them myself through the intermediary of an acquaintance who is in a position to secure them at wholesale trade discount prices.

Yours sincerely,

SPINLOVE TO BRASH

Dear Sir Leslie Brash,   15.7.25.

The whole question of delay in building contracts is intricate and not readily to be explained in a letter, I fear, but the root of the whole matter is that, as the contract allows consideration for bad weather, extra work, strikes, etc., time is not of the essence of the contract. As a practical fact, the only security for prompt completion you have is the builder's care for his reputation, and you could not be in safer hands than Grigblay's.

Please do *not* buy grates or sanitary goods. The former have to suit the fireplaces which I am designing; and the latter have each to fit special conditions, so that it is absolutely necessary that all should be ordered by the builder after you have settled the pattern and price.

It will be of no advantage to you to buy at trade prices. The builder can buy at least as cheaply as you can, and he has already credited trade discounts in making up his tender. If *you* buy, the builder will be entitled to add a fair trade discount to his contract price and you will certainly pay more in the end. This matter of trade discounts is carefully safeguarded in the contract. The sums set aside for the various goods are the actual sums paid to the merchant and not, as I think you suppose, the catalogue retail prices. The builder has already included in his contract for packing, carriage, etc., and it will be impossible for me to prevent extras creeping in if those arrangements are upset. I hope I have succeeded in making the matter clear.

Yours sincerely,

He has, at any rate, had a good try! It would have been better if Spinlove had kept his explanations for Brash's ear, for his letter is likely to raise more questions than it answers. Spinlove, however, appears to enjoy writing letters, although he cannot always enjoy reading those he receives: the next on the file, for instance!

MR. POTCH AGAIN OBJECTS

GRIGBLAY TO SPINLOVE

Dear Sir,   18.7.25.

We are sorry to have to report that the District Surveyor refuses to pass the main drain to sewage tank on the ground that it leaks. As you are aware, there is a very sharp fall on this drain, and we used particular care in making the joints with waterproofed cement so that they should stand the pressure of water test which, between the second and third manholes, has a head of 32 ft. Only four joints showed a drop or two of water after standing several hours, and these have been remade to the Inspector's satisfaction; but water sweats out through the pipes themselves. It only shows in beads after standing for hours, and does not run, but Mr. Potch, the Surveyor, came down yesterday, and has condemned the whole drain. We shall be glad of your instructions.

The pipes are "tested" as specified and there is no flaw in one of them. Bloggs would have put on labourer to keep the pipes wiped dry against the Inspector's visit, he says, but he never thought objection would be made.

Yours faithfully,

We have already seen that, at a pinch, Bloggs can be depended on for "a bit of tack".

SPINLOVE TO GRIGBLAY

Dear Sir, 20.7.25.

I have written to the District Surveyor on the subject of the drain. Please take no further action of any kind, but keep the drain charged, and ask your foreman to mark standing level of water in manholes and keep the covers on. I will visit the site on Tuesday next.

I note the contents of your letter on subject of roofing. If Mr. Grigblay can meet me on Tuesday on this matter I shall be glad.

Yours faithfully,

Spinlove has come quietly to heel in this matter of the roof. It will be noted that the head of water gives a pressure, in the lower pipes, of some 15 lb. a square inch. The "tested" pipes are subjected by the makers to a hydraulic pressure of about 20 lb. a square inch, but this test is applied for a few seconds only, to detect flaws.

Mr. Potch again Objects

Sir,   20.7.25.

It is reported to me that you have refused to pass the main soil drain at Honeywood. I shall be obliged if you will tell me: (*a*) the grounds for your objection; (*b*) the by-law infringed; and (*c*) the work you require to be done.

Yours faithfully,

Spinlove has evidently not forgotten previous interchanges with Mr. Potch. He does well to remind Potch that his powers are limited by the by-laws. Many small builders and others may forget this and Potch, in his ambition to flourish as a public terror, may not trouble to remember it.

POTCH TO SPINLOVE

Sir,   24.7.25.

Honeywood drain loses water and must be relaid. *See By-laws.*

Vent of settling tank to be replaced with 4 in. heavy cast-iron soil vent. *See By-laws.*

I am surprised to be informed by my assistant that copy of our by-laws was sent you last year. As it is unfortunately lost I shall be very glad to present you a second copy to go on with for a time, on receipt of 1s. 2d., post free, as my Council disapproves of putting A.R.I.B.A.'s and others to the trouble to ask unnecessary questions.

I am, Sir,
Yours faithfully

The insolent intention of this letter, although veiled by its illiteracy, is undoubted, and is just what Spinlove must expect from Mr. Potch, who, as has already appeared, practises privately as an architect in the district in which he operates in his official capacity, and so finds it to his interest to pile up official difficulties in the way of his private rivals. To irritate them into precipitate action, to their public discredit with the Council, is all part of his system.

145

Mr. Potch again Objects

Sir,   27.7.25.

You must permit me to inform you that the Honeywood drain does not "lose water", as stated in your letter. After standing for three days fully charged the drop in level of water in manholes is scarcely perceptible—$\frac{1}{4}$ in. or $\frac{5}{16}$ in., not more, in fact, than would be accounted for by absorption and evaporation. The joints are perfectly tight and a slight sweating of water through the substance of the pipes is due to the excessive head of water imposed by the sharp fall in the ground. This condition of head would not arise in practice and the sweating would be of no consequence if it did. The pipes are Dallop's deep-socketed "Tested" laid on concrete and are the best procurable. I have to ask you either to pass the drain or to say in what way the work can be improved, either as regards workmanship or materials.

There is no "Settling Tank". The thing you refer to is an anaerobic tank; its successful action depends upon absence of air, and the ventilation pipe you call for would tend to spoil its efficiency by admitting air. The 1 in. galvanized pipe you object to is to prevent gases accumulating at pressure in the tank and breaking the seal of the trap, and was put in by my orders.

Yours faithfully,

Spinlove does well to ignore the offensiveness of Potch.

Sir,   31.7.25.

I note you now admit water leaks through substance of pipes at Honeywood and which is the reason I stated drain leaks and must be relaid. Unfortunately my inspector cannot wait three days at manholes to check figures as he has other business as well. I have been told drains sometimes gets stopped. The water test is against that happening and not against it does not happen.

My Council does not expect of me to tell Institute architects where to get drain pipes, but most people know such trouble

146

would be cured by treating with one or two coats of pitch, boiling hot.

I happen to be aware what a settling tank is and also all soil vents to be 4 in. heavy cast iron, *see By-laws*. If everyone who did not agree with by-laws could do what he liked my Council would not have adopted same.

> I am, Sir
> Yours faithfully,

Potch seems to know that Spinlove is young and lacking practical experience, for his pitch proposal, if not a joke, is a mischievous attempt to get Spinlove into worse difficulties or, at least, make a fool of him. The "boiling hot" pitch would crack all the pipes and it could not hold back water which is forcing itself, under a pressure of some 15 lb. to the square inch, through glazed earthenware. We may judge from the letter which follows that Spinlove fortified his opinion by discussing the matter with Bloggs.

SPINLOVE TO POTCH

Sir, 4.8.25.

Your letters on the subject of Honeywood are clearly intended to avoid the questions I have put to you. In the circumstances I must ask you to note that the drain you object to demonstrably conforms with your by-laws and is of the best possible workmanship and materials, and that I claim on behalf of Sir Leslie Brash a formal certificate of acceptance from your Council.

I also have to ask you to note that your by-laws do not require that septic tanks should be ventilated, and that, as it is insanitary and against established practice to do so, I have no intention of ventilating the tank at Honeywood.

> Yours faithfully,

Spinlove is winning this tussle in fine style. Potch, of course, is only bluffing, and prevaricating, and obstructing; but Spinlove could scarcely arrive at the point of confidence in which, alone, he could write such a letter, without anxiety and stress. As I was led to remark on an earlier occasion, Spinlove seems to have "been there before", for in nothing does he show such firmness as in thwarting the machinations of Potch.

SPINLOVE TO POTCH

Sir,   14.8.25.

It is now ten days since I wrote to you stating the position I take on the subject of Honeywood drains and calling upon you for certificate of acceptance. As I have received no acknowledgment or reply, I have to ask you to note that unless I receive immediately a satisfactory answer, I must refer the whole correspondence to the Chairman of your Council, in which case I shall protest against the way I have been treated by their official and the offensive tone of the letters I have received.

I am, Sir
Yours faithfully,

Spinlove seems, in a previous existence, to have been a prize-fighter.

POTCH TO SPINLOVE

Sir,   16.8.25.

Re drains at Honeywood. I have been busy and the matter is a difficulty, but have now decided to give you the benefit and enclose certificate, which no doubt meets your satisfaction.

The vent to settling tank must be at your own risk.

I resent your remarks and regret you should feel cause to make same as no intention on my part.

I remain, Sir,
Yours faithfully,

What Potch means by "vent must be at your own risk" he probably could not himself exactly say. He no doubt considers his last paragraph to be an ample explanation and apology. Much of the offensiveness of his letters is, perhaps, due to native ungainliness of mind. He is like a fox which cannot help smelling and is unaware that he smells.

THE STAIRS GO WRONG

GRIGBLAY TO SPINLOVE

Dear Sir,   5.8.25.

As you know, we are at work on the staircases, and we venture to call your attention to the headroom at No. 3 step of back stairs. We think you overlooked that the binder carrying partition runs across door-opening to bathroom, so that unless the bathroom floor is raised one step the binder must be dropped 5 in., and owing to the revised arrangement of the stairs shown in detail No. 27, we do not think headroom will be satisfactory.

Awaiting your immediate instructions,

Yours faithfully,

P.S.—We shall be glad of a further certificate for £3,000.

Apparently Spinlove has done what it is perilously easy to do: he has improved on the contract in his detail drawings without investigating fully all the consequences of the change.

SPINLOVE TO GRIGBLAY

Dear Sir,   6.8.25.

I confirm telephone message directing all work on back stairs to be stopped. I note that the strings have already been got out and sunk, and treads of winders, etc., prepared, so that it is too late to go back to the arrangement shown in the contract drawings. I do not understand why my attention was not called to this matter when the work was set out.

I widened the landing at top to give more room for the swing of the door; this pushed the bottom step out and brought No. 3 step into the position of No. 2, so that it was obvious I had mistaken the position of binder. If you had called my attention to this at the time, the difficulty would not have arisen, as I might have managed with one step less.

I do not like the idea of raising the bathroom floor **one step**.

The Stairs go Wrong

Will you please return drawing No. 27. I do not at present see what can be done. A 9-in. steel joist in place of binder will not settle the trouble. You will notice that I splayed off the angle of the binder to ease the headroom, which I knew was tight.

Yours faithfully,

A ridiculous letter! It is clear Spinlove does not know what the devil to do and wants the builder to tell him. He allows us to suppose that in the contract drawings there was an 11-in. binder which carried 5½ in. floor joists. This binder came below the ceiling and was probably cradled and finished as a beam. In making his detail he pushed the binder up flush with ceiling to give to the starved headroom the extra height required by the alteration in the steps; and overlooked the opening to the bathroom door across which the binder runs.

GRIGBLAY TO SPINLOVE

Dear Sir,   8.8.25.

We regret to say that we have to-day learnt that the binder, floor and partition, are now all in place as shown on the contract drawings. Your drawing No. 27 gives exact particulars of the stairs, but the position of the binder is only slightly indicated. The section of it is not coloured on our drawing, and we had no means of knowing what your intentions as regards other parts of the work were. The binder had been prepared and sent on to the work, and probably fixed, before we received your detail.

It will be necessary either to scrap the strings and winders or take down the binder, etc., which will be the simplest way. We suggest that the difficulty could be got over by putting in a 5½-in. sill in place of binder and trussing the partition, which might also be hung up by tie strapped to purlin. The easiest thing, however, would be to raise the binder and floor. If you do not care to go up one step to bathroom floor, the bathroom might be entered from the corridor instead of the landing of back stairs, in which case the floor need not be raised with the binder. Drawing No. 27 herewith. We shall be glad of immediate instructions.

Yours faithfully,

Spinlove Applies for Fees

Spinlove is a conscientious fellow and we may sympathize with his predicament. It is more than humiliating for him to scrap the strings, etc., for to do so will probably cost about £30. We know, too, that he was not satisfied with the contract arrangement. On the other hand, Grigblay's other proposals are all hand-to-mouth expedients or botches.

SPINLOVE TO GRIGBLAY

Dear Sir,   9.8.25.

I return drawing No. 27 amended. You will see the binder and bathroom floor are to be raised. It is a particular point of the plan that the servants' bathroom should open off their own landing and not off the main corridor, and, as it is only for the servants, the step will not matter so much. [*Ahem!*]

I consider that the discrepancy should have been pointed out to me, as this is a duty specially placed upon you by the contract, and it must be clearly understood that no extra is involved by the making good which I consider to have become necessary owing to your oversight.

Yours faithfully,

Spinlove is pushing things too far. The mistake seems to be entirely on his shoulders.

SPINLOVE APPLIES FOR FEES

SPINLOVE TO BRASH

Dear Sir Leslie Brash,   9.8.25.

Grigblay has applied for a further certificate for £3,000, which I have sent him.

I take this opportunity of enclosing particulars of my own fees, as arranged. The first item—4 per cent on £18,440—became due on the signing of the contract. The second item, 2 per cent on £7,000, is the residue of the 6 per cent on value of work done.

I hope you like the dining-room fireplace which the bricklayers are finishing. The bricks are specially made for this purpose, and Grigblay has imported a particular bricklayer to carry it out.

Yours sincerely,

Two or three months ago Spinlove asked for a modest £400 on account of fees, and after waiting six weeks was fobbed off with £250. As we remember, he then promised to put the matter "on a formal business footing so as to prevent further misunderstandings". He now sends in an account for the fees which, by custom and under the Institute Scale, he is entitled to. The amount indicated is £876 less £250 already paid, or £626.

BRASH TO SPINLOVE

Dear Mr. Spinlove,   10.8.25.

You must permit me to convey to you that I did not at all anticipate that at this early period I should be requested to disburse so preponderant a proportion of your fees. I conceive I am correct in asseverating that professional gentlemen are, by habitual custom, paid their fees *after* the services they refer to have been performed and not *previously* thereto. The mansion is a considerable distance—a very considerable distance I am led to apprehend—from being completed, and yet I am now requested to disburse a sum approximating to 80 per cent of the whole remuneration eventually accruing to you when the works have been satisfactorily completed and your engagement with myself terminated. I confess that I am amazed at a claim which is—if you will allow me permission to so express myself—most extravagantly preposterous.

Although it is not a matter to which I should, under happier circumstances, desire to make deviation, I, nevertheless, consider that you are under serious responsibilities and obligations towards myself which, as in all such monetary matters, have a financial signification. I observe that the contract document protects me with a not unsubstantial guarantee; that is to say, the sums I periodically disburse are amply secured to me by the value of the operations performed. It is on the face of it—if you will permit me to say so—an utterly anomalous conjunction of eventualities which gives me no such security against my architect, to whom I am requested to disburse—by clear demonstration—not 80 per cent of, but *more than double*, the proportion of fees represented by the work accomplished.

I observe that the certificate, which you inform me has been transmitted to Mr. Grigblay, is for the augmented amount of £3,000. May I be permitted to remind you that £2,000 is the payment I am accustomed to anticipate disbursing on these occasions.

Yours sincerely,

Brash's protest is not unnatural, and his reasoning would be sound if his premises were true. This is a very different letter from those he wrote to his young friend in the early days; in fact, it is such a letter as he might write to one of his own years and standing. Spinlove's firm resistance to being bilked seems to have jolted Brash into a higher esteem of him. His wordy expostulation is a little pathetic.

GRIGBLAY TO SPINLOVE

Dear Sir,   12.8.25.

We are unable to agree that the error in back staircase is a matter for which we are in any way accountable, as we had no means of knowing what your intentions *re* bathroom door were. We must ask you to note this, as we cannot accept any such responsibilities for oversights in joinery details, although we do our best to detect them. As the alteration now required is a small matter we will, however, in this instance make no charge, although we are entitled to do so.

Yours faithfully,

I judge this letter to have been dictated by Grigblay himself. He has no doubt had a sharp word to say to his shop foreman and to Bloggs, but as a matter of principle he finds it necessary to remind Spinlove that his bland assumption that the architect is not responsible for misdirections, and for discrepancies in his own thoughts, will not do at all.

153

The Water Comes In

Dear Sir Leslie Brash,   13.8.25.

Had I known you were not aware of the custom concerning payment of architects' fees I would have explained the matter. I now enclose particulars of architects' charges issued by the Royal Institute, from which you will see that two-thirds of the 6 per cent fees—that is, 4 per cent of the amount of the accepted tender—represents fees earned before the contract is signed. The remaining 2 per cent is for general supervision and direction of the work, and is payable in instalments as the works proceed, so that the architect is in the same position as the builder in giving what you term "financial security". At no time is the architect paid for what he has not done.

I shall be glad if you can make it convenient to send me a cheque. One has, of course, to get in one's money.

Grigblay is entitled to £3,000. He would have been entitled to £2,000 several weeks ago had he applied for it. The contract states that certificates shall be for not *less* than £2,000.

With kind regards,

Yours sincerely,

Spinlove seems now to have got Brash's measure in this matter of fees. He has knowledge, of course; but the letters also show him to be the stronger man. By comparison Brash appears to be—if I may be given permission to be allowed to so express myself—a flabby old jelly.

THE WATER COMES IN

Dear Sir,   15.8.25.

I was on the site yesterday and was disturbed to see water standing 15 in. deep in cellar. Some months ago I noticed water, but supposed it was due to rain, only. There is no sign of its coming in through the walls above the standing level of the water, so that there must be a defect in the vertical damp course below that line. Your foreman says he pumped the cellar dry a fortnight ago, when there was nearly 2 ft. of water. I directed him to dig down outside and open up vertical damp course for my inspection. Please let me know directly the work is ready for me to see.

Yours faithfully,

GRIGBLAY TO SPINLOVE

Dear Sir,   16.8.25.

Our foreman has reported to us your instructions to open up vertical damp course; but this is a big undertaking and, as we are certain there is no defect in the damp course, we do not think any purpose will be served by opening up. We have directed our foreman to pump the cellar dry, and we will keep it under observation. In our opinion the water comes up through the floor.

Yours faithfully,

SPINLOVE TO WILLIAM WYCHETE, P.P.R.I.B.A.

Dear Mr. Wychete,   18.8.25.

I am in difficulties with a cellar which lets in water; but where it comes from or how it gets in I cannot understand. The ground is perfectly dry; there was not a sign of water when the excavation was made, and the lower 7 ft. of excavation is in impervious clay. The vertical damp course of 1-in. thick waterproofed cement is continuous with the horizontal damp course which is below the level of the cellar floor. This is 4-in. concrete with $1\frac{1}{2}$ ins. of 3 and 1 cement rendering trowelled to a polish, with skirting carried up 6 ins. and turned into joint of brickwork.

I went on site yesterday after the cellar had been pumped out and wiped dry. We could find no flaw anywhere, but after a time the whole surface of the floor became wet, and after a couple of hours water had collected in one part. The foreman says the floor is "sweating", but does not explain what he means, and I don't think he knows. Can you give me any idea what is wrong, and how I can make the place tight?

Yours sincerely,

The Water Comes In

My dear Spinlove,   20.8.25.

I think the explanation of your scrape is that the impervious excavation holds surface water, which collects against the outside of the walls, like a tank. This gets under the foundations and through the footings, and floods the space under the floor—which, I assume, has 4-in. or 6-in of loose filling—and the water is forced up by its standing head through the concrete. The probability is that this process began while the concrete and rendering were green, so that minute channels were then formed in it; but under the conditions stated the cellar could scarcely be a dry one, as the floor was not damp-proofed.

If there is such a fall in the ground that you can drain the water away by connecting a pipe through the wall into the hard core under the floor, the cure is easy. If not, your only course, in my opinion, is to cover the floor with asphalt and put a concrete floor on top, to prevent the water forcing the asphalt up. This concrete, however, may not be necessary. It is important to dig a sump and keep the water pumped out until the whole of the floor is finished and perfectly set. The builder should have done this originally.

With best wishes to you,

Ever yours sincerely,

Dear Mr. Wychete,   21.8.25.

Many thanks for your letter. I understand the matter perfectly now. There is a sharp fall in the ground, so that there will be no difficulty in draining. Can I make the builder pay for this work? Also, would the District Surveyor be likely to object to the drain going under the walls? If so, perhaps it would be best to put an iron pipe through the wall and under the house, but the rest of the drain, I imagine, could be earthenware? Or could the whole be earthenware if care were taken to carry walls, etc., clear of it?

Yours very sincerely,

Lady Brash takes Charge

Spinlove is here so elated to find himself master of the awkward situation that he loses his head and acknowledges Wychete's careful reply to his question by asking him a hatful of entirely idiotic and unanswerable ones. Needless to say, there is no reply from the great man.

LADY BRASH TO SPINLOVE

Dear Mr. Spinlove,   21.8.25.

Sir Leslie is so *dreadfully* sorry not to be able to have answered your last letter, but he has gone to The Moor quite suddenly! He did not in the least expect it, and asked me to write and tell you.

My daughter is expecting some young friends on Saturday, and we shall hope to see you in the afternoon.

How very close it has been to-day!

Yours sincerely,

MAUDE BRASH.

Will you be my D.P. to Bingham's and stay night? Biff has let me down. *Split-tail behaviours*. Phone early. P.

For "The Moor", I read the moors; Brash has been invited north to shoot grouse. I do not know how Lady Brash manages to convey that her husband is a most unsafe gun, but she certainly does so.

As it is eight days since Spinlove wrote, this stampede to "The Moor" is an imperfect explanation of his getting no answer. The intimation that he lies heavy on his client's conscience will, no doubt, hearten him.

It was "P", by evidence of the handwriting, who wrote a footnote to an earlier letter! "P" must be the daughter.

LADY BRASH TAKES CHARGE

GRIGBLAY TO SPINLOVE

Dear Sir,   27.8.25.

We enclose copy of letter from her Ladyship and await

your instructions *re* same. We understand that the partition referred to is that between bedrooms Nos. 5 and 6, and is to be moved to increase size of dressing-room.

Yours faithfully,

Mr. Grigby (*sic*),

Lady Brash wants the wall in the other big room—not our room—moved nearer from the end as the big wardrobe must go in the dressing-room.

Sunday.

Grigblay knows better than to take instructions except through the architect, although inferior kinds of builders might not be so circumspect. Some might even welcome this opportunity of making hay of the contract and establishing an uncontrolled account for extras.

Lady Brash has here adopted the style of the great lady gratuitously, for this sort of thing has been far to seek since the war. One has only to consider that the person she addresses is superior to her in heart, in mind, in wisdom, in humour, and also—if the word is to have any right meaning—in education, to realize the absurdity of her assumption. We may imagine Grigblay, a middle-aged man, shouldering a pack in Flanders, while Lady Brash was hoarding provisions, decorating her car with flags of the Allies as if for a boat-race, and speaking of Grigblay and his kind as "Tommies".

SPINLOVE TO GRIGBLAY

Dear Sir,   30.8.25.

I have written to Lady Brash. Please tell your foreman to get on with the work.

Yours faithfully,

Decisive but ambiguous! The manner of it expresses "Lady Brash be blowed!" but the sense is "Alter the partition as directed".

Lady Brash takes Charge

Dear Lady Brash,   30.8.25.

Mr. Grigblay has sent me a copy of your letter of Sunday. I understand you want the partition moved so as to make the dressing-room wider. Are you really quite sure you would like this? No. 6 was designed as a dressing-room only, though big enough to take a bed on occasion, and there is a door from it to the bedroom of No. 5. If you widen the dressing-room by, say, 3 ft., you will *reduce the bedroom by 3 ft.* Have you realized this, I wonder? The result will be that you will have a quite small single bedroom with a door opening into a double bedroom also so much on the small side that I am afraid you will be disappointed with it. I mention this because I have used particular care not to have any mean-looking rooms, and because I was originally asked to arrange for a good double room with dressing-room *en suite*, and the plan provides this.

If the partition is moved, the windows will be displaced and both rooms will look lop-sided and ungainly—in fact, they will be spoilt so far as appearance goes. Do you not think it would be simpler to put your big wardrobe in another room and, generally, fit the furniture to the rooms? It is really too late now to attempt to alter rooms to suit furniture. It would be a great pity to shift the partition, and I am sure you would be sorry if it were done.

I hope Sir Leslie is having good sport.

Yours sincerely,

Spinlove's difficulty is no less because it is a common one. He is under obligations to be courteous and patient and amenable to his employer's ambitions; but he cannot ignore his own reputation nor that of his profession, and with this is associated the duty of rendering unfailing services so that his client shall be guided to make wise decisions and protected from hasty and foolish ones. The indications are that Lady Brash is so light-witted and so spoilt that appeals to her better judgment will impress her merely as opposition. When such a woman wants anything she has no attention to give to reasons against it; and in this case the lady's mind is probably incapable of holding two ideas

159

at the same time. The best thing for Spinlove to do would be to make up his mind that Lady Brash does not understand what she is asking, and take an early opportunity of cajoling and flattering her to a sounder judgment.

One awkwardness of the position is that even if Spinlove found sufficient justification to do what the wife demands, he could scarcely act without the authority of the husband. If he writes to Brash for that authority and does not get it; or if the lady knows he has written; or if he acts without writing and is taken to task, he is in danger of becoming involved in—well, let us say, an intermission of marital bliss, which may thereafter encumber him with petty dilemmas, make his work a misery instead of a pleasure and his best offices a personal failure instead of a success.

LADY BRASH TO SPINLOVE

Dear Mr. Spinlove,

I do not want any door and I want it in *that* room as it is the room my sister will have when she comes and it was in our old home and she is used to it so I cannot have it anywhere else as it does not go with the other furniture. Of course I do not want the windows changed only the wall. [*"It" is, evidently, the wardrobe.*]

A man came about sweeping the chimneys. He said his name was Mr. Williams and in new houses the chimneys cannot be swept unless you get on the roof and break the tiles so I really do not know *what* to say. I wish Sir Leslie was at home to see about it. How chilly the wind has been!

With kind regards,
Yours v. sincerely,

Friday.

A touting chimney-sweep has apparently been telling the poor woman that flues are sometimes so built that they cannot be swept.

SPINLOVE TO LADY BRASH

Dear Lady Brash,   3.9.25.

I will see that the chimneys can be swept without anyone

having to get on the roof. I will call at eleven on Saturday morning and settle with you what is to be done. Yes, the wind has certainly been rather chilly.

With kind regards,
Yours sincerely,

This looks more hopeful.
The letter which follows deals with so many points of detail that I will interpolate my comments.

GRIGBLAY TO SPINLOVE

Dear Sir,   4.9.25.
Our foreman took down the partition between rooms Nos. 5 and 6, but her Ladyship now says that it is the one between Nos. 8 and 9 she wanted moved. Her Ladyship seemed very much upset and directed Bloggs to take down the latter partition which he has now about finished. This, as you know, is a double breeze partition. Her Ladyship said you decided to increase dressing-room 3 ft., but we do not think you can intend that on account of linen cupboard. See plan.

[Spinlove mentioned 3 ft. as an illustration only, and had in mind another partition.]

Four feet nine seems the least we can manage with, and that will bring the wall very close up to window. You will remember there was a post on this partition supporting purlin. Bloggs has got this pinned up temporarily, but we shall want a steel joist to take this post, which we think is the best way out of the difficulty. We take it the binder carrying this partition, which is finished as a plastered beam on ceiling below, will remain, and the new binder put in above level of ceiling.

The heating engineer says he does not see how to run his return which came down in the corner of this partition. We told him we would chase wall, but that is an awkward job, as it is only 4½ ins. [*the inner lining of hollow external wall, presumably*], and we are afraid the casing cannot be made flush with wall, as it is a 2-in. pipe, even if we sink back of casing **where the unions come.** We shall be glad of your immediaet instructions as the work is being delayed; also authority for extra.

Watkins started glazing their casements, but we had to stop their men as her Ladyship says they are wrong. We understand sheet or plate is wanted. We had to let Watkins's men go away, which is a pity, as we have had a lot of trouble to get them

[*Watkins must be sub-contractor for the iron casements, and his fixing of leaded glazing is referred to.*]

There is a sweep been hanging about who said he was engaged by her Ladyship to sweep the chimneys. Bloggs told him he had no orders for him, but he afterwards found the man at work and two of the labourers had to see him off the premises. We mention the matter as we should like her Ladyship to understand that we had no instructions to admit the man, and as we are responsible for this work we prefer to entrust it to our own workmen. The parging is green as yet.

[*The builder is under contract to sweep flues to prove they are clear and have been properly built for sweeping.*]

The alteration to the partition will push the lavatory basin in the bedroom so far over that we shall not be able to get the waste into the same head taking those of dressing-room and room beyond, and a separate head and vertical waste will be necessary, and we do not see how this can be made to clear the garden entrance and window below.

[*The dressing-room is perhaps 7 ft. wide, and Spinlove has been able to scheme so that the waste from lavatory-fitting in this room, and those in the bedrooms adjoining on each side, shall all discharge into one rain-water head and be conducted to the ground by one inconspicuous vertical pipe.*]

A lead waste carried diagonally over the head of garden entrance and across to the gully receiving the vertical waste would, however, meet the case.

We shall be glad of your early instructions.

Yours faithfully,

A lead pipe trailing conspicuously across the wall in close

*proximity to one of Spinlove's architectural prettinesses, and
reaching out frantically to the gully, would be a calamity. Such
botches are unworthy of a competent speculative builder—they
disgrace an architect.*

*This letter is an example of the disinterested solicitude of
Grigblay for the success of the work. Few builders would lay the
matter out so fully, but would either put the work in hand, or say
they could not go on and ask for instructions. It also displays in
a remarkable manner how the carefully contrived economies of
means to ends and neat perfections of a skilful design may be
cast into hopeless confusion by merely one act of capricious
interference. However, here is some more of it!*

SPINLOVE TO GRIGBLAY

Dear Sir,   5.9.25.

I was dumbfounded to learn that you have allowed your
foreman to pull down and alter the work in face of my written
instructions to the contrary. I tried to get into touch with Mr.
Grigblay on telephone to-day. Will he please ring me up without fail to-morrow morning?

I confirm my telephone instructions that no further alterations are to be made except by my explicit directions. I am at
a complete loss to understand why it should be necessary for me
to remind you of so well-established a rule. It will certainly be
necessary to put the work back as it was before, and I must
look to you to do so, but kindly note that *nothing is to be done*
until I am in a position to give complete instructions. I shall see
Lady Brash on Saturday and will write to you next week.

Yours faithfully,

GRIGBLAY TO SPINLOVE

Dear Sir,   5.9.25.

Since we wrote yesterday we have heard from our foreman
that her Ladyship has referred to hot and cold water to be laid
on to the drawing-room. We know nothing of this, and ought
to have instructions *at once* as the service pipes are being got

out and this will mean a change in the layout, as it is a long run for the pipes and we do not quite see how we are going to get proper circulation. We understand her Ladyship intends an aquarium to stand in bay, so there will have to be a gully to take waste, and as the Surveyor may object to this being treated as rain water [*sure to do so!*], we shall have to lower the top manhole. [*So that the extension may drain to it.*] We were about to build this manhole, but have stopped the work and also that on drains beyond, as levels and falls will have to be altered, and it is no good doing the work twice over. We think the Surveyor will insist on a vent pipe by gully. [*The extension is at the top end of drainage system and a vent pipe is required in that position.*] Would you wish this on the gable beside the bay window, which seems the best position?

We shall be obliged by your immediate instructions.

Yours faithfully,

Spinlove, we may be sure, has exercised his best ingenuity to arrange that this unsightly 4-inch pipe running up walls and sticking up above eaves of roof, shall be hidden away; and the prospect of its becoming the salient feature of the most sappy part of a studied elevation will cause him anguish.

GRIGBLAY TO SPINLOVE

Dear Sir, 6.9.25.

We write to confirm and record statement made to you by Mr. Grigblay on telephone this morning that he acted in accordance with your instructions (see your letter of 30.8.25) to "go on with the work", which we naturally read to mean to do the work ordered by her Ladyship. Our understanding that the partition between Nos. 5 and 6 was intended, was, we hold, confirmed by your letter.

We note that no further work is to be done until we have your explicit directions, but must point out we are being stopped and that we shall not only have to claim extension of time as well as the extra, but shall have to compensate heating and other sub-contractors and ask you to consider our own position, as we have had to pay off labourers and drain-layers, and we may have to send away plasterers shortly, and these are difficult to get. We shall be glad of a certificate for £2,000 further on account.

Your last certificate, dated 6.8.25, has, so far, not been honoured. If you can help us in this matter we shall be obliged.

Yours faithfully,

Lady Brash, at a touch, has not only brought confusion to the work, but has given both the architect and builder sore heads. Grigblay has been indefatigable in good offices, but the dislocation of his organization is a serious matter for him and he evidently has no intention of being victimized. He is entitled to look to his architect to protect him.

LADY BRASH TO SPINLOVE

Dear Mr. Spinlove,   *Wednesday.*

The men took away the wrong wall!!! It really is all most trying and difficult and so very vexing when they will not do what they are told and putting it in all little squares one cannot see out of and the servants cannot clean properly because of the corners and complaining about it. The men have made a path through the wood all along where the bluebells come for a short cut through the hedge instead of going out at the gate, what Sir Leslie will say when he comes back I really do not know and I thought I should never get the dust out of my eyes they are quite sore still. The man who came about the chimneys complained that Mr. Bloggs was very rude and would not let him because he did not want him to find out and he says because the chimneys are made crooked and cannot get a brush up to sweep them and perhaps the house will be burnt down. If I had any idea what a trouble it was all going to be I would never have consented, but Leslie will not listen to a word I say and the factory chimney was smoking yesterday and all blowing across and I knew what it would be and if they don't put a proper water-pipe it means the garden hose through the window like we had at Pilchins Drake though I am sure I shall never like the house as much as Pilchins and the fish dying. Really

165

I feel so worried with it all I scarcely know where I am. Phyllis is still away she is always such a comfort.

Yours sincerely,

The poor woman has made herself ill in her anxiety to see matters right, and I feel sorry I have said such savage things about her. She opens her heart to Spinlove in a way that shows she has a friendly liking for him and understands he is on her side, although she does not at all understand that the builder is working under his direction. Spinlove ought to have no difficulty in establishing her peace of mind and guiding her to a wise decision if he relies upon her confidence in his good offices and her obvious liking for him, and avoids any assumption of authority. Apparently, however, the receipt of this letter and Grigblay's by the same post have made him again lose his head.

SPINLOVE TO GRIGBLAY

Dear Sir, 7.9.25.

I cannot accept the position you take in your letter, but agree you had grounds for misunderstanding. Later on I will discuss the question with Mr. Grigblay and come to some arrangement; in the meantime, I will do my best to get a decision from Lady Brash.

I have wired to Sir Leslie Brash, which will, I hope, help matters, and I am writing to him. He is still in Scotland and will, no doubt, pass you a cheque on his return. Your application for certificate has my attention.

Yours faithfully,

SPINLOVE TO TINGE, QUANTITY SURVEYOR

Dear Mr. Tinge, 7.9.25.

I enclose particulars of the state of the work and of certificates granted. Grigblay has asked for a further £2,000. You will see he had £3,000 only four weeks ago.

Will you let me have an estimate of value of work done.

Yours truly,

Lady Brash takes Charge

7.9.25.

Brash, Achoe, Glen Taggie, Inverness. Work held up urgent writing Spinlove.

It is difficult to see what purpose Spinlove had in sending such a telegram except to put Brash off his aim for the day.

SPINLOVE TO LADY BRASH

Dear Lady Brash,   8.9.25.

I came down expressly to see you on Saturday, as arranged, and was disappointed to find you out for the day. I have this morning received your letter.

I am very sorry to know you are so worried, but the alterations you want involve all sorts of difficult questions which cannot be settled except at an interview, and your letter makes allusions to matters of which I know nothing. If you will make an appointment, I will gladly come down and settle things with you. Perhaps you could telephone. I rang up and left a message for you this morning, but have heard nothing.

It will not do to delay, as the builder has already had to send away some of the men and the works will be in part stopped if something is not decided at once.

I have received a rather stiff letter from Mr. Grigblay pointing this out and, of course, it all means extra expense.

I could come down to-morrow afternoon if you will telephone before 11, or early on Thursday. I shall not be in town on Wednesday, and have an appointment in London on Thursday afternoon.

> With kind regards,
> Yours sincerely,

P.S.—As I have already mentioned, you need have no anxiety about the chimney flues. I will see they are all right.

It is difficult to imagine a much more tactless letter. Spinlove asks the poor soul not to worry and then tells her of various causes for worry of which she is happily unaware.

167

Lady Brash takes Charge

SPINLOVE TO BRASH (INVERNESS)

Dear Sir Leslie Brash, 8.9.25.

I wired to you last night—"Work held up urgent writing" as I am in a quandary, and Grigblay has been obliged to send away some of the men and others will follow them unless I can at once give directions. As perhaps you know, Lady Brash wishes the partition between bedrooms 8 and 9 moved so as to make the dressing-room bigger, and it was taken down without my knowledge, as also partition between 5 and 6, by an error. There are numerous minor alterations and serious displacements involved in the alterations and I feel sure if these were understood you would wish the partition restored. There is also certain other work Lady Brash wants altered but I have not been told what exactly is required. I have, however, stopped part of the work including the drains or this might have to be done all over again.

I feel it is difficult for you to come to any decision from such a distance but think you would wish to know what is happening as, besides extra cost of the alterations, there may be claims for interference with the work and, of course, time allowance will have to be given. The plastering and some other work is going on as well as circumstances will allow.

Yours sincerely,

What sort of an answer Spinlove can expect to this letter it would be difficult to imagine. If he could not set out definite points for Brash to decide—and it is difficult to see how he could do so—it would have been better for him to confine himself to saying that alterations have been ordered which make it important for Brash to be on the spot as soon as possible. However, this letter will give Brash some idea of what is happening.

LADY BRASH TO SPINLOVE

Dear Mr. Spinlove, *Sunday.*

I really do not know why all this worry with Mr. Blogs not doing what I said and so many questions going on and on and Phyllis away and Leslie and the man about the chimneys again because now is the time and not wait till the house is finished and perhaps have to be pulled down he says. I want the wall moved but not the *wrong one* they have pulled down and the men all smoking and whistling instead of attending and the extra expense which I know Leslie will not pay when he always said the house was for me in case he died first and not for Mr. Grigby to stop the work and do what he likes and make the stairs not wide enough with all the trouble we had at Pilchins over again taking the window out to get it in [? *the wardrobe*] and such small ones [? *windows*] when I wanted them big and not with little squares all over, but Mrs. Spooner says they *will* do it and you can get in quite easily by cutting the squares with a pen-knife and perhaps be murdered so I shall never feel safe in the house when Leslie is away and you cannot have bars in case of fire she says. If I had known that it meant I never never *never* would have agreed with the papers all saying how ugly factory chimneys are and ought to be stopped but I knew what it would be and how am I to get others now the cook and second housemaid have given notice because a new house is damp though I told Leslie all along I could not live in a damp house and the trouble of moving in and the carpets not fitting and things getting broken!!! If Phyllis was here I could get a little sleep and not lie with it all going round and round in my head and how it will all end I really do not know.

Yours v. sincerely,

MISS PHYLLIS BRASH TO SPINLOVE

Dear Jazz,   10.9.25.

I skipped home last night. What *have* you been doing to my poor little Mum? She has made herself ill over this wonderful house of yours. Why cannot the poor thing have clear glass and an Aquarium—she has had one since she was an infant— and the wardrobe that belonged to her grandmother? I know the poor dear is apt to get into states and we have to take care of her, but building without tears is surely poss? Anyhow, come and be nice to her. It's no earthly writing letters and it is very bad for her to be distressed—and what does the dam house matter anyway, you fussy old Architectooralooral Jazz?

Lady Brash takes Charge

Dad jumps in on Thursday week—eight days! Great rejoicings—my sire has slaughtered a nine pointer! *Not* nine pointers, thank goodness. Been staying with Snooty and her lot at St. Austell and doing the Daily Mail dry bathing girl stunt all day. No great larks, but a lovely time.

PUD.

P.S.—Be sure and phone train. I will pick you up at station for yap before you see M.

"Pud" is clearly the daughter, Phyllis; not at all the sort of daughter one would expect the Brashes to produce. "Jazz" is perhaps derived from Jas. or the initials J. S.

(TELEGRAM) BRASH TO SPINLOVE

10 9 25.

SPINLOVE, ARCHITECT, RANGER HOUSE, MAYFAIR, LONDON, W.1. Your telegraphic and written communications received stop desist from all alterations stop returning next Sunday prox ends BRASH.

Brash seems to be a good customer of the Post Office.

BRASH TO SPINLOVE

Dear Mr. Spinlove,   13.9.25.

I arrived home to-day and am greatly gratified with the considerable advance in progress during the interim of my absence. I shall be gratified if you will use your best endeavours to come down here as early as possible to-morrow as the requisite haste brooks no delay. Kindly telephone approximate hour of your probable arrival.

I was so fortunate as to secure a fine trophy, though not a "Royal", to my rifle while in the Northern Highlands of Scotland. This I intend shall be affixed over the fireplace in the interior hall and will augment the embellishments of the apartment, which unless my apprehensions mislead me, I anticipate may be a little plain in decorative accessories.

Yours sincerely,

Lady Brash takes Charge

Nothing much wrong here apparently—not even with the tautology! We do not know what happened at Spinlove's interview with Lady Brash, but we may guess that the buoyant vitality of "Pud" has made all sweet and secure.

Dear Sir Leslie Brash,   15.9.25.

I write to confirm instructions you gave me yesterday in conversation, as follows:

Breeze partition between bedrooms 8 and 9 to be restored but to have door opening between the rooms.

Partition to bedrooms 5 and 6 to be refixed so as to make dressing-room 1′ 9″ wider and doorway to be closed up.

Leaded glazing to be fixed as already supplied.

Hot and cold service and waste connection for Aquarium to be fixed in front hall window.

I yesterday gave directions to this effect and the work is going ahead. I am grateful to you for giving way on the matter of the glazing, and I am sure that after the house is finished you will have no cause to regret your decision. You would soon gather from the comments of your friends that sheet glass was a great shortcoming in such a house and in time you would be likely to have it taken out and lead glazing fixed.

I enclose receipt for cheque which you handed me on Monday and for which many thanks. I note you are sending cheque to Grigblay.

With kind regards to Lady Brash and yourself,

Believe me,

Yours sincerely,

In these matters one can never tell how the cat will jump, but here is a happy ending indeed! When motives are ingenuous and methods frank, a tough dispute often clears away distrust and establishes a higher mutual respect and a deeper sympathy and liking.

As usual, Spinlove has said more than is necessary. By repeating the adroit argument that appears to have won the day for him, he is rubbing in his victory, which is the last thing Brash wishes to be reminded of.

A Storm in a Paint Pot

Dear Sir,   15.9.25.

Value of work done to 12.9.25	..		..	£11250
Retention	..	..	..	1844
				9406
Already certified	..	..	..	7000
			Balance	£2406

Yours faithfully,

As more than half the work is done the maximum retention of 10 per cent of contract, has accumulated.

A STORM IN A PAINT POT

BRASH TO SPINLOVE

Dear Mr. Spinlove,   18.9.25.

An influential acquaintance is financially interested in a new novelty super-paint which will shortly, he informs me, replace all other surface coverings now on the market. It is called Riddoppo and is a *super*-paint giving a most dainty and fascinating interior surface to the inside of houses, as it is free from any odoriferous effects, cannot be scratched by the fingernail and is capable of receiving a high polish. It is elastic so that cracks do not permeate through it and it is also *non-inflammable* and *operates as a fire-proofing coat to both joinery and walls*. I should not be doing justice to the merits of Riddoppo if I did not add that it is *acid proof*, is compounded of entirely new secret elements and that a jet of boiling water or super-heated steam may be directed to impinge upon it for some minutes without deleterious effects occurring. The colours obtainable are very exquisite and varied and we have provisionally selected tints which we desire embodied in the decorative embellishments of the apartments of Honeywood Grange—as we anticipate naming the mansion; these will be

A Storm in a Paint Pot

known as the Pink Room, the Yellow Room, the Blue Room
and so forth, and the tints available will make it possible for
each door to be identified by its independent colour.

Our friend will allow me a special extra discount of ten per
cent and we shall have his advice in the choice of tints and
decorative embellishments as he promises that our house shall
represent the best modern effects possible.

With kind regards,
Yours sincerely,

Silly old man!

SPINLOVE TO BRASH

Dear Sir Leslie Brash,   19.9.25.

I know nothing of Riddoppo, I am afraid, except that it is
advertised in the Tube lift I daily use as a "new novelty super-
paint", but this description, I assure you, is no recommendation but rather the opposite. Grigblay is responsible for the
painting, and the paint specified is well known and the best
results can be obtained from it. I can hardly think that Riddoppo is of any practical value as a fire-proofing, nor that it
will hide cracks opening under it. The ability to resist jets of
acid and super-heated steam will not count for much at Honeywood, and you will not want it "polished"; and as linseed oil
and zinc white have been proved by long years of use to give
perfect results it is surely not an advantage, but a *dis*advantage,
that Riddoppo does not contain them.

I trust that you will not allow your friend to settle the colours
of the rooms. This is a matter which Lady Brash and yourself
should alone decide; it should depend entirely on your individual taste and the completion of the design of the house *as a
whole*. I do not think your friend can have had any experience
in this matter, or he would not make such proposals as you
describe; nor would he make any proposals at all before he
had seen the house in a state approaching completion.

With kind regards,
Yours sincerely,

P.S.—I am sending Grigblay a further certificate for £2,400,
and enclose note of my own fees in respect of that sum.

A Storm in a Paint Pot

There is a touch of the East wind in this letter. Its logic is a shade too devastating, though we may admire the tact with which Spinlove urges that the Brashes, alone, should decide the decorative scheme when his intention must be to guide that decision.

BRASH TO SPINLOVE

Dear Mr. Spinlove,   20.9.25.

I have perused your communication with close attention but you must permit me to indicate to you that the confidence with which you asseverate condemnation of Riddoppo super-paint, of which you admit you know nothing, seems to me—if you will permit me to say so—a little wanting in logical reasoning. You also ignore the fact that Riddoppo is free from odoriferous emanations, a charm which makes it peculiarly attractive to Lady Brash, whose gastric equipment is sensitively disposed to olfactory aggression of every description [*i.e. dislikes smells. Excellent!*].

My friend, a most eminent commercial gentleman, would be the last to be misled by deceptive assertions and as the various meritorious desirabilities of Riddoppo make it most suitable to our desires, I request you will direct Mr. Grigblay to apply it throughout.

Certainly it is our intention to decide on the tints selected.

Yours sincerely,

Brash's friend, though the last to be misled, may be the first to mislead.

SPINLOVE TO GRIGBLAY

Dear Sir,   21.9.25.

Sir Leslie Brash wishes Riddoppo super-paint used throughout. Will you please get me full particulars of this paint and the manufacturers' instructions for using, and I will send you revised specification.

I enclose further certificate for £2,400.

Yours faithfully,

A Storm in a Paint Pot

Apparently Spinlove is not, as before seemed, fully aware of the danger of experimenting with new kinds of paints.

SPINLOVE TO BRASH

Dear Sir Leslie Brash,   21.9.25.
  I have directed Grigblay to use Riddoppo super-paint throughout, as you wish.
  I hope you will reconsider painting the rooms out all in different colours. It is, I assure you, a thing which no one with knowledge of house decoration would propose. Your friend's idea seems to be to turn Honeywood into a paint manufacturers' show room. This, I am sure, will be intolerable to you.
                                    With kind regards,
                                        Yours sincerely,

More kind regards! Spinlove has got well home, but he hits Brash nearly as hard as he hits Brash's friend, the "influential commercial gentleman".

GRIGBLAY TO SPINLOVE

Dear Sir,   22.9.25.
  We know nothing of Riddoppo super-paint, and private inquiries we have made have had no satisfactory result; we therefore have respectfully to state that we cannot accept responsibility for same.
                                    Yours faithfully,

Spinlove should have made inquiries and satisfied himself before calling upon Grigblay to use the paint.

SPINLOVE TO BRASH

Dear Sir Leslie Brash,   23.9.25.
  I enclose copy of Grigblay's reply to my instructions to use Riddoppo.
                                    Yours sincerely,

A Storm in a Paint Pot

Dear Mr. Spinlove,   24.9.25.

I have not been informed of the precise nature of your communication to Mr. Grigblay anent Riddoppo paint, but I must protest most vigorously against what I apprehend to have very much the appearance of a conspiracy to resist the performance of my wishes. This is intolerable and beyond bearing. I assume that Mr. Grigblay anticipates that he will benefit financially by the handsome profit he has doubtless credited to himself on the painting, and is desirous to prevent my obtaining the 10% special discount; but Mr. Grigblay should be informed that it is his business to receive orders and not precisely to give them. It is for me, I apprehend, to decide what paint shall be used in my own residence, and for Mr. Grigblay to assume to dictate to me on this or any other matter is—if he will allow me to say so—perfectly monstrous and unendurable.

I do not know what the man means by "responsibility", and if I may be permitted to be perfectly frank, I do not care. I give the order and the responsibility for giving the order is mine. Mr. Grigblay's responsibility is to do what he is told *at once*.

The colours of the various rooms will be eventually decided later, but in that matter also I consider it is for the owner of the house to give orders and not, precisely, to receive them.

Yours faithfully [*sic*],

Liver!

Dear Sir,   25.9.25.

I am instructed by Sir Leslie Brash to order you to paint with Riddoppo, as already directed. Sir Leslie Brash accepts all responsibility.

Yours faithfully,

Does Spinlove understand fully what that responsibility is? Grigblay understands well enough, but the indications are that Spinlove does not.

A Storm in a Paint Pot

Dear Sir (*sic*),   25.9.25.

I have instructed Mr. Grigblay to use Riddoppo, as you direct.

Mr. Grigblay knows nothing of the discount you speak of and it would make no difference if he did for he is not going to pay it. If profit were his chief concern he would not have tendered for such a house as Honeywood.

I enclose copy of my letter to Mr. Grigblay of to-day and also of my previous letters to him, so that all evidence of our conspiracy may be safely in your hands. These can be attested if you wish. My files are open to your inspection.

I think it is very hard, Sir, that after my unsparing efforts to give you a house which will be entirely satisfactory to you, it should be handed over for a paint manufacturer to celebrate himself by turning it into a colour-cure asylum for lunatics— Red for melancholia, Blue for homicidal frenzy, Yellow for religious mania, etc.—for this exactly describes—if you will permit me to be perfectly frank—the ignorant folly of your friend's proposal; and that because I warned you of the risk of experimenting with an untried paint, utterly discredited by the claims of its lying advertisements, I should be taken heavily to task; and because the builder independently ex-presses the same distrust I should be charged with conspiracy with him to deceive you.

I have arranged to go abroad for a belated holiday on Friday and expect to be back in three or four weeks. I shall be moving from place to place so that I shall be out of reach of letters, as I am in need of rest.

Yours faithfully,

Nerves! Brash has broken the camel's back. Brash's letter which provokes this spirited answer is in autograph. Had it been typed the reference to conspiracy comes very near indeed to libel, and as it was sent to Spinlove's office where the presumption is that all letters, not marked confidential, are opened by clerks, the question of libel may still stand.

It is clear that Spinlove was bound to protest, and undignified and childish as his letter is, he has probably met the matter in the best kind of way. Since his letter is a spontaneous expression of natural feelings, it may be easy to excuse and forget; whereas a stiff protest and demand for the withdrawal, which cannot be refused, might not readily be either forgiven or forgotten. If Spinlove had written on the same impulse, but without losing self-control, he would be likely to have served his own and Brash's interests perfectly. In doing so he might well have said—"I am sure on reconsidering your letter you will feel that it is not only unfair to me and to Mr. Grigblay, but that I am bound to ask for a withdrawal of the word 'conspiracy'."

In point of fact Spinlove is making far too big an outcry over this rainbowed bedroom idea. When the time comes he will no doubt be able to soften the horrors he dreads, but in any case the Brashes are entitled to have what decorations they want, and the enormity of the proposal depends rather on its application than upon its principle. Spinlove's vanity is more deeply concerned than his aesthetic convictions, I fancy.

BRASH TO SPINLOVE

Dear Spinlove (*sic!*),   26.9.25.

I hasten to immediately respond to your communication. I apprehend that the epistolatory intimation to which you take exception was indited with unduly hurried precipitation for which I desire to proffer profound regrets and tender sincere apologies. I employed the word conspiracy, as I anticipate you will on reflection perceive, terminologically and figuratively and solely in its loose phraseological and allegorical application without ulterior signification. [*Bravo! A bag of nuts to Sir Leslie Brash.*]

Lady Brash and myself design to enter into consultation with you on the subject of the decorations before arriving at definite decisions on variegation of tints and, as you are aware, we greatly appreciate the attentiveness of the care you have expended on the operations, and the excellence of Mr. Grigblay's meritorious performance of the work.

With best wishes from us both for a successfully regenerative holiday.

Always yours sincerely,

P.S.—I shall be gratefully appreciative of occasional messages signifying your whereabouts for telegraphic communication, if necessary. In the interim of your absence I will keep a close inspection on the operations and communicate with your office.

As Spinlove's friend Dalbet said "a real good sort!" Ridiculous as the old boy is, this is not merely a generous but a sympathetic letter. It is, however, a little surprising, as was that it replies to. There is somehow a lack of reserve—a background of intimacy— which the facts before us do not explain. Perhaps the upheaval when Lady Brash took control is accountable. Anyhow, Spinlove can go away and enjoy his holiday. There is a note "Answered 27.9.25." on the corner of the letter, so that Spinlove appears to have acknowledged it in his own hand.

SIR LESLIE BRASH TAKES CHARGE

There is a partial hiatus in the file owing to Spinlove's being on holiday abroad. If he has left adequate drawings and instructions behind him, Grigblay will endure his absence with an equanimity Spinlove probably has no idea of, and on his return all will be found safe and satisfactory—unless, possibly, it is not. The chief dangers are Brash's interference and the immovable steadfastness of Bloggs, the foreman, who is likely to follow what he deems to be his instructions with a devotion which no obstacles will discourage.

SPINLOVE'S ASSISTANT TO BRASH

Dear Sir,   12.10.25.

Regret was not at office when telephoned inquiry received.

Have heard nothing from Mr. Spinlove except one word wirelessed from aeroplane near Barcelona ten days ago. On inquiry ascertain this not code word but given to understand means Mr. Spinlove in good health and enjoying holiday.

179

Sir Leslie Brash takes Charge

At present Mr. Spinlove believed to be Corsica or Athens unless breaking journey Constantinople; therefore difficult to cable, but in any case scarcely possible make your question clear or for Mr. Spinlove to reply without drawings at hand. In circumstances think best hold off work terrace steps until return. Have directed Mr. Grigblay accordingly.

Yours faithfully,
R. S. PINTLE,
for J. SPINLOVE.

Pintle seems to have modelled his style on the penny-a-word diction appropriate to inland telegrams. Spinlove should not allow this.

PINTLE TO BRASH

Dear Sir,   15.10.25.
Your telephone message directing proceed work terrace steps received Have instructed Mr. Grigblay accordingly.

Yours faithfully,

MISS BRASH TO PINTLE

Dear Sir,   15.10.25.
If you feel at liberty to do so, will you say what the single word was which Mr. Spinlove wirelessed, as there is a great difference of opinion here.

Yours truly,
PHYLLIS BRASH.

PINTLE TO LADY PHYLLIS BRASH [*sic*]

Madam,
In reply beg state word wirelessed by Mr. Spinlove Oct. 2nd *YOICKS*. This not code word but informed means Mr. Spinlove in good health and enjoying holiday.

Yours respectfully,

Pintle has, it will be seen, made "Pud" a lady in her own right.
180

Sir Leslie Brash takes Charge

He evidently supposed the letter was from Lady Brash and was ignorant of the titular distinction. "Pud" will laugh, and her dad's ambitions may be flattered. Pintle is apparently a draughtsman who has taken charge in Spinlove's absence.

(TELEGRAM) BRASH, PENZANCE, TO SPINLOVE
LONDON

On further cogitation decided desist from work terrace steps ends Brash.

PINTLE TO BRASH

Dear Sir,   18.10.25.
   Am in receipt your telegram and ordered work terrace steps be abandoned.

Yours faithfully,

BRASH TO PINTLE

Dear Sir,   22.10.25.
   My telephonic communication from Penzance was I apprehend too hurriedly precipitate, as on inspecting the work on my return I find I was a little misled in my preventative precautions and I desire that Mr. Grigblay shall now proceed with the steps.

Yours faithfully,

PINTLE TO BRASH

Dear Sir,   23.10.25.
   Your instructions regarding terrace noted and have again cancelled previous order, as directed.

Yours faithfully,

The word excised hints that even the purely vicarious duties of Pintle do not save him from an impulse of rebellion

181

Sir Leslie Brash takes Charge

PINTLE TO GRIGBLAY

Dear Mr. Grigblay,   23.10.25.

Sorry, but old man Brash written now definitely terrace steps *are* to go on. Am doing best keep things straight but O.M.B. not able make up mind.

                                                  Yours truly,

Pintle addresses Grigblay personally apparently to propitiate him, and because he is ashamed of writing these contradictory orders. He has, of course, no business to write letters behind the scenes. He is clearly a second-rate fellow deficient in loyalty. We may suppose the copy was made and filed without his cognisance.

GRIGBLAY TO SPINLOVE

Dear Sir,   24.10.25.

We note that work on terrace steps is now to go on and we have given orders accordingly. May we remind you that in eleven days we have laid our men off this work or put them on again no less than *four times*. We must point out that such confusion of orders is not reasonable and is beyond what we are entitled to expect. If there is any question, the work had better stand till Mr. Spinlove can decide what is to be done. This disorganization of our arrangements is a serious matter for us, and we regret we shall have to make a charge to cover loss of men's time.

                                                Yours faithfully,

As before, Grigblay shows he will not stand nonsense.

PINTLE TO BRASH

Dear Sir,   25.10.25.

Enclosed copy of letter received to-day Mr. Grigblay which perhaps you ought to see.

                                                  Yours truly,

Spinlove takes Charge

Dear Sir,   26.10.25.

I shall be obliged if you will signify to Mr. Grigblay my apologetic regrets that the necessary preventative precautions should have incommoded him. In the circumstances I am greatly pleased to accept the suggestion he makes and I desire him to desist from operations on the terrace steps until Mr. Spinlove's return.

Yours faithfully,

Five times!

SPINLOVE TAKES CHARGE

GRIGBLAY TO SPINLOVE

Dear Sir,   30.10.25.

We understand you are back and enclose list of extras ordered by Sir Leslie Brash during your absence. They are of a minor character and as Bloggs received the orders when the men were actually at work, he had to do what he was told or stop the work. We have kept time sheets as the work cannot be measured and must be charged day-work.

We understand from Bloggs that the bedrooms are to be papered. As you know, they are being finished with a felt-faced float for distempering. We shall be glad of particulars of papers at once. Bloggs was given orders to dark stain oak, but we await your directions.

Yours faithfully,

Builders are always ready to render day-work accounts—that is accounts based on the cost of the men's time and of materials— instead of accounts based on measurements priced at the contract rates, and it is only fair they should do so when the work involves pulling down or small separate jobs; but the method is unsatis-

183

factory for the owner because, as the builder will be reimbursed for all his outgoings and he receives in addition (usually) 15 per cent on the net cost for establishment charges and profit, there is no inducement to economy; and because, as the workmen and the foreman are aware of the circumstances, there is a tendency for everyone to ease off on day-work. In addition to this, the logging of the men's time is in the foreman's charge and, as he is accountable to the builder for keeping down the cost of labour covered by the tender, the day-work time sheets are apt to record hours which, properly, should be charged against the contract. Day-work accounts, unlike measured accounts always pay the builder; and from what has been said it will be realized that a dishonest builder can make them pay a great deal too well.

THE AFFAIR OF THE COTTAGES

(CONFIDENTIAL) GRIGBLAY TO SPINLOVE

Sir,   30.10.25.

I think I ought to let you know at once that a fortnight ago Sir Leslie Brash sent me drawings and specification for block of four cottages he wants erected down at bottom by lower road, and asked me for a price. The name on the drawings is Mr. Cohen Snitch, but a young man in our prime costing says they are copied from published plans by Mr. Sutcliffe Regenstook, A.R.I.B.A., and we have turned them up in our file of the "Builders' Record" of May 7th, 1923. The specification is a ready-made affair with just a tender-form without any conditions, and the bricks, chimneys, windows, and all sorts are to be "same as at Honeywood".

Now, apart from the work being only half described and position on site, drains, roads, and water supply, etc., left out, we don't do speculative work and don't care to tender without proper particulars and quantities. At the same time we should be quite willing to do the work under our present contract

184

schedule and leave it to Mr. Tinge to measure and settle the account, but we do not think this would suit the old gentleman as what he is after is a cut price and cut fees, without doubt. Not in any case should we agree to a proposal of the kind without consulting with you, and this was the reply we made and were then asked to return plans etc.

Since then Bloggs tells me Nibnose & Rasper's manager sneaked in down at bottom looking for mushrooms Bloggs thought, but young Rasper turned up after, and had the face to ask questions about water. Bloggs told him we were managing without any and saw him off, so it's pretty clear what is going on; but I'm not going to have Nibnose & Rasper learning how to build from me, and if Sir Leslie Brash brings them on to the ground he will have to pay me for a night watchman and a new lock-up or I shan't be able to keep a plank or a ladder or a drain pipe or a bag of plaster or anything else on the job without a man sits on it. That young Rasper would strip the tiles off the roof if you so much as turned your head to cough. I don't forget the trick he played me with that old six hundred gallon cast iron tank I loaned them and then they told me they hadn't had it. I happened to go along by, and there was my brave tank set up ten feet in the air on a staging and daubed over so it won't be recognized. Ho says Master Johnny Rasper, all of a surprise; *Is that yours?* Forgot where they had stole it.

Sir Leslie Brash sent me a plan and a picture of a gimcrack garage affair with pink asbestos slates and blue doors and a bit of bargeboard painted yellow and a flag at the gable. He had torn it out of Hutt and Gambols' reach-me-down bungalow catalogue, but had cut off the firm's name and the price for fear I should know too much, and he wanted me to give a price for two of them joined together for his cars to go in at the North West end by trades entrance. It would be a pity to put a thing like that up against his house, as I think you will agree; besides we can't build the stuff H. & G. spew about all over the country nor at their price if we did, and I think the old gentleman should be told so.

With apologies for troubling you but thought you ought to know it.

Yours faithfully,

The Affair of the Cottages

A very pleasant chatty letter—the letter of a friend! It has apparently occupied Grigblay's evening hours. Brash's intention, no doubt, is to save his pocket by cutting out architects' fees—for no doubt he made a bargain with Mr. Snitch; and he may feel, also, that Grigblay's work is unduly expensive and that this is due to Spinlove's complicated methods and exacting demands. He may also wish to "be his own architect", and believes that by uttering the words "two three- and two five-room cottages" and getting someone to "draw out the plan" and by agreeing a price with the builder, he is being it. Whatever the results are he will be slow to see defects in "my own work", and if the plans do not give him what he wants he will enjoy "making improvements" and take great credit to himself for the ingenious botching and makeshifts by which the shortcomings are made good. He will helplessly protest against the builder's account for extras, whether it is fair or not, and will always believe that he was "swindled".

As for Mr. Cohen Snitch, his kind is common. He has a knowledge of building sufficient to enable him to hold himself out as an architect in those wide fields that public ignorance puts at his disposal; and his many diverse activities bring him commissions which his reputation as an architect would deny him. The obligations of a profession of which he is not a member do not weigh with him; and he enjoys the same advantage over the accredited architect as the man who ignores the rules of a game has over one who observes them.

It is difficult to believe that Brash is not aware that he is treating his architect shabbily; but we have already seen that Brash can outface such consciousness. He perhaps regards the whole affair as a matter of fees. He is paying Spinlove for the house, but sees no reason why he should pay him when he can manage without his services; his instincts, in fact—or let us say his antecedents—do not allow him to distinguish between obligations due to a professional man and the consideration expected by a commercial agent. If Brash is conscious that Spinlove is giving Honeywood a devotion for which he can never be paid except in thanks, he probably merely regards his architect's services as remarkably good value for the money, and is too unaware of any reciprocal obligations to take any pleasure in acknowledging them.

186

The Affair of the Cottages

What is the unlucky Spinlove going to do about it all? He first flies for rescue to his friend Wychete, it seems.

Dear Mr. Wychete,   1.11.25.

I am sorry to bother you again but a most awkward thing has happened. I enclose copy of the builder's letter which gives the facts. I found it on my return from a four weeks' holiday abroad. Mr. Snitch is a house and land agent. I met him once, as he was appointed by the adjoining owner to agree a watercourse. The cottages will probably be three hundred yards or more from the house, but associated with it as is evidently the owner's intention—note the similar brickwork, chimneys, etc. I should be most grateful for any hints what to do.

With kind regards,
Yours sincerely,

P.S.—Could you possibly send me a line at once? I shall have to meet the owner in a few days, at latest.

SPINLOVE TO BRASH

Dear Sir Leslie Brash,   1.11.25.

I returned to the office yesterday. Mr. Grigblay has sent me a list of variations and extras ordered during my absence, and there is a question you have raised about the terrace steps. I can come on to the site on Friday or Saturday, if you will let me know when I can meet you, so that these and any other matters may be settled on the spot.

I had a delightful time abroad.

With kind regards,
Yours sincerely,

Spinlove has apparently put off meeting Brash until he may hope to have had Wychete's reply.

WYCHETE TO SPINLOVE

My dear Spinlove,   2.11.25.

Your luck seems out. The position is certainly awkward, as

you say, but the probability is that your client does not realize the unfairness to you—though one would imagine he intends a snub. Much depends on your personal relations and upon the kind of man he is. You alone can judge how far expostulation or protest may be made to weigh with him. Mr. Snitch's action seems most unprofessional, but he does not belong to our camp and in any case we do not know what happened; there is nothing to prevent your client employing him if he wishes, and it is no good taking any steps to get Mr. S. to withdraw. Even if you were able to do so it might not persuade your client to entrust the work to *you*.

Adopting Regenstook's design is, of course, a breach of copyright, and would give him grounds for an action for damages. Copying your details also comes very near to the same thing. Your client's intention is clear, and the wrong is of the same kind though so different in degree that you would scarcely be in a position to claim damages.

I should be interested to know the end of the story. You must not lose time or your client may accept the other builder's tender.

Ever yours,

SPINLOVE TO BRASH

Dear Sir Leslie Brash, 3.11.25.

I confirm telephone message fixing Friday at 10 a.m. for our meeting on site.

Mr. Grigblay has mentioned to me that you asked him to tender for a block of cottages which, for certain reasons, he felt unable to do without first conferring with me. I am, naturally, so much interested in Honeywood that I should be indeed grieved not to be allowed to design the accessory buildings, particularly as you mentioned these cottages to me as matters in which you would want my advice.

However, we can speak of this on Friday, but I write to warn you, before you commit yourself in any way, that the plans you sent Mr. Grigblay are not an original design at all, but have been copied from plans by another architect which were published a short time ago in one of the building papers. The designer holds the copyright in his plans and you will be liable to action for damages if you proceed. In the same way my detail drawings of Honeywood are my copyright and cannot be used for the proposed cottages without my consent.

Yours sincerely,

Spinlove is quite right in his statement of the fact of the copyright ownership, but he manages to suggest a masterfulness in architects which exceeds the life.

SPINLOVE TO WYCHETE

Dear Mr. Wychete,   6.11.25.

I am most grateful to you for your letter. Directly I got it I wrote to my client and warned him of the breach of copyright, but when I saw him two days later he told he had "provisionally accepted" (as he termed it) tender for the cottages from a local firm, Nibnose & Rasper. He had, however, accepted the tender in fact; by "provisionally" he meant that he was at liberty to accept, or not, a supplementary estimate for outbuildings.

Well, there was a great to do. He was most indignant with Snitch for fobbing him off with someone else's design and charging thirty-five guineas for it as an "inclusive fee", and he means to make him disgorge, for he has already paid the fellow.

He was quite nice to me—in fact particularly so, for he is a self-important man and rather obstinate in favouring his own ideas [*ahem!*], and I really do not think it occurred to him that he was injuring me. He thought he would save fees and get a cheaper building, and that it was entirely his own affair.

The tender he has accepted is for £1,350 for the block of four cottages—an impossible price. A great deal of the work is left out of the specification, to say nothing of drains, paths and water supply, and though the specification calls for the building to be completed in all details etc., Nibnose & Rasper attach to their tender a letter which, rather slyly, excludes work not described. There are no conditions of contract.

I had to point all this out to Brash and insist that the cottages will cost at least £1,700 before he has finished, and perhaps nearly £2,000, and that there was nothing in the contract to prevent the builder putting in the cheapest and most shoddy work, and that he would have a huge bill for extras and be at the builders' mercy—in fact Brash began at last to understand what an architect is for.

The next difficulty was how to get Nibnose & Rasper to withdraw with merely nominal compensation or none at all. Owing to a previous muddle they have a quite unfounded grievance against me; however, Brash wrote and told them he had discharged Snitch and appointed me his architect, and I got Nibnose to my office and, after cross-examining him on what he had included for and what not, he was obliged to agree that, as a basis for a contract, his tender was a farce. He was quite reasonable; said he had done his best with the particulars supplied, that there were big risks—and so on. Finally it was agreed that he and Grigblay should tender to a new design and that the lowest tender should be accepted. So that's that, and I am enormously obliged for your hints, without which I do not know what would have happened; and Brash, if he only knew it, is still more deeply indebted to you.

I am putting up temporary shed of larch slabs as garage, which will look quite inoffensive pushed back among the trees.

With many thanks and best wishes,

Yours very sincerely,

Spinlove seems in fine fettle. His recent holiday has done him good. He has evidently carried Brash quite off the ground upon which he had taken so formidable a position, and won his surrender.

LADY BRASH CAUSES A DIVERSION

SPINLOVE TO GRIGBLAY

Dear Sir,   10.11.25.
I had to call your foreman's attention to boarding on flats over bays, which is specified to run with the fall, but has been

laid across it to suit the joists which run the wrong way. I must ask you to nail ⅜″ boarding over present boarding with feather-edged border so as to get neat finish of lead on to brick cornice. [*Boards are apt to curl up at edges under lead, and prevent free drainage of water if laid across the fall.*]

The trefoil piercings in skirtings of panelled rooms have been omitted. This makes the broken battening and openings in top of capping useless. Please put stout cop-bronze wire mesh behind piercings. [*The purpose of this arrangement is to give free ventilation behind the panelling, for if air is bottled up between panelling and damp walls the warmth of the house will favour dry-rot. The wire gauge is against mice.*]

The eaves gutter at N. of kitchen wing stops short of the gable verge. I am aware that the verge is tilted bu the finish is un-workmanlike. The stopped end should be 1″ in front of line of verge. [*The tilting of the tiles at gable verge throws the water back so that the eaves gutter probably is effective in catching all of it. It is the rigid exactness of modern building that makes this immaterial deviation an offence.*]

Now that the heating service is working will you please see that the windows are *kept open.* I have called your foreman's attention to this before. [*The heating is put on to dry out the house, but if the windows are kept shut the steam-laden air, which can take up no more moisture, cannot escape, condensation takes place and the object of having the heat on is in great part defeated. The windows are kept shut because of the blinking draught, and in pursuit of snug comfort. Even at the best of times the luxury of shutting oneself up for a day with a mate and a radiator in an unventilated bathroom with a few cans of paint, a plumber's furnace, two clay pipes, a quart of boiling tea and a pound of putty, is rarely enjoyed.*]

The lead tacks of soil pipes, as well as of waste pipes, are to be wiped on the front angle. This has not been done. The service pipes carrying taps are to be *vertical.* The double tacks above and below taps are as specified, but in the pantry the pipes are *horizontal.* They must be carried along under sink and then taken up vertically to match scullery taps.

The nozzle of a tap fixed on a horizontal pipe tends to sag

191

*down after a time. A vertical pipe, properly fixed, resists the
leverage of the hand screwing down the tap.*]

Please give these matters your attention.

Yours faithfully,

*Spinlove has been away from the works for some weeks and,
if these are the only matters he has to complain of, Grigblay
is doing well.*

SPINLOVE TO GRIGBLAY

Dear Sir,   15.11.25.

Sir Leslie Brash rang me up to-day to tell me Lady Brash
is complaining of a *smell* in the house. Will you find out what
is the matter? I could get no description of it except that it is
an unpleasant smell.

Yours faithfully,

*Most of them are so or they would not be smells; and it is
difficult to describe a smell even when it will bear description,
which is rare. Lady Brash's famous "olfactory sensitiveness"
has claimed tribute.*

BRASH TO SPINLOVE

Dear Mr. Spinlove,   17.11.25.

Would it be practicably feasible to insert french windows in
the drawing-room, and what would be the amount of the probable anticipated estimate? A friend has pointed out that it will
not be practicably possible for a person seated in the middle
of the drawing room to get a view of the gardens owing to the
excessive height of the bottoms of the windows. This is dis-
turbing. Alternatively, and as a different proposition, could not
the windows be lowered a foot or two? What would be the
probably approximate estimate for doing so, including, of
course, the bay windows? I comprehend the necessary desir-
ability of disposing the windows of the bedroom chambers in
a lofty situation in view of the danger of a fall, but this desir-
ability scarcely obtains in the downstair apartments.

Lady Brash causes a Diversion

Lady Brash informs me the smell is much worse. It is desired that the necessary steps towards eradication may be *at once* put in active operation, as Lady Brash spends several hours of each day in the house.

Yours sincerely,

Dear Sir,   19.11.25.

Have you done anything about the *smell?* Sir Leslie Brash referred to it again in a letter I received on Saturday and he has rung up to-day to say that Lady Brash was in the house on Sunday and that the smell was "dreadful". Please take steps to have the nuisance ended at once, as it is causing great annoyance. I wish you had not allowed the plumbers to use the den as a shop. They have made the place in a disgusting state—litter of all kinds, bacon rind, banana peel thrown about, crusts and bones and tea leaves—your foreman ought to be told to look after things better.

Yours faithfully,

Spinlove is evidently getting rattled; but until Lady Brash is appeased there will be no peace for anyone.

Dear Mr. Spinlove,   19.11.25.

I really think I ought to write to you about the smell! It was *quite* dreadful on Sunday they all noticed it and Mrs. Bingham said it made her eyes water she is so subject to hay fever like my dear mother was and I take after them *both!!!* I could never consent to live in a house with a smell like *that* which goes on and on even after I get home like the monkey house in the Zoo especially the drawing-room. Whatever Sir Leslie may say something will have to be done or none of our friends will ever come to see us!!!

How fast the leaves are falling!

Yours v. sincerely,

Lady Brash causes a Diversion

Dear Lady Brash,   20.11.25.

I do not know what the particular smell is that you do not like. I have asked Mr. Grigblay to try and find out. Of course many of the materials used by the workmen have strange smells, but that is unavoidable and they will all disappear, I can assure you, before the work is finished. If you find the atmosphere of the house so unpleasant it would perhaps be wiser *not to go into it* just at present, or why not ask Mr. Bloggs to *open the windows;* have you thought of that I wonder?

Yes, I noticed the leaves were beginning to fall.

Yours sincerely,

Spinlove's solicitude leads him to ascribe to the lady a degree of imbecility which is scarcely flattering.

Dear Sir,   20.11.25.

We have noted the various instructions you gave our foreman, which are receiving attention. He has searched for the smell complained of but has not succeeded in discovering it. His report is as follows:

"About her Ladyship's smell there is not anything to complain about as I can see. The paint is nothing at all scarcely. There was a bit of a hum in the kitchen but that was just a coat the gasfitter's mate had there. He said it was fish and I reckon like enough it was. I told him take it outside. The plumber's shop is swept out."

We do not know what more we can do in the matter.

Yours faithfully,

Dear Sir Leslie Brash,   21.11.25.

I have twice written to Grigblay about the unpleasant smell, and I have to-day heard from him that they cannot detect anything which is not as it should be. In writing to Lady Brash yesterday I suggested that she might perhaps see that the windows are opened.

In answer to your question, french windows are impossible. They could not be fitted to the existing openings, could not be made to match the other windows and would be disastrous architecturally, as you would at once realize if I made you a sketch of the altered elevation. If you had said originally that you wanted french windows I could have designed them suitably, but the style of the house would have been entirely different.

It would be possible to lower the windows, but if you did so the transom—that is the intermediate horizontal member of the frame—would come right across the line of vision of anyone standing. The top of cills is 2′ 9½″ from the floor and this is as low as can be managed. I may point out to you that the reason you cannot see the ground outside when seated away from the window is that the ground slopes away. In any case the top of the terrace wall will appear above the line of the window cill to anyone seated in the room, so that even if you lowered the windows you would have no better view of the garden.

I had intended to suggest to you, when the subject was allowed to drop, that instead of painting the doors pink, yellow, blue—for I am sure you would dislike the array of differently coloured doors—the name "Pink Room", "Yellow Room", etc. might be lettered on each door. I could design a scutcheon upon which the words might appear, and this might be of the appropriate colour if you wish, or the coloured scutcheon without the words might serve. Personally I would recommend the words without the scutcheon.

I hope you will not think me unduly persistent, but I am sure you would regret a parti-coloured corridor.

With kind regards,
Yours sincerely,

Apparently the conversations grew heated when the rainbowed bedroom proposals were discussed, and Spinlove had to change the subject. It is a torturing effort for the designer to get the heads —or transoms—of casement windows above the eye, and the cills duly low, while at the same time keeping the proportions of windows satisfactory.

Lady Brash causes a Diversion

Dear Mr. Spinlove,   22.11.25.

I have considered your remarks anent the windows and suggest you will raise the floor of the room which will, I apprehend, give the same equivalent effect as the lowering of the windows to which you demur, and prevent the terrace wall obstructing the view. There will be no objection to going up two steps into the drawing-room—in fact most pleasing effects may be obtained in this manner, and we can postpone using the apartment until the operations are completed. What will the cost of this work be? I recall that £300 is included in the contract amount to meet contingencies of this kind.

I am not at all averse to your proposal for identification of bedroom doors. If you will have a door painted and appropriately lettered as you propose, I will give you an ultimate final decision.

We are contemplating moving into the house for Xmas day. Do you think that a feasible proposition?

I have seized the opportune occasion to purchase certain cottages and shall in consequence not now find the necessity to erect those conveniences. Will you please advise Messrs. Nibnose & Rasper with the appropriate intimation.

Yours sincerely,

Dear Jazz,   24.11.25.

You ought to hop down as soon as poss. Mum is worrying dreadfully over the smell in the house. She spent most of this morning and part of the afternoon listening for it; it did not squeak to-day but was apparently known to be in hiding. I have not been in the house myself on a good hunting morning when the scent was lying well, but two people besides M. found on Sunday, so something must be wrong.

Dad started an innocent little frolic with a dentist ten days ago; it became a serious game and poor Dad is now seventeen down with nine to play. He is staying up in town till after the final round, which is why I write. Will you phone to-morrow, please?

PUD.

SPINLOVE TO GRIGBLAY

Dear Sir   25.11.25.

I am directed by Sir Leslie Brash to say that he does not now intend to build any cottages.

Will you please tell your foreman to see that all windows are securely *shut* before the men leave on Saturday, so that I may satisfy myself about this reported smell.

Yours faithfully,

SPINLOVE USES TACT

SPINLOVE TO BRASH

Dear Sir Leslie Brash,   28.11.25.

I am sorry to know you are having such a bad time of it.

As you will no doubt have heard, the smell Lady Brash comp'ained of is that of the *new oak*. It is a penetrating smell certainly, but most people like it. It will entirely disappear in a short time, in fact I do not think it will be noticed after the oak has been waxed.

I am afraid it will not be possible for you to get into the house for Xmas. There is much more to be done than appears. In six weeks' time it might be possible, but it wou'd be better for you to wait. The house is drying out well, and I do not think there would then be any actual objection to its being lived in, but if you waited, say, till March you could be certain of no ill consequences.

As regards raising the floor of the drawing-room, there are grave difficulties and objections which I think you have not realized. Ten or twelve inches off the height of the room would make it appear very low. This is a big room and the height to ceiling is no more than is necessary, for it fixes the height of the first floor throughout. To raise the floor would mean raising the panelling to about 18 in. from the ceiling which would look very ugly, and also rebuilding the brick chimney, for the opening of the fireplace would be much too low. The transom of the window would also come very awkwardly; people looking out would have to stoop or stand on tip toe. It would be dangerous to have the steps close up to the door; a landing outside would be necessary which would stand out, with the steps, four or five feet into the hall, and, of course, the new floor would have to be carried on joists. The concrete floor is prepared for nailing the floorboards to it, and the only reason this has not been done is that I told Grigblay to hold off so that the concrete should be thoroughly dry. The cost of the alteration would, as you may judge, be a considerable sum—£200 very likely.

The £300 contingencies, you mention, is not available for extra work of this kind. It is to cover the contract work—that is to say to pay for work which may be found necessary but which is not described in the contract because it may not be. Part, at least, of this sum has been spent. If there is any left unexpended, it will, of course, be credited in the final statement of account.

I have written a tactful letter to Nibnose & Rasper letting them know you do not now intend to go on with the cottages. As you remember, they agreed to cancel their previous contract on the understanding they should tender, against Grigblay only, to the new design I was preparing; but I hope they will not make any trouble.

With kind regards,
Yours sincerely,

SPINLOVE TO NIBNOSE & RASPER

Dear Sirs, 28.11.25.

My client desires me to present you with his best compliments and inform you with his profound regrets that he has now decided not to build the cottages for which you were so obliging as to consent to submit a tender.

Sir Leslie Brash asks me to tell you that he looks forward on some future occasion to the pleasure of availing himself of your services.

Yours faithfully,

If this suave and buttery letter is Spinlove's idea of a tactful one, he has much to learn. It not only reeks of insincerity, but is intolerably condescending in tone and would be likely to give offence to anyone and under any circumstances. "Nibrasp" will perfectly understand that the purpose of it is to disarm their claim to compensation; and as the firm has already, in its own opinion, been unfairly deprived of the contract for the house, anything more provocative and inflaming could scarcely be devised. Spinlove ought to have written somewhat as follows: "An unfortunate thing has happened. My client has an opportunity of buying cottages close at hand so that there is now no reason for him to build. I am afraid you have been put to a good deal of trouble and Sir Leslie Brash is sorry for this and will bear it in mind, and hopes to be able to make use of your services on a future occasion."

BRASH TO SPINLOVE

Dear Mr. Spinlove,   29.11.25.

I am glad to be in a condition to intimate that I am now emancipated to freedom from the dental surgeon's sanctum—though still unable to make spectacular public appearances.

I am naturally disappointed to be apprised that our occupation of the house a Christmas is not practicably feasible. Christmas Day eventuates precisely fourteen days subsequently to the contract date of completion. I advisedly apprehended that certain extra days would be allowed to Mr. Grigblay to perform his undertaking, but six weeks is surely a very excessive apportionment of latitude? It is, of course, in your hands to see that Mr. Grigblay is kept informed of his obligations, but I desire that you will intimate to him that I consider his procrastination beyond what is reasonably to be anticipated, and that I shall certainly not feel inclined to remit any proportion of the sums which may become due to me as penalties for delay.

I note your remarks anent the lifting of the drawing-room floor. I do not precisely apprehend the full interpretation of your remarks as I am not in a condition to immediately make the public appearance involved by the journey to the site, but I am prepared to accept your views, although they do not favour my ideas, as the amount of the anticipated estimate is altogether more than I can contemplate.

As regards the "contingencies", I apprehend that the money is mine and that I am, therefore, at liberty to spend it as I choose—however it is not necessary to deviate upon that eventuality. The mansion certainly more than satisfies our anticipations. I look forward shortly to viewing the experimental lettering on doors.

With kind regards,
Yours sincerely.

"NIBRASP" ASKS COMPENSATION

NIBNOSE & RASPER TO SPINLOVE

Dear Sir,   29.11.25.

We were just a little surprised at your letter—but nothing to worry about—as this is the second time we have been passed over by you and we are getting used to same.

We shall be glad if you will present our respects to Sir Leslie Brash and inform that gentleman that we shall be glad to serve him at any time that he may honour us with his orders and abide by them, but we do not much care for the way he has served us so far, for what we expected is not *comp*liments but *comp*ensation.

We may remind you that when Mr. Nibnose saw you at your office on this matter it was clearly understood that we would agree to cancel our contract if we were given a fair chance to tender to a new design against Mr. John Grigblay only. As Sir Leslie has chosen to disregard his side of the bargain and break your word to us, we must respectfully ask a sum representing our reasonable profits in compensation, viz: $7\frac{1}{2}\%$ on the amount of our tender.

Yours faithfully,

"Nibrasp" asks Compensation

"Nibrasp" are entitled to compensation for the cancellation of their contract, since the acceptance of a tender constitutes a contract binding on both parties each of whom is entitled to compensation for breach by the other. The sum that would be allowed by the Courts in compensation would depend on the circumstances. It might happen that a contractor or a building owner would, by a breach by the other, be involved in losses far in excess of the direct loss of profits or loss of the bargain.

SPINLOVE TO TINGE, QUANTITY SURVEYOR

Dear Mr. Tinge,   1.12.25.

While I was away on a holiday my client obtained tender for £1,350 for a block of cottages from a new builder, Nibnose and Rasper, which he accepted. He has now decided not to build and the contractors ask $7\frac{1}{2}\%$ on the tendered price as compensation for breach. Is this a fair claim? The firm states that $7\frac{1}{2}\%$ represents their expected profits. Is this right?

Yours truly,

TINGE TO SPINLOVE

Dear Sir,   2.12.25.

$7\frac{1}{2}\%$ is about right for profits.

Yours faithfully,

Tinge, as usual, keeps strictly to facts. It is for Spinlove, and not Tinge, to decide whether the claim is a fair one. All Tinge will say is that $7\frac{1}{2}\%$ is a reasonable estimate of profits.

SPINLOVE TO BRASH

Dear Sir Leslie Brash,   3.12.25.

I enclose copies of my letters to Nibnose & Rasper and of their replies. The amount they claim is about right I will make an appointment with Mr. Nibnose and agree the best terms I can get.

Yours sincerely,

201

"Nibrasp" asks Compensation

We must suppose that Spinlove explained to Brash, when he decided not to build the cottages, that "Nibrasp" could claim compensation; but he does not appear to have any authority to agree the amount, and although 7½% may represent expected profits it does not follow that "Nibrasp" could make good a claim for that amount.

SPINLOVE TO NIBNOSE & RASPER

Dear Sirs,   3.12.25.

Sir Leslie Brash could not foresee the circumstances which now make it impossible for him to build, and he is aware that he is liable to you for compensation; but there are special circumstances which have to be considered in settling the sum to be paid and I think it would be satisfactory if Mr. Nibnose could call at my office to agree the figure. If you will ring up I shall be glad to make an early appointment.

Yours faithfully,

Spinlove, as agent, here pledges Brash to pay compensation. Even if Brash had agreed to pay—and it does not appear he has ever done so—it was a serious error in diplomacy on Spinlove's part to tell "Nibrasp" this. He should have opened negotiations by saying that his client resented paying compensation and that unless "Nibrasp" substantially reduced the amount of the claim they would get nothing.

SPINLOVE TO BRASH

Dear Sir Leslie Brash,   4.12.25.

On my return to the office this evening I found your telephone message telling me to come to no understanding with Nibnose & Rasper until I had seen you. I am sorry to say that I wrote to them last night in the sense of my letter to you. I enclose copy of the letter. You will see that the amount of compensation is left open, so that this may be merely a nominal figure.

Yours sincerely,

"Nibrasp" asks Compensation

We have here another example of the ineptitude which over-takes Spinlove when he gets away from the actual business of building. How can "Nibrasp" be put off with nominal compensation—nominal standing for "in name only"—when the payment of actual compensation has been promised?

BRASH TO SPINLOVE

Dear Mr. Spinlove,   5.12.25.

I was astounded to peruse your communication to Messrs. Nibnose & Rasper, in which you take it upon yourself to engage me to disburse compensation without any kind of authority from me to do so, and in face of my emphatic objection, expressed to you in verbal conversation some weeks ago, to do anything of the kind. If anyone is to pay compensation I apprehend it is Mr. Snitch for selling me sham bogus plans and preparing documents which you tell me are incomplete and which Messrs. Nibnose & Rasper knew to be incomplete.

It is obvious that I am being robbed and swindled by a pack of extortionate rogues and that so far from doing anything to protect me you are—if you will permit me to say so—actually playing into their hands. However, one thing is definitely certain; I will not pay Nibnose & Rasper, or Snitch, or any jack one of these scoundrels a halfpenny, and you can tell them so with my compliments. Mr. Snitch has now very obligingly offered to charge only ten guineas "to cover expenses" for cheating me, and if Nibnose talks any more about compensation I request you to refer him to Russ & Co., for I will fight these thieving rogues if I have to sell everything I possess to do it, before I will pay them a farthing.

Yours sincerely,

Ease off on the kidney omelettes, my good sir, and walk to the station of a morning! It is true that Spinlove was at fault in pledging his client without written authority, or without a written note of oral instructions the wording of which his client has approved and which he has confirmed to his client; but he seems to have no doubt that he was correctly representing his client's views, and in any case Brash's claim against Snitch for fees paid,

203

and *"Nibrasp's" against Brash for compensation are entirely due to Brash's acting without his architect's advice or knowledge. Spinlove has, indeed, rescued his client from a much worse disaster.*

SPINLOVE TO BRASH

Dear Sir Leslie Brash,   6.12.25.

I much regret that I should have wrongly interpreted your wishes, but when some weeks ago I told you that Nibnose & Rasper were entitled to compensation you made no comment, and I clearly understood you accepted the situation. I have to-day written to the firm repudiating their claim; at the same time there is no doubt they can enforce it. Mr. Nibnose is coming to see me and I will get the best proposals for settlement I can.

May I remind you that I had nothing to do with your contract with Mr. Snitch, nor with your contract with Nibnose & Rasper, but that I have spent a good deal of time in trying to get matters arranged in your best interests.

Yours faithfully,

Spinlove's nerves are not this time involved.

SPINLOVE TO NIBNOSE & RASPER

Dear Sirs,   6.12.25.

I confirm appointment with Mr. Nibnose at this office at 11 on Thursday.

I regret to have to say that in conveying that Sir Leslie Brash was willing to compensate you I misinterpreted what I understood to be my client's views. I am now directed by Sir Leslie Brash to inform you that he does not agree you have a claim for compensation against him.

Yours faithfully,

But they have! All Brash has done is to roar "I won't pay."

"Nibrasp" asks Compensation

SPINLOVE TO GRIGBLAY

Dear Sir,   7.12.25.

May I ask you whether you are aware of what is going on at Honeywood? When I was in one of the bedrooms yesterday with your foreman, there was a sudden uproar downstairs and, while I was asking Bloggs what all the noise was, a rat with a terrier after it ran into the room and bolted into the floor-space where the electricians had a trap open, and men came rioting up the stairs before they could be stopped. I had noticed several dogs tied up and Bloggs said the men brought them "for a bit of a rat hunt in the dinner hour", but I never supposed there were *rats in the house*.

It is really disgraceful and I should certainly have to ask you to replace your foreman if the work were not so nearly finished. Suppose Sir Leslie learnt what was going on, or that Lady Brash saw a rat! The rats have no doubt been attracted by the litter of bits of food in the den which the plumbers used as a shop, but the men have no business to bring food into the house at all. It must be stopped and the rats cleared out, at once. Bloggs says they will go when they cannot get water, but I have heard of them gnawing through lead pipes for it, and with all these spaces under the floors on the South side, the house will become rat-ridden before it is finished. I shall want to see those spaces thoroughly cleaned out. There are shavings and rubbish there. The main thing is to get rid of the rats at once. Poison must not be used or we shall have more *smells*. I am astonished you should allow such a state of affairs.

Yours faithfully,

P.S.—We put the terrier into the floor and got the rat.

From the postscript we learn that the august architect pocketed his indignation and joined the hunt.

BLAY TO SPINLOVE

Dear Sir,   9.12.25.

We regret the occasion for your letter which we were quite

unaware of. We are sending down an expert who will fume out rats, and have given our foreman strict orders, and trust you will have no further grounds for complaints.

We should like to call your attention to the Riddoppo paint next time you are on the site, as our foreman painter is not altogether satisfied.

Yours faithfully,

BRASH TO SPINLOVE

Dear Mr. Spinlove,   8.12.25.

I have to solicit your condolences and ask you to make excuses for the somewhat rough asperity of my last communication, as I was at the time suffering from a dental relapse in a molar which has proved unexpectedly refractory and you will be sorry to hear me say that the distress was extremely chronic. [*It is to be hoped he will be very sorry indeed to hear Brash say it, but then—why say it?*]

Messrs. Russ & Co. are dealing with Mr. Snitch. With reference to Messrs. Nibnose & Rasper, I apprehend that you have noted my asseveration that I have given you no authority to agree any sum in disbursement for compensation. At the same time I desire you to proceed with negotiations directed to determining what amount will satisfy these people's demands. The proposal must then be submitted for consideration to Mr. Russ.

Yours sincerely,

Here is a return to sanity!

SPINLOVE TO BRASH

Dear Sir Leslie Brash,   10.12.25.

I am very sorry to know you have been so poorly and hope you are all right again now.

I saw Mr. Nibnose to-day. He is hurt at the way he has been treated and was inclined to be stiff, but he is a fair-dealing man and, of course, I had plenty to say of the irregularity of the contract arrangement. Finally he agreed to accept £25, in full settlement as a "friendly compromise", on the understanding that if the money is not paid within seven days his offer is to be deemed to have been refused.

I did full justice to your views, but was only able to lead Mr. Nibnose to make this offer by telling him that if he did so I thought he might regard the matter as settled. This was the best I could do and I think you will be wise to accept, for I believe it is your only chance of an amicable settlement.

Yours sincerely,

Spinlove seems to have managed well and his letter is, for a change, strictly to the point.

Christmas is approaching and on the morning of the contract date for completion Spinlove receives missives twain of good cheer from Grigblay. The first is as follows:

DIFFICULTIES AND DELAYS

GRIGBLAY TO SPINLOVE

Dear Sir,   10.12.25.

We have received notice from Mr. Potch, District Surveyor, refusing certificate of occupation on ground that window in bedroom No. 5 is not of area required by by-laws. This is the room which was made larger by moving partition to the orders of her Ladyship.

Yours faithfully,

It seems we have not yet heard the last of Lady Brash's famous big wardrobe. By enlarging the room to receive it, the floor area has been increased to more than ten times the window area, which is the maximum allowed by the by-laws, and it seems Spinlove overlooked this.

The second message of glad tidings is more diffuse, but it does not lack sap.

Difficulties and Delays

Sir,   10.12.25.

I think best to send you a private word that we are going to
have a serious trouble with this paint of the old gentleman's.
If you ask me I should say that this new novelty super-paint
is a bit too new, a lot too much of a novelty and, if you will
pardon me, a damned sight too super, and I think that Sir
Leslie Brash who ordered it ought to put on his best spectacles
and have a good look to see how he likes it before we go on
and finish. As you know I refused responsibility, and I also
kept the men's time from the start, and lucky for me for this
job is going to cost someone a bit of money.

The painters say the stuff is treacly and don't smell natural,
though it flows nicely after the brush and no complaints; but
from what our painter told Bloggs I had a good look into
things to-day and it's like this. A coat goes on and dries hard
and quick, but when the next follows it seems to soften the
coat below, and the more coats the worse it gets, at least that's
the best I can make of it. As you know, we have four coats
on most parts and the finish on one or two doors, and on
kitchen and lavatory walls. It seems fairly hard and has a nice
oily gloss and a good surface, but if you look closely there is
a rim of paint hanging along the bottom edge of doors and
bulging out along top of skirtings of painted walls, and where
the light is reflected you can make out a kind of a drag and
ripple in the surface, in places. In my belief the paint is beginning to creep; it may be hard, but so is bitumen hard and bitumen will flow out like honey give it time. This is only beginning
and it isn't going to stop and we shall have R.N.N.S.P. creeping
out over the carpets in a few months or I'm mistaken.

It would suit me best to finish and leave Sir Leslie Brash to
settle with the manufacturer, but that would be just so much
waste, for when you go down you will see what I say is right.
I haven't squirted any boiling acids at it nor yet french polished,
but if that is to be done it had ought to be soon before Riddoppo super crawls out of the front door and off home, which
is about what it's aiming for.

Perhaps Sir, you will let me know what you would wish me

to do, as there is no call to have more trouble than can be helped and I gather the paint is no concern of yours any more than mine.

You will pardon me troubling you but thought it might help to keep things straight.

Yours faithfully,

This letter is an autograph, as were the other friendly messages that have engaged Grigblay's evenings with such advantage to Spinlove.

SPINLOVE TO POTCH, DISTRICT SURVEYOR

Sir,   12.12.25.

I am informed by the builder that you have refused certificate of occupation for house at Honeywood on the ground that the window in bedroom No. 5 is not the minimum size required by by-laws. It is true that this room has been increased in size since the plans were approved, but I must point out that the glass area is still more than one-tenth of floor area: viz: glass— three times $3' 6'' \times 1' 4'' = 15$ feet; area of floor $10' 9'' \times 12' = 129$ ft.

Yours faithfully,

BRASH TO SPINLOVE

Dear Mr. Spinlove,   13.12.25.

I have desired Messrs. Russ & Co. to transmit cheque for £25 to Messrs Nibnose & Rasper as a "friendly compromise" in ultimate liquidation and final settlement of their iniquitously monstrous and fraudulent claim. I never so resentfully grudged disbursing a remunerative payment more than in this instance, but as Mr. Russ, after his interview with you, confirms endorsement of your opinion, I have no other alternative course but to stand and deliver.

Yours sincerely,

GRIGBLAY TO SPINLOVE

Dear Sir,   13.12.25.

I write to call your attention to the Riddoppo paint which

209

was ordered by Sir Leslie Brash. This is showing signs of creeping and we are afraid the trouble is only beginning. We are going on with the painting, as ordered, until we receive other directions.

Yours faithfully,

Appearances are that Spinlove has had a talk with Grigblay and arranged that he shall write this formal notification. It is to be observed that in this matter Spinlove is not responsible to Brash, who ordered the paint himself contrary to his architect's advice. Grigblay, as we see, takes the position of being a disinterested person, and Spinlove will be wise to do the same or he may, before he knows it, fasten responsibility upon himself by one of those redundancies which are so characteristic of his letters.

SPINLOVE TO BRASH

Dear Sir Leslie Brash,   16.12.25.

I enclose copy of letter I have received from Mr. Grigblay, and await your instructions. I understand that by "creeping" is meant that the paint is slowly flowing down the walls, doors, etc.

Yours sincerely,

Spinlove is justly entitled to disclaim responsibility, but if he had any sense of humour—and we know he has none—he could not blandly have passed the matter over to Brash without full explanation. Spinlove's original objection was rather to the scheme of decorations than to the risk of the paint's failure, as paint; and Brash has good cause for grievance that he was not particularly warned of that risk. It is true he would probably, in giving rein to his temper, have scorned the advice, but he can none the less complain that he was never given a chance of doing so. Spinlove's excuse, of course, is ignorance: he has not had the experience which would have made unnecessary the experience he is now getting.

BRASH TO SPINLOVE

Dear Mr. Spinlove,   18.12.25.

I do not precisely apprehend why you refer Mr. Grigblay's

objection to the super-paint to me. That is a matter of technical craftsmanship upon which I anticipate you are competent to adjudicate. I am aware that Mr. Grigblay has all along evinced a protracted resistance opposed to Riddoppo, but after viewing the edifice to-day I can only asseverate—with my respects to Mr. Grigblay and acknowledgments to yourself—that I never viewed a more smooth or glossy or delightfully-tinted surface-colouring. I desire that you will direct Mr. Grigblay to proceed with the work, and oblige me by desisting from making these obstructive representations.

Yours sincerely,

SPINLOVE TO POTCH

Sir,   20.12.25.

Permit me to remind you that I have received no reply to my letter of eight days ago. The builder informs me that no certificate has been received by him. As the owner intends to occupy the house very shortly I shall be obliged by your attention to the matter.

Yours faithfully,

POTCH TO SPINLOVE

Sir,   18.12.25.

I duly received your favour informing me that three times 3′ 6″ into 1′ 4″ makes 15 feet, but did not understand you wanted me to check same for you. Unfortunately my Council does not allow me to use up their time teaching London architects to square dimensions, but to oblige you my office boy has kindly gone over and makes it 14.

I am, sir,
Yours faithfully,

As Potch's principle is always *to hit below the belt, he will feel he has fetched Spinlove a walloper—and even Spinlove must admit a touch.*

Difficulties and Delays

SPINLOVE TO POTCH

Sir,   19.12.25.

The slip was perfectly obvious and whether 14 or 15 feet is of no kind of consequence. You admit the window area is 14ft. and floor area 129, and I must ask for certificate without more delay or I shall apply to your Council's Clerk.

Yours faithfully,

POTCH TO SPINLOVE

Sir,   29.12.25.

I have received your letter stating I agree your measurements of floor and window at Honeywood, but can find no record of agreement in this office and shall be glad of reference and date as my assistant says nothing on files.

I am, Sir,

Yours faithfully,

This is a mere quibble intended to obstruct and annoy.

SPINLOVE TO POTCH

Sir,   31.12.25.

I understood you accepted the figures I gave—namely, 14ft. super for the window and 129ft. for the floor of bedroom. I must ask you either to forward certificate without delay or appoint someone to agree dimensions on the spot.

Yours faithfully,

SPINLOVE TO BRASH

Dear Sir Leslie Brash,   31.12.25.

The holiday has prevented my replying sooner to your letter.

It is well understood by Mr. Grigblay and myself that the Riddoppo paint is being used by your orders and under your responsibility, and it would suit Mr. Grigblay to finish the painting and have done with it. He pointed out to me what he thinks to be a serious defect and I considered it my duty to report his views, which are quite disinterested, to you. I agree that, superficially, the finished painting looks well; the work has been carefully and skilfully done. It requires a practised eye to notice the defect, but apparently a creeping action has begun. If you look at the bottoms of doors and along tops of skirtings below painted walls you will see rims of paint, and a drag or ripple in the surface can also be discerned in places. Mr. Grigblay thinks the defect will ncrease. The painting is being proceeded with, as you ask.

With best wishes to Lady Brash and yourself for the New Year.

Yours sincerely,

This is an adequate and wary letter. Spinlove does well to make no recommendation. To do so would associate him with future difficulties and, in fact, no one except the manufacturers of the paint can advise Brash.

POTCH TO SPINLOVE

Sir,   31.12.25.

I do not know what sort of foot rule you use but I go by English Standard (Pinchlocks' Double Folding Pocket 4s. 3d.); and suggest you get a new tape as yours is stretched.

My inspector notes glass—three times $3' 5''$ into $1' 3'' = 12' 10''$; floor $10' 11'' \times 12' 2'' = 132'$.

I am, Sir,
Yours faithfully,

The measure 12ft. 10in., by the system employed in building operations, represents 12 feet superficial and $\frac{10}{12}$ of a superficial foot or $12\frac{5}{6}$ feet super; actually, 12 square feet and 120 square inches.

SPINLOVE TO GRIGBLAY

Dear Sir,   1.1.26.

I enclose copies of letter to the District Surveyor and his reply My measures are taken from the half inch joinery detail, and from brick dimensions of room, allowing 2″ on each wall for plaster and skirting. Will you ask your foreman to check my figures against Mr. Potch's and let me know where the discrepancy is. *Urgent.*

Yours faithfully,

BRASH TO SPINLOVE

Dear Mr. Spinlove, 2.1.26.

I must request to be permitted to reiterate over again that I am not equipped to adjudicate in a technical matter appertaining to craftsmanship and which I apprehend belongs to the province of my professional adviser—by which term I designate yourself—to see that the painters perform their functions in an efficient manner.

I again inspected the mansion yesterday and Mr. Bloggs indicated what he deemed irregularities but which are, I apprehend, of quite immaterial significance.

With reciprocations of your seasonable good wishes from Lady Brash and myself,

Yours sincerely,

Most lordly and most melancholy! Brash's self-sufficiency will not allow him to "apprehend" the facts.

SPINLOVE TO BRASH

Dear Sir Leslie Brash, 4.1.26.

My services are, of course, entirely at your disposal, but I am unable to tell Mr. Grigblay how to deal with the defective paint for I know nothing of Riddoppo, which, as you are aware, is a "new novelty super-paint compounded of new secret ingredients". You will recall that I advised against its use and that neither Mr. Grigblay nor myself were able to accept responsibility for it. The blemish is, so far, inconspicuous, but it may be a symptom of inherent defects.

Yours sincerely,

Spinlove here is "reiterating over again" the very thing Brash

has asked him to "*desist from intimating*", but his tenacity is here very much to the point. When Riddoppo begins to "*crawl out of the front door and off home*"—as Grigblay expects it one day will—this letter will safeguard Spinlove from being involved in the catastrophe. The very long head James wears through these interchanges he owes, no doubt, to Grigblay having "*put him wise*", as they say in America.

BRASH TO SPINLOVE

Dear Mr. Spinlove,   7.1.26.

I have received your further communication anent Riddoppo. I can only once again asseverate that the blemishes indicated by Mr. Bloggs are of insignificant importance and that the painting satisfies the anticipations of the person most vitally concerned who is paying for it, and who I apprehend to be not precisely Mr. Grigblay nor my architect, but, to be brief, myself alone.

The lettering on the doors is esteemed by us as a distinct advance in the improvement of the house, and you will be gratified when I intimate to you that we agree that the particoloured variegations of tints originally proposed would not have provided the refined appearance now obtaining. Will you be so obliging as to have the door of the chamber apartment now lettered "Salmon" altered to "Strawberry", as the connected association is unpleasantly distasteful to Lady Brash.

We are proposing to arrange to move in our furniture on the 22nd inst. prox.

Believe me,
Yours sincerely,

Brash is evidently pleased with the house. We may detect in his letter a note of bland, proprietary self-congratulation.

SPINLOVE TO GRIGBLAY

Dear Mr. Grigblay,   8.1.26.

Sir Leslie Brash wishes the painting with Riddoppo completed as he does not consider the defects of any importance.

He proposes to move in furniture on the 22nd. Will that be possible? I enclose a list of matters which need attention.

Will you please have the door now lettered "Salmon" altered to "Raspberry".

Yours faithfully,

Spinlove has made a slip here.

GRIGBLAY TO SPINLOVE

Dear Sir, 8.1.26.

Our foreman has checked measurements and says Mr. Potch is right for glass area. Your figures are correct clear of window-frames. The iron casements stand in $\frac{9}{16}$ in. full. Mr. Potch's dimensions are also right for area of room but he has measured above skirtings. Our foreman suggests why not fill in recess with cupboard fixture so as to reduce floor area.

Yours faithfully,

It is to be noted that in most right designs—if not entirely in all—the size of casements is a unit of the elevations which cannot be varied, and that the minimum of one-tenth of floor area for windows gives an excessive amount of light to some rooms with some aspects, if aesthetic judgment rather than hygienic theory is the guide. The consequences are that to obtain a good disposition of windows in the elevation and an adequate, but not excessive, window area to rooms is a matter which particularly exercises the ingenuity of the designer. The bedroom in question was properly lighted by a range of three casements, but the moving of the partition has increased the floor area up to, or over, the maximum size allowed by the by-laws in respect of these three casements. If a fourth casement is added it will be likely to play "Old Harry" with the elevation and to over-light the room, and as the only way of arranging four casements will probably be to take the window out, remake it with new head and cill and re-centre it in the elevation, the breaking down and making good of brickwork is likely to show up on the elevation for some time. Though everyone else may soon forget the ungainly room and never notice the botched elevation, Spinlove will remember his

216

regrets to the end of his life. Potch does not know this and would not understand if it were explained to him; the annoyance, humiliation and cost to his rival and the man who employs him, is his aim.

SPINLOVE TO POTCH

Dear Sir,   9.1.26.

I find that your measures of windows are taken to the glass line, and of floors to walls above skirtings.

My measures are taken to the line of the frames as this, in my experience, is customary, and I claim that the floor area is properly measured up to skirtings and not above them.

Even if you insist on the window area being estimated as the area of actual glass, the floor area, measured to skirtings, is still only two-thirds of one square foot more than ten times that of windows and, I submit, so small a discrepancy depending on an unusually exacting computation of window area, does not justify the withholding of the certificate. The addition of another casement is an extremely awkward matter and will ruin the elevation and is surely a scarcely reasonable demand?

The owner wishes to move in on the 22nd, so time is short. I hope, therefore, that with these explanations before you, you will feel able to draw the certificate.

Yours faithfully,

This is a quite foolish letter. Spinlove seems to be so distressed at the prospect of having to mutilate his elevation and spoil the room that he is reduced to begging for mercy, which, as he must know, is perfectly useless. A man like Potch reacts only to impulses of greed or funk and, as Spinlove is incapable of "working it", he must fight.

Spinlove's measure of window area is 14 ft.: Potch's 12. The difference represents only $\frac{1}{2}$ in. on face of each frame, but involves a floor area of $11\frac{2}{3}$ ft.

SPINLOVE TO BRASH

Dear Sir Leslie Brash,   11.1.26.

I was speaking to Mr. Grigblay on the telephone to-day and

I fear it will not be possible for you to move in on the 22nd nor, indeed, this month. As you know, there are a good many odds and ends remaining to be done and the painting of various cupboard fittings Lady Brash has ordered have yet to be finished, and I do not think you ought to fix a date much before February 12. I am also sorry to say that the Local Authority has refused certificate of occupation on the grounds that the window in bedroom No. 5 is not big enough, but I am hoping to get this matter settled quite shortly.

Yours faithfully,

POTCH TO SPINLOVE

Sir,   12.1.26.

You should not have made the window too small if you did not care for the trouble of altering it larger. My Council cannot change its by-laws to suit A.R.I.B.A.s and if time is short you would be better correcting your mistakes than wasting more of it writing letters instead.

I am obliged to you for pointing out what my duties are, but it would be better if you spent your time some other way as it happens I have had more chance of learning it than what young London office architects have.

I am, Sir,
Yours faithfully,

Spinlove's letter produces an insult from the Potch mechanism as surely as his penny would a bit of chocolate out of an automatic machine.

The Model By-laws *which Local Authorities are at liberty to select from and "adopt" at will speak of "floor area" and "area of windows clear of frames". Spinlove has either been misled by a bluff on the part of Potch and overlooked this last definition, or the words "clear of frames" may possibly have been omitted from the Marlford District Council's version. In the latter event Spinlove would get his measurements upheld by appeal to the Local Government Board.*

Difficulties and Delays

SPINLOVE TO GRIGBLAY

Dear Sir,   15.1.26.

I cannot reduce floor area by putting cupboard fixture in recess as this is wanted to take Lady Brash's wardrobe.

I enclose detail of a small casement window. This, as you will see, is to go over the lavatory basin and will come very nearly central between the ranges of adjoining casements. I am sorry to have to order the work, but the Surveyor insists.

Yours faithfully,

BRASH TO SPINLOVE

Dear Mr. Spinlove,   14.1.26.

I really must asseverate my protestation at the successive procrastinations anent completion. Permit me to remind you that the builders contracted for eventual occupation on or before December 11th last year; I was then informed I might arrange to take up residence shortly after Xmas, and subsequently the 22nd was the extended date fixed. I am now informed that the middle of next February prox. is the anticipated day, and am given to apprehend that this date may eventually be eliminated and so on infinitum (*sic*), which is, as you will agree—if you will permit me to express myself so—a most preposterous succession of prevarications and procrastinations.

In addition to these delays and postponements, for which I apprehend the contractor is responsible, you now inform me that the necessary certificate entitling me to occupy the house is not forthcoming because, forsooth, you have made one of the windows too small! Are we ever going to get into the house at all?—that I apprehend to be a question to which it is now incumbent on me to request a definite assurance. Why is the window not large enough? I apprehend that to be a matter on which I was entitled to rely upon your judicial discretion.

Yours sincerely,

Our sympathies may well be with Brash's impatience, though not with his grievance, which is unreasonable. He and Lady

219

Difficulties and Delays

Brash have, in fact, been accountable for greater delays than they complain of; but for one reason or another there always are delays, and Grigblay, all circumstances considered, has done well not to be more behindhand than he is.

(CONFIDENTIAL) GRIGBLAY TO SPINLOVE

Sir,   17.1.26.

I noticed your correspondence with Mr. Potch in the office and have seen your detail of little port-hole makeweight. I fancy it goes against the grain for I know something of the way architects feel, so I take the liberty to let you know that Mr. Potch is not so particular with his own building nor yet with that of some others, and I can drop him a hint that will make that certificate come by special messenger. If you do not care for that—and I would rather not start any mix up with Mr. Potch—why not brad a bit of ovolo down on the floor against the skirting just to make it easy for the poor housemaid to sweep the dust out of the corners and not tire her pretty self? ½in. wide would bring the floor area down to limit and leave a bit over for good manners. No trouble to take up again before the family move in.

With apologies for troubling you but thought you might like to do it.

Yours faithfully,

SPINLOVE TO BRASH

Dear Sir Leslie Brash,   19.1.26.

The 22nd was named by *you*. I said "before the end of the month", and were it not for the many fittings which have been ordered only after the house is on the point of completion, there would be no reason why you should not move in this month.

You must permit me to excuse myself. The window of bedroom No. 5 was big enough for the room as I planned it, but the room was made too big for the window when, by your orders, the partition was moved. The grounds for the Council's objection are trivial and since I last wrote I have succeeded, I think, in arranging matters, and there will be no delay on this account.

Yours sincerely,

Spinlove has certainly advanced in discretion and force; his early diffidence and shyness, and consequent indecision and impulse to be plausible and to explain and justify himself, have in great part disappeared. The reason is, no doubt, that he now knows the person he has to deal with and feels himself master of the position now that his knowledge of past history, rather than his judgment in making new, is involved.

SPINLOVE TO GRIGBLAY

Dear Mr. Grigblay, 18.1.26.

I am much obliged for your letter. Will you please have the skirting fillet fixed as you suggest and return my detail No. 49.

Yours very truly,

SPINLOVE TO POTCH

Sir, 22.1.26.

I write to notify you that lighting of bedroom No. 5 at Honeywood has now been amended to comply with the by-laws, and to apply for certificate of occupation.

Yours faithfully,

SIR LESLIE BRASH MOVES IN

(CONFIDENTIAL) GRIGBLAY TO SPINLOVE

Sir, 28.1.26.

I went down to Honeywood to-day to have a look round and you may tell Sir Leslie Brash the house will be ready for him on February 10th, unless he orders other work to keep himself out of it. The road etc. will take a couple of weeks to finish and had better stand till the old gentleman has got his furniture in. I've seen something of the mess these heavy lorries can make of a new road and this one is none too heavily bottomed. Bloggs will be clearing up next week.

While I was down there Mr. Potch paid us a friendly call. He ran to bedroom No. 5 as if he'd buried a bone there, and I followed and found him huffing and blowing his nose; but I soon stopped his nonsense and we shall get the certificate in a day or two.

Riddoppo super is beginning to act up and I shall be glad to be out. Potch went away with a bit of it on his behind end, but I don't know where he got it for the surface is dry and firm though it does not look to be so underneath, for in places it is beginning to ride up over itself, and it is hanging from the bottoms of doors again for all it was cut away once, and a bead of it laying along top of skirtings. There is one place where furnace flue goes up kitchen wall, where it is beginning to craze like a really fine old picture. In my opinion it will all have to come off again, unless it's kept on to prevent the house catching fire, but it can't be burnt off, because it's fireproof, and it can't be pickled off because it's acid proof, so there you are! It is a pity the makers, who had such a lot to say about laying it on, didn't spare a word or two about getting it off.

Apologizing for troubling you but thought best to tell you.

Yours truly,

GRIGBLAY TO SPINLOVE

Dear Sir,   31.1.26.

We have received certificate of occupation from the District Council's Surveyor.

We note that your client wishes to move in on the 8th, instead of the 10th as arranged, and we think there will be no objection to this.

We enclose rough approximate statement of account and shall be glad of your final certificate. The detailed statement will follow in due course.

Yours faithfully,

Sir Leslie Brash Moves In

Grigblay is entitled to a certificate for the whole value of the work less 5 per cent, on completion.

Tel.: Forgetmenot 178.   *HONEYWOOD GRANGE,*
Postal Address: Thaddington.   *MARLFORD,*
Station: Wedgfield Junc.: 4 m.   *.KENT*
      (*Taxi* 5s.)

My dear Mr. Spinlove,   13.2.26.

Here we are eventually! We commenced to take up residence at Honeywood Grange on Thursday and occupied the sleeping apartments last night for the first occasion. Although there still remain a vast number of dispositions of furniture to adjust I desire, on behalf of Lady Brash and myself, to intimate that we are completely charmed and delighted with the mansion. We consider it to be most elegant in every respect and anticipate that we shall esteem the convenience and appropriateness of the various different arrangements still more as time progresses, and we already have had occasion to appreciate the recommendations you have suggested and your forethought in providing beforehand many excellent devices. We shall anticipate seeing you here when we have settled down.

Believe me with best regards from Lady Brash and myself,
Yours very sincerely,

So that's that; and a handsome letter for even a grateful client to write.

SPINLOVE TO BRASH

Dear Sir Leslie,   14.2.26.

Very many thanks to you and to Lady Brash for your most kind letter, which, I can assure you, gave me great pleasure. I shall look forward to seeing the house when you have settled down. One cannot really see a house properly until it has been furnished.

I am sure that Mr. Grigblay would very much appreciate a line from you telling him you are pleased with his work. He has taken great pains to make it a success.

223

Sir Leslie Brash Moves In

With kind regards and good wishes to Lady Brash and yourself,

Yours sincerely,

*   *   *   *   *   *

And so the file ends; but it ends at the point where the folder will hold no more papers: the last score of letters have, in fact, been packed under the clip to bring the chapter to a close—for a chapter, only, it is. There must somewhere in Spinlove's office be another chapter enshrined in another folder. That second chapter[1] may be a short and uneventful chapter, or it may be neither short nor uneventful nor even the last. The Honeywood account has to be settled, and the numerous items of that account may raise many questions of fact and lead to a review of events gone almost out of memory. Question of extras may arise in which the architect, although involved by his own acts of omission or commission, has to keep the scales balanced between builder and client, and gild for the latter, as best he may, the often bitter pill called, "final balance due". Last, this second chapter will contain the history, be it long or short, of the inevitable small defects and the possible big ones, which reveal themselves after a house has been occupied and which, should they appear within nine months—or more or less—and so far as they are due to improper workmanship or materials, the builder is engaged under the terms of his contract to make good. Yet a third chapter clipped, perhaps, within another folder may lie upon Spinlove's shelves; but we, who have come to know him, may hope that it does not exist. It could only be a record of pains and miseries—a chapter of bitter memories; for while the builder's liabilities end when he has redeemed those of his faults which reveal themselves within the limit of nine, or other, months fixed by the contract, the architect's liabilities are for all defects due to his negligence, whether faults of himself, of manufacturers, of specialists or of builders, which may appear within the limit of six years fixed by the law. We know, however, nothing of what other files may lie in Spinlove's office. The last page of The Honeywood File *is the front cover, and that we now close.*

[1] This second chapter has now been published under the title *The Honeywood Settlement.*

224

INDEX

Index

THE
HONEYWOOD
SETTLEMENT

a continuation of The Honeywood File

PREFACE

The Honeywood File described the building of a house, and the present volume carries the history to conclusion ten months later when the last defect has been remedied, the last dispute settled, and the last account paid.

The aspirant to architectural practice – unlike the general reader – is more interested in building houses than in occupying them; but the proof of a pudding is in the eating, and by showing the consequences that flowed from events recorded in the earlier book, *The Honeywood Settlement* completes the lesson of *The Honeywood File*.

H.B.C.

CONTENTS

Contents

INTRODUCTORY REMARKS

THE matter before us purports to be a correspondence file from the office of James Spinlove, a young London architect. The file is concerned with the building of a country house for a certain Sir Leslie Brash, and consists of a folder within which are clipped, in order of date, letters received and carbon copies of those dispatched. The colours of the picture presented are necessarily somewhat brighter than life; the characters are also entirely imaginary and the episodes inventions; yet, since the whole of the didactic value of the book and much of its interest depends upon the reader's acceptance of the picture as true to life, it has been the author's particular concern to make it so by enhancing verisimilitude. The detachment of the commentator is, however, no such elaborate affectation as appears; for the commentary has been provoked by the reaction of characters to the events, and new events have had birth in those reactions so that the author is, in general, identified with the commentator in not knowing, from one page to the next, what is going to happen.

The file we are about to open is the second and last of those covering the history of the building of Honeywood Grange. In the closing commentary of *The Honeywood File* it was mentioned that somewhere in the architect's office there must be a second Honeywood File, for the first file ended when the folder would hold no more papers, and the circumstance that the last letter coincided with the completion of the house was merely an example of Author's luck, for if the business of building a house ended when the workmen left it, this world would be a happier place than it is for owners, architects, and builders.

There is the vexed question of defects which, in a greater or less degree, manifest themselves in all new buildings, and which, so far as they appear within a certain time and are due to improper workmanship or materials, the builder has to make good under the terms of his contract; or, so far as they are due to negligence on the part of the architect, the architect is responsible for under his. Then, the builder's final Statement of Account has to be dealt with. This is likely to include charges

9

for extras and to raise questions of fact long gone out of memory. When these disputes have been settled it devolves on the architect to reconcile his client to those extra charges that are due to his interferences, and to those others imposed on him by the oversights or afterthoughts of his architect. Lastly, there is the architect's account for balance of fees due. As this account includes items for expenses and disbursements, and special charges for services additional to those directly involved by the contract work; and as, besides, these expenses and charges are based on the architect's status and style of living and the cost to him in time and trouble, and are to be justified only by their reasonableness, it sometimes happens that owner and architect discover, perhaps for the first and only time, that their ideas of reasonableness differ.

It is such matters as these that make the existence of a second file inevitable; but the bulk of that before us is exceptional and is not explained by Spinlove's habit of writing unnecessary letters which provoke unnecessary replies. Every reader of *The Honeywood File* will, however, recall that Spinlove is involved in more ways than he is aware of. He has, for instance, given his client light-hearted estimates, some of which have been wildly astray; and, although the contract lays down that no extras shall rank unless the claim be made and accepted at the time the work is done, Spinlove was not particular in enforcing the builder's observance of this rule. Spinlove is also unconscious that he has fallen into a trap set for him by the persons who supplied the facing bricks, and who have thereby established a claim for extra payment.

Spinlove warned his client not to give orders direct to the builder's people, and laid stress on the dangers of the extras that would attend any interferences with the work; but Brash's attention to this excellent advice wandered, and when her Leslie was gunning in Scotland Lady Brash began pulling down work that afterwards had to be restored—one of the least economical ways of building known to the trade.

Trouble is also promised by Brash's insistence on the interior of the house being decorated with a new, untried, patent paint called Riddoppo, against his architect's advice and in spite of the builder's objections. Riddoppo is advertised in tube lifts as a New Novelty Super-Paint, fire and acid resisting, proof against assaults of boiling water and super-heated steam, and capable of receiving a high polish; but these rare merits have not prevented it from showing such a marked tendency to "creep" or flow downwards, that Grigblay, in a private letter to Spinlove—in which his incorrigible, ironic humour veils a natural annoyance—describes "Riddoppo Super" as getting ready to crawl out of the front door and off home.

Sir Leslie Brash, his wife Maude, and his daughter Phyllis—who prefers to be known as "Pud"—occupied Honeywood Grange on 10th February 1926. The house backs upon a spinney through which the entrance drive passes to the adjoining highway, and looks out over a terrace upon a fine prospect to the south, east, and west, marred only by a pump-house chimney two miles away which reacts unfavourably on the nerve-centres that serve Lady Brash for brains. It is a brick gabled house, with leaded lights in iron casements set in solid oak frames; and the design has affinity to Tudor architecture. The oak floors and staircases and the oak panelling and open brick hearths and fireplace surrounds to the reception rooms, are in sympathy with the same tradition. Brash, however, allowed a friend, who was a director of the paint company, to persuade him to paint each bedroom out in a different colour, thus turning the upper part of the house, as Spinlove complained, into a colour-cure asylum for lunatics.

Sir Leslie Brash, the building owner, is a man in advanced middle-age. He is an accountant and financial expert of some importance whose native generosity of heart is veiled by pomposity and irascibility. His architect, James Spinlove, is about thirty: he is well qualified and is painstaking and conscientious, but temperamental; and he lacks experience of life and of affairs, so that he is apt to turn for guidance when in difficulties to the builder, John Grigblay. Grigblay is a provincial builder of good standing and repute, and high integrity.

The last sheet in the first file was a copy of a letter of Spinlove's acknowledging a warm message of appreciation and thanks from Brash, who had just gone to live in the house. This letter was dated 14th February 1926, and when we open the second folder we find the following:

11

SIGNS OF DAMP

JAMES SPINLOVE, A.R.I.B.A., TO JOHN GRIGBLAY, BUILDER

Dear Sir,   23.2.26.

I should like your Statement of Account at once. When may I expect it?

Yours faithfully,

It is a pity Spinlove—like the rest of us—does not get his deserts, or he would receive by return a postcard bearing the words "Say, Please", and obtain great benefit from the hint. He is on the best of terms with Grigblay who has taken great trouble to make the house a success and whose friendly help and advice he has acknowledged on several occasions and been indebted to on many more, so that his gracelessness is merely a habit with Spinlove in addressing those under his direction. It is a bad habit, and one that has already got him into difficulties he might otherwise have avoided.

SIR LESLIE BRASH TO SPINLOVE

Dear Mr. Spinlove,   28.2.26.

I very much regret to have to intimate that my anticipations anent the windows at Honeywood appear to be now eventuating. You will recall that I previously communicated to you, on behalf of Lady Brash and myself, our strong preference for big sheets of thick glass in place of little thin sheets all jointed together with narrow strips; but you persuaded us to adhere to the present device. The consequent results are precisely what I anticipated. The rain percolates freely through the glass, which is very thin, cheap glass; and also, I apprehend, through the joints where it is connected by the little strips which are so weak that *iron bars* have in some cases been found necessary to fortify their strength. Every morning the maids have to remove the accumulated wet that collects on the new oak window-boards, which are exhibiting stains in consequence, and the water even runs over the edge on to our new carpets!

12

Signs of Damp

The situation of Honeywood Grange is excessively exposed to the weather, and it is clearly obvious that large continuous sheets of thick glass is the appropriate desideratum, as—if you will permit me to remind you—I previously prognosticated.

We continue to be delighted with the house and to appreciate the anticipatory forethought of its architect. We notice no signs of damp other than that above intimated except in the box-room, the outer wall of which was lately found to be streaming with water; and the domestic staff complain of wet marks near the ceiling over the fireplaces of their domain on the uppermost story.

I desire that you will intimate to Mr. Grigblay that these matters require immediate attention. There should be no difficulty in cutting the glass to appropriate sizes and effecting substitution of one pane at a time so as to avoid unnecessarily exposing us to the weather.

Yours sincerely,

Brash certainly takes these disasters in an accommodating spirit. He is evidently well satisfied with the house.

SPINLOVE TO BRASH

Dear Sir Leslie Brash,   1.3.26.

It is not possible, I assure you, for rain to beat through the glass quarries, which are not, as you suppose, unduly thin. Iron saddle-bars are essential to leaded lights. Large sheets are made thick for purposes of strength only. It is certainly possible for heavy driving rain to find its way in through the joints with the leadings, but this cannot be the case with your windows. Messrs. Watkins, who did the work, are most reliable people; and it happens that, knowing the house was exposed on the south and west, I spoke to their man on this particular point and found that he was already jointing the quarries to the cames, or leads, with a mastic stopping—a precaution not in ordinary found necessary.

I have no doubt whatever that what you describe is merely *condensation*. In a quite new house the moisture in the walls, due to the large amount of water used in bricklaying, is continually being evaporated, and the warm air becomes charged with steam which condenses on the cold surface of the glass. If the windows are left a little open the trouble will diminish, and it will entirely disappear for good and all with the summer.

The wet surface of the boxroom wall is due to the same cause. This is a solid wall, and the plaster was finished with an ordinary steel-faced float and so left. The window and door should be kept open for the next few weeks.

With kind regards,

Yours sincerely,

P.S.—You will find that wet will collect on the windows irrespective of rain, and on the boxroom wall only when mild, humid weather immediately follows cold.

Spinlove is evidently informed by experience or he could scarcely write with the assurance he exhibits—which, however, does not extend to explaining the cause of the damp in chimney-breasts. It will be noticed he says nothing of this. The reasons he gives, and the advice he offers, are sound; but we may suppose that Brash has raised a great shout over a very small matter, for the conditions at Honeywood Grange are such as least favour condensation. The brickwork was built during the summer months and the outer walls are formed of a 4½-in. inner and a 9-in. outer wall, with a 2-in. space between, so that evaporation must be relatively small. In houses that specially favour condensation— such as those built in the winter and stuccoed or rough-cast on the outside as well as plastered within, so that water is bottled up in the walls—the evaporation induced by the warmth of the occupied house is so considerable as to produce most disquieting conditions of damp. Water collects in puddles on window-boards and runs down walls to form pools on the floor below; and under such conditions of weather as that described in Spinlove's post-script, wallpapers covering outside walls may become soaked with water. Brash's boxroom is a mild instance of this pheno-mènon; and when Spinlove speaks of "steam", and mentions that this particular wall is built solid and its plastered face left as finished with a steel float, he gives the explanation of it, though Brash may not know what he is talking about for he probably

14

recognizes steam only as the vapour from boiling water (which is not steam), and has no idea that steam is invisible, or that atmospheric air is charged with steam which comes into evidence as vapour, or "condensation", only when pressure is reduced or temperature lowered.

The inner 4½-in. lining of a hollow wall speedily dries out and acquires a temperature approximating to that of the room, so that condensation cannot take place upon it. A solid brick wall, on the other hand, tends to retain its moisture and is therefore a better conductor of heat than a dry one; and, as there is no hollow space providing an insulating blanket of air, the warmth of the room is dispersed into and through the wall which, in consequence, remains cold and invites condensation. If this boxroom wall had been papered—and in the degree that the paper was thick and porous—condensation would have been discouraged and for the reason that explains Spinlove's reference to a steel float. A steel float which gives a compact, smooth, polished finish to plaster, promotes condensation by the abrupt transition of temperature presented at its surface; but a float faced with felt leaves an open grain behind it so that the air invades the interstices of the plaster surface, there is a gradual transition from the temperature of the room to the temperature of the wall, and condensation will not then take place under any conditions likely to arise in a house. Incidentally, distemper lies well on a felt-floated wall: it looks "solid", as a house painter would say—a result that can be otherwise got only by papering before applying distemper. In using the ordinary method of finishing with a steel float in the boxroom and other back quarters, Spinlove was observing a right principle of economy.

GRIGBLAY TO SPINLOVE

Dear Sir, 2.3.26.

As proposed to you by Mr. Grigblay, we held off with metalling the entrance drive until the owner had got his furniture in, and our foreman tells us that the heavy lorries have done a lot of damage to the bottoming. Mr. Grigblay looked in yesterday and thinks you ought to see what has been done, as we must make a claim for restoring and Mr. Grigblay thinks

Signs of Damp

the best thing will be to put a 5-ton roller over the 9-in. pitching and then level up with 4-in. chalk rubble before laying the 3 ins. of metalling, as the present bottoming is rather light.

Bloggs will be on the site till middle of next week finishing the paths, etc., and clearing up. We have an expert ganger who will look after the road.

Bloggs says there are various little jobs her Ladyship wants done in the house, and we are attending to them. We propose to put these in a separate account.

Yours faithfully,

Heavy motor lorries are a great tax on private roads, which require better foundations than were formerly necessary. Spinlove is indebted to Grigblay for having warned him to postpone the finishing of the road: it would otherwise have been badly broken up. The additional layer of rubble was in any case desirable.

It will be noticed that Grigblay says nothing of Spinlove's demand for the Statement of Account. In point of fact, the reason Spinlove wants the account at once is a good reason why Grigblay should wish to hold it back. However exact Spinlove's methods may be—and we have no evidence that they are particularly exact —they will fall far short of the orderly, detailed records which are a necessary part of the daily routine of a builders' office, so that Spinlove will have to depend in great part on his memory in determining that certain charges are justified and in fortifying himself to disallow others. Thus, if a builder delays rendering his account, the architect is at a disadvantage in fulfilling his duties as arbiter of what is just and unjust, and is more or less at the builder's mercy. There is also a psychological reason favouring delay in making claims, of which everyone is conscious and which seems to depend upon repugnance to reopening old disputes or returning to forgotten battlefields. When an owner is in bland enjoyment of his accomplished ambition, and his architect immersed in fresh activities (and anxieties), neither has much appetite for renewal of controversy. In addition to this, a builder is obviously in a bad position if he renders his account before he knows what may be required of him in the matter of making good defects; for if he is to be met by exacting and crotchety demands

16

he will be inclined to reimburse himself by claims for doubtful extras which he otherwise might prefer not to raise; or if, by some misfortune, he is involved in a demand for costly restitutions that become the cause of an action for damages, he will wish, as an offset to the claim against him, to be free to inflate his account to the full limits that plausibility and legal ingenuity can effect. Thus there are good reasons why a builder should delay sending in his account till the time within which he is under contract to make good defects—usually nine months—has expired, or is on the point of expiring; and this no doubt explains why protracted delay in rendering the final statement of account is common. It must be remembered, however, that a builder does not make out his statement of account until he has brought up to date his prime-cost account which shows what the actual value of material and labour is; and as some invoices reach him only months after the materials have been delivered, an early rendering of the State-ment of Account would dislocate his organization.

SPINLOVE TO GRIGBLAY

Dear Sir,   3.3.26.

I will go on to the site on Monday and settle what is to be done to complete the entrance road.

I understand that the work Lady Brash has asked you to do relates only to fittings. This, as you propose, should be rendered in a separate account. You will, of course, let me know if any kind of structural alterations, or decorations, are asked for.

I shall be glad to know when I may expect your Statement of Account.

Sir Leslie Brash mentions that damp is appearing on the chimney-breasts of the second floor. Will you therefore leave necessary ladders on the site so that I can examine the listings?

Yours faithfully,

Spinlove is wise in directing the builder to make a separate account of the odds and ends of work which are necessary to enable an owner to fit himself and his belongings into his house; but he will have to see that none of this work is work that should properly be included in the contract to "complete" and make good

17

defects. *Such accounts are otherwise apt to become inflated by a carpenter employed to fix coat-rails or shelving, charging against that work time spent unhanging and easing doors.*

(TELEPHONE MESSAGE) BRASH TO SPINLOVE

11.20   4.3.26.

B. notes you on site Monday. Hopes stay night. White tie. Phone. R.S.P.

Tell him *Yes.* J.S. 4.3.

O.K. R.S.P. 4.10. 4.3.

Spinlove has begun to record and file telephone messages, as he ought to do—though not quite in this manner. We recognize in "R.S.P." his assistant Pintle, whose style, even in these few words, also identifies him. He is an excruciating person and ought to be sacked, unless—as his toleration by Spinlove might suggest —he has on some occasion saved his master's life.

We noticed before that Spinlove had established intimate social relations with the Brashes and as Brash is precisely the sort of man who would be well aware of the disadvantage of this intimacy should his architect let him down; and as he is, besides, somewhat a self-important, unapproachable person, the thing is not exactly what one would expect.

GRIGBLAY TO SPINLOVE

Dear Sir,   4.3.26.

We have not overlooked that you wish our Statement as soon as possible, and we will press on with this work, which is in hand. In the meantime we shall be glad to receive a certificate for, say, £3,500 on account. We may remind you that we sent you a rough approximate Statement on 31st January, which we think must have escaped your attention.

Yours faithfully,

THE DRAINS SUSPECTED

Dear Mr. Spinlove,

It is dreadfully close here, the house always smells stuffy and the drains must be *very* bad for I have tried disinfectants but it only makes it worse instead of better so something will have to be done or I am afraid we shall all be *affected*! There was a *horrid* smell the other day and I am sure it was the scullery sink or something and it might get into the larder though I told them always to keep it shut as tainted food is *not pleasant* and I am *most* particular even the dogs are not allowed to and it is *specially* at night though Leslie will not believe me.

How peaceful after all the stormy weather we have been having!

Thursday.   Yours sincerely,

Lady Brash complained of a bad smell on an earlier occasion before the house was finished. That, after some trouble, was found to be the pungent aroma of the new, untreated oak, which the lady did not like. Spinlove apparently does not answer this letter. He was, as we know, going to the house a day or two later.

Dear Sirs,   6.3.26.

Yes, I set aside your letter of 31st January, as the work was then not completed and you were not entitled to a certificate. The matter has since escaped my attention, and the Statement covered by your letter cannot be found in this office. I am at a loss to understand how you justify a certificate for £3,500, and shall be glad if you will let me have a copy of the missing Statement.

Yours faithfully,

The Drains Suspected

A lame business! Spinlove seems to have put aside the State-
ment without looking at it, or he would have questioned it at the
time.

Dear Sirs,   9.3.26.

I enclose specification for work in completing entrance road.
I ought to have your estimate of the extra cost, as Sir Leslie
wants to know this.

I am annoyed to find that wet gets into the chimneys and
shows on the second-floor breasts. I could see nothing wrong
with the listings, and Bloggs assures me the soakers were
properly lapped and turned up—in fact, I saw the work being
done. It is, therefore, evident that the water strikes through
the cement and runs down behind the upturned edge of the
soakers, and I learn from Bloggs that the cement was *not*
waterproofed with Puddlyte. The listings will have to be replaced in Puddlyte cement as specified. The work should be put
in hand at once, a small bit at a time, as weather allows; and
care taken to keep tarpaulins rigged to prevent rain getting in.

Lady Brash tells me she finds the house "stuffy", and that
she has not felt well since she went to live in it, and that two
of the servants have been unwell. She suspects something is
wrong with the drains. This is not possible, but, as a fact, did
the District Surveyor test the whole of the drains and give you
a formal certificate of acceptance of the sanitary work? If so,
kindly send me the certificate by return.

                                            Yours faithfully,

It seems that Spinlove employed lead soakers laid in with the
tiles and turned up against the brickwork where roof slopes butt
up against chimneys, but replaced the usual lead cover-flashings,
turned into the brick joints and covering the upturned edges of the
soakers, with cement fillets in the angle between tile and chimney-
face. These "listings" are a perfectly sound, water-tight device,
although they are associated with the tradition of humble build-
ings rather than of important works of architecture. Spinlove, we
remember, had several knowing ideas for a sham medieval roof

which he could not get carried out; but he seems to have had his own way in this matter.

The Local Government Board's model bye-laws secure that all drains shall be planned on established scientific principles of sanitation, so that architects are relieved of the preoccupation of trying to save money by following ideas of their own; and inspections and tests by District Councils' Surveyors reduce—in practice though not in law—the architect's responsibility for seeing that the work is properly carried out. Spinlove's letter suggests that he is in need of evidence of this official approval to enforce the assurances he offered Lady Brash of the soundness of the drains. His urgency will be readily understood by those who read The Honeywood File. *If Lady Brash gets the idea into her head that something is wrong with the drains, nothing less than a course of hypodermic injections is likely ever to get it out again.*

GRIGBLAY TO SPINLOVE

Dear Sir,   10.3.26.

The whole of the drains were duly tested with water and the p'pes with smoke by Mr. Gallop, the drain Inspector; and the whole were inspected on two occasions by the District Surveyor, Mr. Potch, whose certificate of approval we enclose. We are sure there is nothing wrong as the work was done under the supervision of Bloggs; and as Mr. Potch could not find fault with it no one else is likely to be able to. [*This letter was evidently dictated by Grigblay.*]

As regards the listings, this is not in our opinion the best method of flashing to chimneys; but we have no reason to think that the work at Honeywood is defective, as it was carefully carried out to your instructions. We have respectfully to point out that Puddlyte to listings was not, as you state, ordered by you. Puddlyte cement is specified for bedding and jointing weathered brick members only.

We do not know to what the damp in chimney-breasts is due, but Mr. Grigblay expects to be that way on Friday and will take the opportunity.

We have noted your provisional acceptance by telephone to-day of our estimate of £64 12s. for remaking entrance road.

The Drains Suspected

We have ordered the pitching and enclose details of our measurements and rates on which our estimate is based for you to check.

Yours faithfully,

Spinlove is making a muddle of things. He ought to have asked the quantity surveyor what the approximate value of the work on entrance road was, and left it to be measured and valued at settling-up. Apparently he accepted Grigblay's estimate so that the work could be put in hand, but subject to measurements being checked and rates agreeing with the Contract Schedule. This, however, is a task for the quantity surveyor, and in any case Spinlove had no business to learn what those rates are, for the priced bills of quantities, which constitute the Contract Schedule, are properly kept under seal. A builder has a right to expect that they will be so kept, as otherwise the architect is in a position to vary the contract in the interests of his client, and unprofitably for the builder, by substituting work for which the builder has included a low price for that for which he has allowed a good one. Such a proceeding by a building-owner is manifestly unfair and, by an architect, dishonest; for the architect is, by the terms of the contract, constituted arbiter between client and builder.

It is not usual for the District Sanitary Inspector to test with smoke, but he has the right to do so and there were reasons why Mr. Potch, the District Surveyor, should instruct him to so test at Honeywood.

Dear Lady Brash,   11.3.26.

As I promised, I enclose the formal official certificate of the Local District Surveyor showing that the whole of the drains conform with the regulations of the Local Government Board and Public Health Acts; and that the pipes, both below and above ground, have been subjected to smoke and water tests; and that the whole of the work was approved as sound and to his satisfaction. I hope that this will entirely banish any doubts you may have. May I assure you that I have none whatever myself? As I told you, I personally overlooked the whole of the arrangements, and you may rest assured that everything is safe and sound. Even if a defect had developed in the drains since they were tested and passed, which is unbelievable, it could not by the remotest possibility lead, as you imagine, to contamination of the air in the house.

With kind regards,
Yours sincerely,

P.S.—Will you please return the certificate when you have done with it?

Here we see our young friend making his old mistakes. In his anxiety to emphasize his assurances, he represents sanitary security as a very difficult and dangerous matter to arrange and a still more difficult matter to prove—which are the particular things he should have avoided. He also depicts himself as persuaded, only, of the purity of Honeywood: he does not, as he should, assert a fact, but reasons his conclusions although he knows that the person he addresses is incapable of reasoning and unable to weigh the evidence if she were. On the top of all this he actually admits the possibility of a defect and, without knowing what that defect may be, pledges his word that it cannot set up unsanitary conditions. It would probably have been better if he had left Brash to open the subject, as he would do were it more than a figment of his lady's imagination. Why the exasperating fellow cannot hold his tongue, after all he has suffered from unnecessarily wagging it, is beyond understanding. It is inconceivable that there can be anything wrong with the drains, but Spinlove has given his client reason to think it possible.

DEFECTS APPEAR

(HOLOGRAPH) GRIGBLAY TO SPINLOVE

Sir,   12.3.26.

I looked in at Honeywood when I was passing to-day. You can take it from me that there is nothing wrong with the listings and, if there were, they would not let water into the flues to run down and lie in puddles on the back hearths of fireplaces as it has been doing. There had rightly ought to be a damp course across the chimney, and flue pipes in the stacks; for the rain drives across from the S.W. something cruel, and the proper thing to live in up at Honeywood is a submarine, but I can make all right with a bit of soap. The house is dry, but the water drives right through the 9 inch, that's certain, for the wall at the bottom of the hollow is soaked; but nothing is showing inside, though the maids were quack-quacking about a bit of sweating there is which is only what you must expect in a new house. [*"Sweating" is here loosely and inexactly used by Grigblay to signify condensation.*]

The matter I am taking the liberty to write to you privately about is this New Novelty Super-Paint the old gentleman insisted I use and which is going to be a bit more of a novelty than he bargained for. The ripple is much more than it was, and is forming in ridges. Sir Leslie may think it looks pretty so, but he will change his mind when it begins to fold over on itself and break away in flakes—which is what comes next, for I found a place behind a radiator in the bathroom where it is doing a bit of private rehearsal. The worst place is on the wall of the kitchen where the furnace flue goes up behind. The maids have brushed it over and washed it down till there isn't any paint left, scarcely.

As you know, sir, I refused to take responsibility for Riddoppo and gave warning before the painters left the job that it would all have to come off again—except what came off of itself—and I hope you will bear it in mind, because when Riddoppo gets a move on and shows how super it knows how to be (and we shan't be long now) the dogs will begin to bark; and as I don't want to be bit, and you, I take it, don't want either, and as I have perhaps had a little more experience of mix-ups of this kind than has happened to come your way, I take the liberty, with all respect to your superior judgment, of dropping you a friendly hint—which is just to take no kind of notice; and if the old gentleman says anything or makes any complaint, to hold out that the paint is no concern of yours any more than it is mine, for I understand you objected to

Riddoppo and only carried out instructions in passing on Sir Leslie's orders to me. Please be very careful, sir, what letters you write to Sir Leslie; and do not write any if avoidable, for lawyers are wonderful fellows at proving words mean the opposite to what they do.

I hope no harm done by me addressing you, but thought best, as I am afraid there is trouble ahead.

I am, sir,

Yours faithfully,

For a builder to write such a letter to an architect is most unusual, although the understanding established between Grigblay —a builder ripe in years and experience—and Spinlove—an architect mature in neither—would render it easy for Grigblay to make the same communication in conversation; for Grigblay's individuality is masterful, and Spinlove, although he has great tenacity and can show spirit on occasion, impresses us as lacking personal force. Grigblay has, however, formed the habit of dissipating the evening preoccupations of his active mind in well-purposed letters to Spinlove, which, though intimate and fatherly in tone, are perfectly respectful, and that is all there is to say about it. It is necessary to call attention to the oddness of the circumstance, or an experience few architects are ever likely to have might be supposed usual.

The meaning of the letter is that Grigblay, in visiting the house, is reminded of the imminent failure of the inside paint work; and that he is uneasy. Apparently, he feels that his original disclaimer, and Brash's acceptance, of responsibility for Riddoppo, does not perfectly secure him; and he is afraid that Spinlove may be led, by characteristic exuberances, to countenance an interpretation of the facts prejudicial to Grigblay's position. Spinlove, of course, cannot by anything he may write or say commit Grigblay; but he may readily mislead Brash as to what Grigblay's obligations are, and thus foment contest.

FIRST NEWS OF EXTRAS

Dear Sir,   12.3.26.

				£
Our estimate for certificate is as follows:				
Amount of contract	..	..	..	.. 18,440
Less 5 per cent retention	..	..	922	
Received on a/c	..	..	.. 15,500	
				16,422
				2,018
Add balance variations account, say	..	..		1,500
				£3,518

We shall be glad to receive your certificate as this matter has been standing over some time.

                                                        Yours faithfully,

On completion of the work to the architect's satisfaction—an event which befell on 10th February—the retention of 10 per cent of the value of work done was reduced, under the terms of the contract, to a 5 per cent security for the builder's performance of his covenant to make good defects appearing within nine months. Grigblay was at any time entitled to require the value of extra work to be included in the computation of Spinlove's certificates, but does not appear to have asked for it.

Dear Sir,   13.3.26.

Mr. Grigblay visited Honeywood yesterday and is of opinion that the damp on chimney-breasts is due to rain driving into the brickwork of the chimney. It also drives through the parging into the flues which may account for complaints made to Bloggs of the flues not drawing. We think that the trouble can be cured by treating the face of the brickwork with soap, unless you prefer application of some special waterproofing. If you will let us know what you wish we will estimate cost of same.

                                                        Yours faithfully,

First News of Extras

Grigblay's proposal to supply an estimate is intended to make clear to Spinlove what he is slow to discern for himself, namely, that the architect, and not the builder, is responsible for the architect's mistakes. Having regard to the exposed situation and the extreme, though not exceptional, porosity of the facing bricks, Spinlove ought, as Grigblay says, to have put dampcourses through the stacks and piped the flues. He will, no doubt, on the next occasion when a similar conjunction of circumstances arises, benefit by this experience; but it was no part of the builder's duty to foresee the trouble: a builder has preoccupations enough without thinking for the architect; and though he would, for his own credit and in a spirit of collaboration, warn the architect when he saw dangers ahead, he may have learnt that such interferences are not always welcomed and that when they are, and the precaution proves ineffective or for any reason is afterwards regretted, the trouble he puts himself to lands him in trouble he could do without.

Perhaps this is Spinlove's first experience of building with sand-faced bricks in an exposed position. In that case he will have good reason to appreciate the device of the hollow wall which he has apparently carried out with exact care. If the ties binding the $4\frac{1}{2}$-in. inner wall to the 9-in. outer wall were not of a particular pattern, the rain, which Grigblay discerned to stream down the inside of the outer wall when driven by heavy wind, would creep across to the inner; and if the clearing-battens, hung in the space between the walls when the bricks were being laid, had not been carefully maintained, droppings of mortar would have lodged on these ties with the same result. If, also, Spinlove had neglected to carry the hollow space down through the dampcourse which stops water rising from the ground into the wall, or had mortar droppings been allowed to accumulate at the bottom of the hollow, the water flowing down the inner face of the outer wall would have soaked across into the lower part of the inner wall. We gather that none of these things has happened, for it is evident that the south front of Honeywood Grange is being severely tested and Grigblay noticed nothing wrong. How severe that test may be in an exposed situation is only fully known to architects' and builders of experience.

Rain will drive right through a 14-in. wall of London Stocks

27

First News of Extras

laid in lias lime mortar faced with the best sand-faced, hand-thrown bricks; and run from the under side of concrete lintels over window openings so as to collect in pools on the floor It will penetrate 9-in. walls of impervious Fletton bricks laid in hydraulic mortar and cement stuccoed in two coats. It will even make a 14-in. wall, similarly stuccoed, so damp as to recommend renewal of the cement stucco with special waterproofed rendering. Stone and concrete walls present their special problems, but it will be seen that Spinlove has done well in dealing with a brick one, and in securing, under thoroughly bad conditions, that his client has a dry house.

(PERSONAL) SPINLOVE TO GRIGBLAY

Dear Mr. Grigblay,   13.3.26.

I have duly received your letter. I am aware that you always objected to the use of Riddoppo, and I also advised against it so that Sir Leslie cannot very well hold us responsible. I certainly should say nothing on the subject unless Sir Leslie himself raised it.

I note what you say of wet in the chimney, and have written instructions to-day.

Yours truly,

The tone of this letter suggests that Spinlove resents the implication that he needs guidance, so that it is a pity his attempt to show he is not such a fool as Grigblay thinks should make it clear that he is a much bigger one. The issue does not, as Spinlove implies, turn upon Brash's holding the architect and the builder accountable, but upon whether the facts make them legally responsible; and if Spinlove is going to address himself to the subject as though the point were open and debatable, he will be certain to prejudice his own and Grigblay's positions exactly as Grigblay fears, and lead Brash on to make claims which, though they may be untenable, will be likely to embroil everyone in the distresses preliminary to litigation. It will also be noticed that Spinlove brackets himself with Grigblay as though they were in the same boat. They are not. Their responsibilities are different.

28

First News of Extras

Dear Sir,   13.3.26.

I note that the damp in chimney-breasts is due to rain driving into the stacks, and shall be glad if you will treat the whole of the brickwork of all chimneys above roof with two coats of "Dessikex" damp-proofing, applied as directed by the manufacturers. I prefer this to treatment with soap. The work should be put in hand at once.

                                    Yours faithfully,

A pound of soft soap in a bucket of boiling water, allowed to stand overnight and sprayed freely on to brickwork with a garden syringe, is a reliable damp-proofing which Grigblay seems to have confidence in; and soft soap is also effective in waterproofing mortar or concrete with which it is mixed. As Grigblay has had great experience of wet walls and Spinlove very little, it would be wise for Spinlove to use what Grigblay has practical experience of, rather than what recommends itself to him by report or by advertisement. There are proprietary remedies for damp walls, of proved worth; but the yearly increase in their numbers is rather a sign of the obstinacy of the complaint than of the efficacy of the cures.

Dear Sir,   15.3.26.

I do not understand why there has been such delay in rendering your final Statement of Account. You now send me a summary showing extras £1,500. I was totally unprepared for this, and can only suppose there is some mistake. Have you taken the provision for contingencies into account, and the saving on the provision for well-sinking and pump, for instance? A considerable part of the variations will come into a measured account which the quantity surveyor must deal with; and the value of that work has still to be ascertained. I shall be glad to have a rough summary of the variations account on which you base your claim. I must prepare Sir Leslie Brash for what is ahead as I am sure he has no idea that extras have mounted up in this way, and I have no knowledge of their ever having been ordered.

I enclose certificate for £2,500, which is as much as I feel entitled to certify at this time.

Yours faithfully,

We have no doubt that Grigblay's estimate of extras is right; and when Spinlove says he is totally unprepared for such a figure he only tells us what we expected to hear. It is not surprising that he should lose touch with the account, as his careful contract arrangements were upset in various ways for which he was not responsible; but he ought to have been prepared for a heavy bill, and with greater experience he would have been. He might also have found opportunities to let his client know what was happening, but it is doubtful whether experience would have prompted him to do so. When the interferences of the client, or adventitious circumstances, make hay of the careful safeguards of the Conditions of Contract and of the detailed forethought of the drawings and specification, the whole position gets out of hand for the architect; and if the building-owner, after being warned (as Spinlove warned Brash) of the results of interferences and alterations, persists in following his own devices, his architect cannot, without risk of impertinence, make any gesture of checking him.

SPINLOVE TO BRASH

Dear Sir Leslie Brash,   15.3.26.

Mr. Grigblay has asked for a further certificate on account. This was due to him, on completion of the work, in February. I find he is entitled to the sum of £2,500, and have to-day sent him a certificate for that amount. This makes the total of certificates £18,000. The contract amount, as you know, is £18,440, but there will be the cost of extra work—garage, alteration to kitchen and other variations and additions and so forth—to add, which will, I am afraid, run into several hundred pounds. I am pressing the builder for his Statement of Account giving particulars of these extras.

Yours sincerely,

P.S.—As this money was due to Mr. Grigblay more than a month ago, he will probably be glad of a cheque at once.

First News of Extras

Spinlove's ideas of administering the gilded pill are raw, but promising. A degree of tact which may appear excessive is allowable on these painful occasions. The owner has to be informed of—and reconciled to paying—a bill of extras for which he is unprepared; and the easier the gradations by which the revolting intelligence is imparted to him, the happier for him; and the happier for the builder; and the happier also for the architect, whose forethought for his employer's peace of mind is not unusually prompted by a care for his own.

Spinlove's postscript is due to Brash's habit, in the past, of holding back payments to the builder to the extreme limit allowed by the contract.

(CONFIDENTIAL) GRIGBLAY TO SPINLOVE

Dear Sir,   15.3.26.

In reply to your favour I take the liberty of writing to make clear, as there seems to be some confusion on the matter, that I painted with Riddoppo only on your statement that those were the orders of Sir Leslie Brash, and that he accepted responsibility for same; and I ask you to bear that fact in mind, as it is the position I take and hold to. I ought to have refused to touch the stuff, but I wished to oblige Sir Leslie so far as I was able; and as he would not take my advice he must settle the matter with the man whose advice he did take instead—and that, I suppose, is himself.

I write very frank and open, sir, because this is a serious matter for someone, if it isn't for me. It's not going to cost a hundred pounds, nor two hundred, nor yet three, with the cleaning of the stuff off the walls and joinery and the loss of going to a hotel—for they can't be expected to live in the house all those weeks it will be before the work is done. Therefore, sir, I ask you to let Sir Leslie clearly understand that I have nothing more to say on this matter, as it will save a bit of trouble and be the best for everyone, including,

Yours truly,

This was evidently dictated by Grigblay.

31

First News of Extras

Dear Sir,   16.3.26.

We have to acknowledge certificate for £2,500, which we have sent on to Sir Leslie Brash, and hope we shall receive his cheque per return, as it is a long time since we had anything on account and we were entitled to 40 per cent more than this six weeks ago, which please note and oblige,

Yours faithfully,

This letter is curt to the point of being threatening. We have already seen that although Grigblay is lavish of good offices and kindly forethought, he is impatient of sloppiness. All he says is perfectly just, and Spinlove deserves to be told it. It is the architect's duty to see that the builder, as well as the client, gets his dues. Spinlove has shown no consciousness of his remissness in holding back the certificate for so long, and has not in any adequate way apologized to Grigblay for so disobliging him. He is, further, not entitled to withhold £1,000 on the plea of his ignorance of the state of the account. It is his duty to inform himself.

Dear Mr. Spinlove,   18.3.26.

I have duly received your communication anent certificate and will arrange for cheque to be transmitted in due course. I cannot, however, accept responsibility for Mr. Grigblay's neglect to present his claim at an earlier date. I apprehend with satisfaction that these payments are now drawing to a final termination, but I am considerably astonished at your off-hand —if you will pardon the expression—intimation of additional extras running into the total amount of *several hundreds of pounds*. I am aware that accumulated additional extras have accrued, but the exact anticipated total of my eventual liability is a matter of more importance to me than you appear to divine; and though a matter of half a dozen hundred pounds one way or the other may seem of insignificant importance to you, it is, I may inform you, of *considerable importance to me.*

32

I desire that you will be so good as to ascertain the exact figure forthwith and also clearly intimate to Mr. Grigblay that the accountancy is in your hands and that I am not prepared to acquiesce in any inflated extortions. Surely it is not at Mr. Grigblay's discretion to decide what additional extras he shall demand?

I have re-perused your communication to Lady Brash anent the surveyor's certificate of sanitary efficiency, a second time. Are you *confident* in your conviction that our sanitary provisions are entirely without blemish? In the concluding passage terminating your letter you surmise the possibility of a defect in the arrangements having eventuated *subsequently* to the previous tests. This I apprehend to be a matter for further imperative investigation.

Yours sincerely,

Brash's avoidance of the low word "drain" marks a refinement that is rare.

(PRIVATE) SPINLOVE TO GRIGBLAY

Dear Mr Grigblay,   18.3.26.

I perfectly understand the position you take and it has my approval. I shall myself most certainly refuse to accept responsibility for Riddoppo.

Yours truly,

Spinlove's assurance will further increase Grigblay's doubts. The disparity may be subtle but it is vital. The point is not what action Grigblay may in future take, but what his position, in fact, now is. Spinlove's approval or disapproval cannot alter those facts, and Grigblay is in no way concerned with it. It is clear, also, that Spinlove does not appreciate his own position, and Grigblay can have little confidence that he will not allow Brash to believe he has a claim against both of them.

SPINLOVE TO BRASH

Dear Sir Leslie Brash,   20.3.26.

The delay with the certificate was not Mr. Grigblay's fault.

He made his claim before the money was due, and in setting that matter aside I overlooked it. I should be obliged, therefore, if you will regard the certificate as dated 10th February, which is the day it fell due.

I cannot yet say what the total of the account is, as much detailed measuring and pricing, and checking of the daywork accounts and merchants' vouchers, etc., is necessary in order to arrive at it. Grigblay will duly render a Statement of Account which it will be necessary for me to check and certify. The actual "accountancy"—as you term it—will be done by the quantity surveyor, who ranks as auditor in ascertaining the exact sums due in respect of work which I find to be properly authenticated as extras. I shall hope, however, to be able to give you an approximate figure in the course of a week or two.

I can assure you that the drains are all right. It is inconceivable that they have developed any defects since they were tested.

I have discovered the cause of damp above the attic fireplaces, and have told Grigblay to put this right at once.

Yours sincerely,

P.S.—Will you please return the surveyor's certificate?

Spinlove has laid out the mechanism of settling builders' accounts, so that Brash will have a right idea of it, quite neatly.

He is, however, too emphatic in his pride of drain. The development of defects in Honeywood drains is not inconceivable. We heard of a clay subsoil at the time the cellars were dug, and the movements of clay in response to changes of temperature and humidity may lead to early cracking of cement pipe-joints such as would cause failure under the water test; and the heavy lorries already referred to may have done similar damage. Such defects, however, do not ordinarily lead to insanitary drainage, as the conditions of the tests, which exact perfection, do not arise in use; and if by accident they did arise, the amount of pollution of the subsoil would be insignificant.

GRIGBLAY TO SPINLOVE

Dear Sir,   22.3.26.

We note your instructions *re* waterproofing to chimneys. Our

34

price for this work, which includes the necessary ladders and scaffolding, is £42 12s. We will use "Dessikex" if you wish, but we happen to know what this stuff is made of, and we should prefer to apply two coats of either Sorrellming or Flutate, both of which are colourless and can, in our experience, be relied on. The work, however, cannot be put in hand till the summer as, whatever we use, the brickwork must be quite dry and ought to be warm when the application is made.

Yours faithfully,

BRASH ON DRAINS

BRASH TO SPINLOVE

Dear Mr. Spinlove,   24.3.26.

I am gratified to know that the cause of damp in the domestics' domain has been ascertained and that immediate renovations will at once be accomplished; and I have noted your arrangements for checking Mr. Grigblay's charges.

I am, however, unpleasantly disconcerted by your reference to the question of the sanitary purity of Honeywood, which is —if you will pardon me for so expressing myself—somewhat peremptory and offhand. Of course, where domestic effluents are concerned, obnoxious exhalations are in a limited degree unavoidably to be anticipated, and I should be the last person to be unnecessarily discriminating in such a matter; but where delicate ladies are concerned—and Lady Brash's mucous membrane is peculiarly sensitive to olfactory aggression—[*we were told something like this once before*]—it is most desirably expedient that the odoriferous emanations of which I speak— and which I need not more particularly define—should be limited to the exterior atmosphere, and not permitted to invade the interior of the domicile. Lady Brash increasingly complains that Honeywood is a stuffy house, and one of our domestic staff—cook, to be precise—has described her sleeping quarters as "fuggy"—I use the word as reported to me, and may there-

35

fore repeat the expression without apology. I also understand that whiffs of a repulsive nature are from time to time encountered in various parts of the house, but though Lady Brash has on a number of occasions hurried me to the seat of an unsavoury effluvium newly discovered, I have not yet been so fortunate as to arrive on the scene of offence before dissipation has eventuated; and accordingly I am not, I regret to say, in a position to indicate a precise description of the quality of the various noxious emanations which are proving incompatible with Lady Brash's *joie de vivre* and, I fear, prejudicial to her good health. I anticipate, however, that I have, in this lengthy communication, sufficiently indicated the seriousness of the situation, and I shall be gratified to be informed that its prompt amelioration has your immediate attention.

Yours sincerely,

This letter suggests that it is not the drains that require the attentions of an expert, but Lady Brash. We must feel sorry for the poor woman, but this need not prevent us from being far more sorry for Spinlove.

SPINLOVE TO BRASH

Dear Sir Leslie Brash,   26.3.26.

I was naturally disturbed by the contents of your letter, but after reading it attentively more than once I cannot help feeling that the case is not so bad as you think, for I am convinced that the drainage system at Honeywood, both inside the house and out, is perfectly sound; and if it were conceivable that anything had gone wrong it could not possibly give rise to such a state of affairs as you describe. It is incredible that the house can be "stuffy" or "fuggy" except for reasons which may give rise to that condition in any house—such as overheating of radiators, accumulations of dust, dirty carpets, lack of ventilation, etc.

I will, of course, give the matter my particular attention and do my best to discover the reason for the complaint, but I shall not be able to spare a day before the end of next week. In the meantime perhaps you will be able to find the true source of the unpleasant conditions, which certainly can have no connection with drainage.

With kind regards,

Yours sincerely,

Spinlove is not happy in the wording of the sentence in which he seeks to discredit the idea that the house can be stuffy.

SPINLOVE TO GRIGBLAY

Dear Sirs,   26.3.26.

I enclose a letter I have received from Sir Leslie Brash. I have had previous complaints of smells in the house. As I cannot go down for a fortnight, and have no time to waste, and you have work going on in the neighbourhood, I will ask Mr. Grigblay to take an early opportunity of calling at Honeywood and to let me know what he makes of it all. Perhaps he will be able to see Lady Brash and establish her peace of mind, which I have, unfortunately, not been able to do. You will remember there was the same kind of trouble over the smell of the new oak when the house was being built. They may have been overstoking and keeping the radiators too hot.

I note that waterproofing of chimneys will have to stand over till the summer.

I still have not yet received your summary of variations account.

Yours faithfully,

The stuffy, close, stale air associated with radiators is due to the hot iron causing the paint on it, and on adjoining surfaces, to smell until it has thoroughly dried up, which, in the case of oily paints, takes some time; and also to the rising currents of heated air carrying up dust particles. There is, rightly speaking, no such thing as "scorched air", though the term is sometimes used as an explanation of these unpleasant associations of radiators. Radiators, however, only in part warm by radiation; a great part of their heat is disseminated by convection, and the repeated circulation of the same air against the heated iron dries it and vitiates it. Many heating systems by hot-water radiators are

37

enervating and dispiriting to live with. These conditions are much aggravated when the radiators are allowed to get above a certain temperature, and are remedied by good ventilation.

Dear Mr. Spinlove,   30.3.26.

Your communication encourages optimistic anticipations, though you must allow me to intimate the suggestion that it is not reasonably consistent with what you previously indited to Lady Brash. You must permit me, however, to object most strongly to the astounding suggestion that the conditions I complain of are due to improper neglect of cleanliness at Honeywood. The house, I must beg permission to inform you, is *not* unventilated, dusty and dirty, and I am amazed that one from whom I have learnt to anticipate polite behaviour on all occasions should so far forget decorum as to offer any such monstrous explanatory solution of the matter in complaint.

That the house is stuffy, and impregnated with obnoxious effluviums of some kind, there is abundant evidence to substantially prove. The source of the annoyance, which is a danger to health, is for you to definitely determine, and for Mr. Grigblay to curatively ameliorate without delay.

Yours sincerely,

Dear Sir Leslie Brash,   2.4.26.

I assure you that you entirely misread my letter. I admit that my wording was ambiguous, but I had no intention of suggesting what you suppose. My argument was that a defect in the drains could not possibly give rise to the conditions you describe; that those conditions were such as would be occasioned by overheated radiators, dust, lack of ventilation and so forth and that—as you knew these conditions did not exist at Honeywood—the explanation *must lie in some other direction*. That is all I meant to say. It never entered my head that you would suppose I could mean that Honeywood was in such a condition; and *if* I had supposed it *was*, I should, of course, have been careful not to let you think I thought so. Please accept the will for the deed. [*The finishing touch!*]

I do not know what more I can say until I come down to investigate for myself. That cannot, however, be immediately, as I have to go out of town on business, but I will get in touch with you as soon as I can next week.

With kind regards,
Yours sincerely,

This letter is a wretched performance. Spinlove not only says a great deal too much, but makes it appear that his offending letter was written in the belief that his explanation of the "noxious emanations" was the true one. He then indicates that he does not consider the matter of any pressing importance, and by making plain, with characteristic tenacity, that he regards the whole thing as a mare's nest, he returns, like a fly, to the bald place from which Brash has just driven him.

GRIGBLAY ON DRAINS

GRIGBLAY TO SPINLOVE

Sir,   6.4.26.

I had a chance yesterday and called at the house to examine into all these effluviums and emanations and other polite stinks that are going about, but can make nothing of it. Every house in my opinion has its own smells, different in different houses, if you sit down and wait for them. There were only two real Oh Mys at Honeywood on Tuesday: one was Lysol and the other was her Ladyship who was carrying so much scent that though I have as good a nose as most it had ought to be forty feet long to reach anything else when the lady was by. She had such a lot of things to tell me, too, that it was difficult to find out anything for myself. The plumbing everywhere is a picture to see; there never was a better job. Rumble was on it, and he's a craftsman if there ever was one: it's a pleasure to look at his

39

wiped joints. No spigotting anywhere, you may be sure; no rubber cones; solid lead tacks wiped on front angles and screwed and plugged; all joints between lead and iron or stoneware made with brass thimbles—beautiful; but you know all about it, sir, having ordered and saw the work being done.

All I could get at was that the bedrooms smelt funny, and the scullery—and why wouldn't that smell, I should like to know? There was an intelligent young girl there who had taught herself how to pull the cobweb grating out of the wash-up, and there she was with a bit of telegraph wire with a sharp burred end to go pushing into the trap when it gets blocked every half hour and cut a hole in the lead before anyone has time to discover what a clearing eye is for. They had hung up this grating and the key of the back door, so that they shouldn't be wasted, to keep the clock going, because the weight had been lost plumbing the rain-water well.

There was talk that a smell came in at the window; so I told this same slut if you don't like stinks you shouldn't make them, for she had the grease-trap outside all clogged and mucked up with kitchen filth, the container not having been emptied all the time they've been there—nor never would be if I hadn't noticed. The gully by the back entrance was flooding over. They had taken the grating out and broke it with a sledge-hammer in case someone should remember what it was for, so as to make it easy to pour down the water they wash the floors with without the trouble of taking scrubbing-brushes and clouts out of the bucket first. That was what Jossling found stopping the trap when I told him get it cleared, along with a vacuum-cleaner fitting and a few other trifles that wouldn't be missed. That is all I could find wrong with the drains; but it's none of her business, says cook, and the chauffeur says it is none of his, so there you are, and we shall have more complaints before long unless Sir Leslie is told what is going on.

As for the smell in the bedrooms it is difficult to say. The cook had a lot of complaint and said it gave her asthma. It will give you measles, I told her, before ever it will give you asthma, and I think she feels more contented now; but there certainly was a close, stuffy smell in the fifth room on the second floor, in particular, though it had never been used; and my opinion is

Grigblay on Drains

that smoky air from outside is drawn down the chimneys by the pull of other flues, or perhaps it's down-draught. These damp flues where the rain beats into them would be likely to lead to that kind of trouble.

There was a close air in three other of the maids' rooms that was not accounted for by the windows being shut, nor yet by two towels and a newspaper pushed into the chimney-throat of one of them to plug it in case of ventilation. Her Ladyship says her own room on the first floor is very stuffy; I could not notice anything, but, there you are! I am not in the perfumery myself, and a musk-rat or a civet-cat or whatever it is, spiced up with a touch of Lysol—which is about in saucers and everywhere it has no occasion to be—smells to me after half an hour pretty much like badger. Her Ladyship uses the Lysol so she won't notice the drains, and the scent so she won't notice the Lysol, which is a queer way to go to work if you ask my opinion.

However, I told the lady I could find nothing wrong except perhaps some down-draught in the chimneys, and that everything would be all right in the summer. She seemed satisfied and was very grateful and friendly and had lunch specially served to me though it was early; so I hope we shall have no more old tommy-rot about the drains.

> I am sir,
> Yours faithfully,

The erratic script of this letter, conjoined with Grigblay's authentic voice, indicates that he typed it himself. We may well suppose that, if persuasion of any kind could do so, Grigblay's massive resources consoled Lady Brash. Grigblay, however, here definitely oversteps the mark. He takes a great deal too much on himself: he involves Spinlove in a kind of disloyalty to his client, and the extreme intimacy of his facetiousness is subversive of discipline and, definitely, not allowable, but—as Grigblay would say —"there you are!" Spinlove has allowed himself to look to Grigblay for direction in a degree which a more substantial individuality would not tolerate.

Grigblay on Drains

Dear Sirs, 10.4.26.

I am much obliged for Mr. Grigblay's report on drains, etc. Things are very much as I supposed. I have written to Sir Leslie Brash calling attention to his servants' neglect, and have no doubt the complaint of bad smells is now disposed of. Please fix the sink grids. I do not understand how that in the scullery could be taken out.

Will you let me have your final Statement of Account without further delay? I have several times asked for this.

Yours faithfully,

Dear Sir Leslie Brash, 10.4.26.

I came back to the office to-day to find awaiting me there a letter from Mr. Grigblay who, in my absence and at my orders, made a thorough investigation into the cause of the smells complained of, as no doubt you may have heard. He finds the "closeness" of the bedrooms to be due to the windows being kept shut, and also, perhaps, to slight down-draught carrying smoky air down the chimneys. This is due to the stacks being damp, and will disappear when the summer comes. The chimney-throat in one of the servants' rooms was found to be stopped up. This should be discouraged, as the flues ought to be open to ventilate the rooms.

Mr. Grigblay, however, found a most insanitary state of affairs, productive of bad smells, in the scullery; due, not to any fault in the drainage arrangements or defect in the work, but to the neglect and deliberate ill-usage of the appliances provided, by your servants. The grating of the sink waste has been mischievously forced out so that the trap gets choked with filth; and this is cleared by violently ramming a steel wire down and damaging the pipe, instead of removing the screwed eye provided to make such ill-usage unnecessary. Then the grease-trap into which the sinks discharge has never been once emptied; and as a consequence the whole thing is clogged with congealed fat and stinking filth. This allows grease to get into the drain which it is the special purpose of the device to prevent. The iron receptacle in the gully should be lifted out and emptied once a week. In addition to this, the gully by the yard entrance has had its grid removed and deliberately broken, and a scrubbing brush and floor clouts and other things had been thrown into the drain, stopping the trap and flooding the yard with sewage.

I was certain, as I told you, that there could be nothing wrong with the drains, and Mr. Grigblay's report is very much what I expected. If the servants are told to use the fittings and arrangements as they are intended to be used, the smells you complain of will cease.

I am very glad to be able to give you this definite assurance.

> With kind regards,
> Yours sincerely,

Spinlove so stresses the facts as to overweight them; and it is not tactful in him to triumph over Brash with cock-crows of "I told you so", and to remind him of his fault by rubbing his nose in it: nor is it tactful in him to appear enormously relieved in being able to give the explanation; for great relief can only be a reaction from great anxiety, and Brash will suppose Spinlove to be concerned for Honeywood's drains, when it is Honeywood's brains that are worrying him. This drain-trouble appears to be entirely of Spinlove's making. If he had written the brief, compact letters of a confident man, instead of the diffuse ones of a man anxious to appear plausible, Brash would have been fortified against his wife's complainings, and the lady, perhaps, herself assured. He is wrong in supposing that emphasis carries conviction; the opposite is true. "I saw Jones at Brighton" is more conclusive that Jones was there than: 'I am certain I saw Jones at Brighton", and much more so than: "I am absolutely positive . . ."; and it is only fatuous writers of advertisements who suppose otherwise.

BRASH TO SPINLOVE

Dear Mr. Spinlove,   13.4.26.

I am astonished to be informed of the improper neglect to observe sanitary amenities on the part of the kitchen staff, and have emphatically directed that it shall cease forthwith. It is scarcely necessary for me to signify that it is not incumbent upon me, as master, to keep myself personally acquainted with the conditions obtaining in the purlieus of the establishment; but I have now expressed my disapproval of past procedure in suitable terms to the person I hold to be responsible, and I confidently anticipate that no repetition of the previous objectionable circumstances will be repeated in the future.

You must permit me to express, however, that I fail to see how irregularities in the culinary domain can account for consequent olfactory intrusions in the sleeping quarters; nor do I comprehend in what way a down-draught in the chimneys can be applicable to the question of sanitary purity. I desire, therefore, that you will transmit Mr. Grigblay's report anent the matter of which I am speaking, so that I may be enabled to acquaint myself with the signification of your communication in more exact detail.

Yours sincerely,

If Brash saw Grigblay's letter the fat would, indeed, be in the fire!—which is proof that Spinlove should not allow such letters to be addressed to him. An architect should be able at any moment to lay all correspondence dealing with his client's business freely before him—in fact, the client has right of access to such correspondence, and also to possession of the whole of it after the work is completed. This follows necessarily from the relation of Agent and Principal which subsists between them. It is clear that Spinlove cannot do what Brash asks; and, even if there were no other reasons, Grigblay's letter, though it is not so marked, is clearly a private or confidential letter.

MORE NEWS OF EXTRAS

GRIGBLAY TO SPINLOVE

Dear Sir,   14.4.26.

We have been pressing on with our Statement of Account as you ask, and are arranging with Mr. Tinge to meet us for the purpose of measuring variations. We find that the total balance of extras on the variations account will be in the neighbourhood of £1,800 and shall be glad if you will pass us a further certificate for £1,000.

Yours faithfully,

Dear Sir,   16.4.26.

I am astonished to learn that your account will show extras to the amount of perhaps over £1,800. I was quite unprepared for anything of the kind, and I am sure Sir Leslie Brash will be shocked at the figure. I certainly have not authorized extras on any such scale, and have no idea how the figure is made up. I must have a summary of items, showing how the amount is arrived at, before I can consider drawing a further certificate.

Mr. Tinge has no authority to measure any work except as I may direct, and it is necessary for me to have the summary before I can do this.

Yours faithfully,

Dear Mr. Tinge,   16.4.26.

Grigblay is preparing his final Statement of Account. Will you please note, however, that no work is to be measured except as I may direct, as I have reasons to fear that the account is inflated with unauthorized extras? I have asked Grigblay for particulars of the work to be measured, and will let you know what is wanted in due course.

Yours truly,

Spinlove's arrangements are good, though his manners to Grigblay are not. The measuring of work by the quantity surveyor, or even by the architect, does not establish an authorized extra, but it certainly supports a claim for one. The quantity surveyor, also, has to be paid for the work he does in fees that are added to the account, so that it is the architect's duty to see that no other measuring is done than the needs justify. Extras

45

often consist in differences between the value of work specified in the contract and the same work as carried out; and as the only way to arrive at this difference is to measure and value the whole of the work replaced together with that which replaces it, and strike a balance, it might happen that the surveyor's fees for measuring and pricing £2,500 of work twice over is tacked on to a resulting extra (or omission) of only £50. For this reason it is sometimes expedient for an architect to agree a figure with the builder. On the other hand, the builder will be inclined to charge as day work (time and material) extra work which ought in the interests of the client to be measured and priced at the contract rates, or at rates commensurate therewith.

FURTHER DEFECTS

BRASH TO SPINLOVE

Dear Mr. Spinlove,   19.4.26.

May I be permitted to remind you that you have omitted to transmit Mr. Grigblay's report on the odoriferous effusions which, I regret to say, still persist?

We continue to be delighted with the house, which will be quite perfect when sanitary amenities have been safeguarded, but we have observed various slight defective flaws in the building work. These are not so far imperatively serious, but need preliminary attention. Dripping taps can speedily be renovated, I conceive, also little cracks in the plaster ceilings which may otherwise increase. Stains in the wallpapers are, I fear, a more serious apprehension. There are openings in the woodwork, specially in the overmantels to fireplaces in the first story, and *most alarming gaping cracks* in the exterior oak window frames, particularly on the outside. Steps should at once be taken to prevent these cracks increasing in dimensions. Some are several inches in length, and in breadth wide enough for me to almost insert the terminal edge of a sixpence. I have prepared and transmit under this cover, for your convenient guidance, a scheduled list of the defects I have noticed as obtaining; but your trained eye will no doubt have no difficulty in discerning others.

With regard to the Riddoppo, this has a delightful lustrous appearance, and its variegations of different tints is charming, but it leaves stains where the under bottoms of doors rub over the carpets, which will only imperfectly brush out; and it has failed, I am informed, near the range in the kitchen. Mr. Grigblay should be notified

> Yours sincerely,

Brash's "scheduled list" is missing from the file, but if it is fairly represented in the above letter the "defective flaws" are nothing to complain about (so far) except, of course, Riddoppo. Brash has not realized what is happening to his new novelty super-paint.

(PERSONAL) SPINLOVE TO GRIGBLAY

Dear Mr. Grigblay,   20.4.26.

I reported to Sir Leslie the substance of your letter describing your investigation of supposed smells, and he has since twice asked for a verbatim copy of your letter. I cannot possibly send it him—besides, it is a private letter—so will you let me have a version suitable for sending to Sir Leslie? I enclose the original in case you should not have kept a copy.

> Yours truly,

Spinlove is unwise in allowing Grigblay to write to him confidentially, but more unwise in his method of disguising the fact. He has a frank, straightforward nature; slyness is foreign to him, and must be distasteful. He could perfectly well have replied to Brash: "Grigblay reports as follows: He says . . ." and completed an accurate paraphrase in that form. If Brash were so obtuse as to press for the original, he could be told it was a private letter.

Further Defects

Dear Sir Leslie Brash,   20.4.26.

The blemishes of which you send me a list are only what appear in all new houses, and do not point to serious defects. Grigblay will do all necessary restoration, but this will be in six months' time when such defects as there may be have fully developed. Of course, if anything goes wrong he will send down and put right, but it appears that nothing has. Certain sulphates or other exudations appearing on the face of new plaster kill the colour in wall-papers, which is why I recommended only tinted lining papers designed to serve as a foundation for the better papers you may afterwards decide to hang. The cracks in the oak frames are of no consequence. They are characteristic of English oak.

Yours sincerely,

P.S.—I will send you copy of Mr. Grigblay's letter to-morrow.

This pretence of an afterthought in order to gain time is regrettable: thus does one deceit involve others. Spinlove's comments are well-informed, but by omitting all reference to Riddoppo and thus including its failure with defects that are "not serious", he may be applying Grigblay's advice to "take no notice" too drastically.

Dear Sir,   22.4.26.

We enclose report for Sir Leslie Brash, and return original of Mr. Grigblay's letter.

Yours faithfully,

Dear Sir,   6.4.26.

I called at Honeywood on the 5th instant to examine into the effluviums and emanations complained of, but I could not

48

ascertain any olfactory aggressions indicating blemishes in the sanitary provisions.

There was a bit of odoriferous exhalation in the scullery, and a whiff of noxious emanation in the yard, because the domestic staff had removed the grating out of the scullery sink instead of emptying the grease-trap. Unsavoury effluviums from the yard gully are due to the grating being missing and the drain being too small to pass the size of scrubbing brushes used.

The obnoxious exhalation in the bedrooms is due to windows being kept shut and chimney-throats stopped; but it is likely that there is down-draught in some of the flues owing to them being damp as yet.

Yours faithfully,

Spinlove asked for a report so worded as to be suitable for sending to Sir Leslie Brash, and it is probable that Grigblay supposed it was intended he should adopt Brash's euphemisms, and that his inveterate habit of irony, his lack of literary accomplishment and his impatience of nonsense, did the rest: he did not understand what was wanted and resented the folly of what he was doing. Grigblay's habit of veiling his irritation by irony is so ingrained that he is likely to be in great part unaware of the gorgeous effects he sometimes gets. Some such explanation seems necessary. We can imagine that Grigblay is unaware here, as elsewhere, of the vividness with which his letters reveal his state of mind.

SPINLOVE TO GRIGBLAY

Dear Sir,   23.4.26.

I am much obliged for Mr. Grigblay's report on drains, but I think that Sir Leslie Brash might misinterpret certain passages. I have, therefore, altered some of the terms and return the report. If Mr. Grigblay will copy it as amended and sign, I will send it to Sir Leslie.

I am still awaiting your summary of variations account.

Yours faithfully,

Further Defects

Dear Sir,   24.4.26.

We have rewritten report as you suggest and enclose same.
We hope that this now ends the matter.

Yours faithfully,

Dear Sir,   6.4.26.

I called at Honeywood Grange on the 5th instant to investigate complaints of smells, but could find nothing wrong with
the drains.

A smell in the scullery was due to the removal of the grating
of the sink, and to the container of the grease-trap not being
emptied. The flooding of the yard gully is due to the grating
being missing and scrubbing brushes getting into the trap.

The stuffy smell in the bedrooms is partly due to windows
being kept shut and chimney-throats stopped up, but it is likely
there is down-draught in the flues owing to their being damp
as yet.

Yours faithfully,

*A very colourless version! Spinlove has ventured, it will be
noticed, to touch up Grigblay's grammar.*

Dear Mr. Spinlove,   24.4.26.

I note your comment anent the subject of blemishes. So long
as we are not inconveniently incommoded I am quite willing to
permit matters to stand over for the present, on the understanding that Mr. Grigblay is previously advised beforehand and
comprehends that the increase in defects due to the remissness
of his attentions is a matter for which he solely is responsible.
I certainly consider, however, that it would be advantageously
to his interests to intervene before the increase in blemishes
becomes more aggravated, as I apprehend that a small defect
is more readily ameliorated than one of greater magnitude, and

that the anticipated augmentation of cracks, for example, is better prevented than cured. That, however, is a matter for your and Mr Grigblay's eventual decision.

Since I wrote, a new defect has appeared, which needs immediate attention, as it is causing the establishment considerable unnecessary inconvenience. On Thursday afternoon last, at about 4.25—so far as I can precisely ascertain—it was observed that when the push in the drawing-room was depressed the front door bell rang; and it subsequently transpired that all the other pushes rang the front door bell, and that the bell-pull at the front door rang the bell in the lady's maid's room on the second floor instead of its own. As the indicator has also ceased to appropriately function, the consequent inconvenience can be imagined, and is not—may I be permitted to say?—what I feel is compatible with a house designed by a qualified architect and erected by an expensive builder. I shall be gratified if you will ring up the house to-morrow and instruct us in what it is desirable to do.

Your communication omits to intimate anything regarding Riddoppo super-paint. My apprehensions on this question are commencing to engender considerable doubts, as a small narrow strip was yesterday observed to have detached itself away from the wall above the skirting of the inner lavatory compartment adjoining the front entrance, and investigation indicates that similar disasters threaten to immediately eventuate in various other different positions. Inspection also substantiates that serious ridges and rims of paint, which break away from the surface in little crumbs and flakes that adhere to the carpets, are accruing in diverse localities, which conclusively demonstrates that *Riddoppo is beginning to commence to disintegrate*. Immediate attention is most desirably expedient, and I request that Mr. Grigblay shall be informed that I expect immediate remedial precautions to be embarked upon at once.

May I intimate the due reminder that you have not yet transmitted Mr. Grigblay's report on the sanitary anomalies? These cause me increasing apprehension. Also the damp places over the chimneys continue, although the promised remedy was intimated to be on the point of eventuating several weeks ago. Other evidences of damp places are now ocularly discernible

51

in the corners of some of the first-floor sleeping apartments.

I have transmitted cheque to Mr. Grigblay but still await promised figure of total sum of extra cost.

Yours sincerely,

We have seen Brash making heavy weather of "blemishes" which do not amount to defects, or are of no importance. He has yielded to the weakness, common with owners of new houses, of crawling over every part with the minute scrutiny of an ant, instead of enjoying his well-planned and soundly-built house. The Riddoppo failure is, however, a serious matter.

SPINLOVE TO BRASH

Dear Sir Leslie Brash,   27.4.26.

I do not know in the least what has gone wrong with the bells, but, as I telephoned to-day, I have arranged for Grigblay to send an electrician to the house to-morrow.

I enclose copy of Grigblay's report on drains. I am sorry I omitted to send this before.

The necessary work in preventing damp appearing in chimney-breasts will have to be put off till the summer when the brickwork has dried out. I will inquire into the cause of the other damp places you speak of. The house has hollow walls, and there cannot be much wrong.

I assure you that your fear of faulty drains is without foundation. I really do not know what more can be done.

I am sorry to hear that the Riddoppo paint is proving unsatisfactory. As you know, I never had confidence in it, and Mr. Grigblay objected to its use.

Yours sincerely,

There is a directness and brevity in this letter which, though perfectly appropriate to the occasion, indicates that Spinlove is busy in other directions and is getting tired of Honeywood. He has not followed Grigblay's advice of repudiating responsibility for Riddoppo, but he perhaps does better at this juncture in implying that the matter is Brash's concern, only.

SPINLOVE'S SELF-LOCKING DOOR

MISS PHYLLIS BRASH TO SPINLOVE·

Dear Jazz,   30.4.26.

This is to warn you to form a solid British Square and prepare to receive cavalry, as Dad is on his high horse. You *are*
a mutt. Dad even suspects a practical joke. This is what
happened; no guy, honest indian.

We had a big house-warming dinner-party to-night, very
swell and solemn, all the poshest of the posh, no one under
about seventy, all good Gargantuans with digestions treasured
by leading physicians—Dad simply wallows in that sort of
occasion:—when the writing wobbles it is because I am
laughing.

Mum and I were out with the car, and didn't get to home
sweet home till nearly seven, to find the kitchen staff—as Dad
calls them—waiting *outside* the kitchen door, which was open
just wide enough to allow a choking smell of burning glue and
feathers to be nosed. They could not get in to finish cooking the
dinner, nor to stop its cooking. The back entrance was bolted,
the windows all fastened—except the little top ones—and the
door jammed; it would not open nor shut. I pushed my arm
through and found the door of the cupboard, just inside, pressing against the knob of the kitchen door. The knob of the cupboard was against the other, so that the door would not move
either way. How it got fixed no one knows. The servants found
it so at half-past five, after they had run to see an aeroplane
stunting at the front. The gardeners had all gone, not a man
was about, and so the loonies just waited, with sauces burning
and everything going wrong inside, and nothing being done to
get the dinner ready. The chauffeur fetched a ladder and reached
through one of the little top windows with a golf club and un-
did a lower window, and, by heaving himself up against the
door, freed it. You can imagine the to-do with all the arrangements knocked sideways. Of course, it would not have mattered
if it had not been such a swanky occasion; but not a word was

Spinlove's Self-Locking Door

said, and the seventeen seventies sat solemnly marking time in the drawing-room with cocktails and caviare sandwiches, while the servants struggled and sweated in the kitchen and the hired men gloomed in the hall, till nearly a quarter to nine. It is a thousand pities you were not invited—as you should have been—as the triumphant architect of the arrangements.

Ever yours,

PUD.

Spinlove appears to have a friend in the enemy's camp.

This accident is extraordinary. Spinlove ought to have been more wary than to allow any door to open against another in such a way as to block its swing: such a chance is always in mind for the planner. It happened, however, that the kitchen arrangements at Honeywood were altered after the trenches had been dug and the foundations begun, and this unlucky fouling of doors may be the bequest of that revision. Afterthoughts and alterations are frequent cause of such mishaps. When the plan is originally made the whole scheme is subject to minute concentration; but when alterations are devised there is great danger that all consequences of the changes will not be foreseen.

Fantastic as this misadventure may appear, it will seem so to the experienced architect or builder only for the grotesque catastrophe associated with it. It is, in fact, typical of the kind of accidents that frequently happen. Pud's description makes pretty clear what occurred. It is a thing that the most exact detailing by the designer and anxious care of the builder could scarcely accomplish, so that had the thing been—as Brash's irritation led him to suggest—a practical joke, it would have done honour to the ingenuity and assiduity of its perpetrators.

The sketch shows what apparently happened. The title I have given it seems justified; for if anyone hereafter discovers a right use for the device, Spinlove ought most certainly to have credit for the invention.

BRASH TO SPINLOVE

Dear Mr. Spinlove,   30.4.26.

It was with considerable astonishment—will you permit me

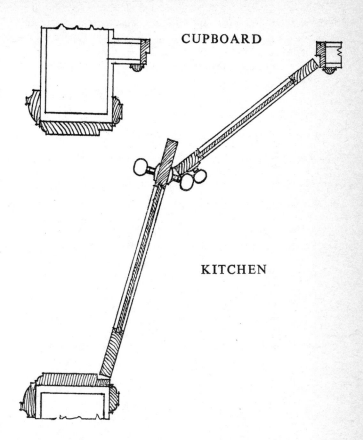

CUPBOARD

KITCHEN

SPINLOVE'S AUTOMATIC SELF-LOCKING DOOR.

Spinlove's Self-Locking Door

to say?—that I read the copy of Mr. Grigblay's report on the sanitary abnormalities obtaining at Honeywood; as this, so far from elucidating the circumstances elaborated in your letter on the subject, intimates no reference whatever to many of them. This is a matter I will take an early convenient opportunity of investigating in oral conversation with you as, also, other important matters somewhat lightly—if you will pardon me—touched on by you.

Yours sincerely,

Oh, what a tangled skein we weave
When first we practise to deceive!

Dear Sirs,   1.5.26.

Sir Leslie Brash rang up to-day and told me that the kitchen door in some way jams against the handle of the cupboard, and the servants were not able to get into the kitchen. Will you please send someone over to put things right? The cupboard door had better be hung the other way round and a spring catch fixed so that it remains fast when closed.

Sir Leslie Brash also spoke of the Riddoppo paint as developing serious defects. He had previously referred to this matter in a letter. I reminded him that it was used by his orders and against my wishes and your advice. Could Mr. Grigblay call or send over a painter to see what can be done?

Yours faithfully,

Spinlove seems to have suffered puncture! There is a note of moral deflation in this letter. Our young friend makes no attempt to put the blame on the builder, as he has taught us to expect, but actually accepts responsibility for the kitchen door fiasco. He seems also to have given ground deplorably in the matter of Riddoppo. Apparently Grigblay's urgent representations have made no impression on him. Is Mr. Spinlove losing heart? If so, he had better give up practice at once. The letter that follows offers some explanation.

RIDDOPPO BOILS UP

Dear Sir Leslie Brash,   1.5.26.

I write to confirm telephone conversation this morning.

I still think that the explanation of the stuffy smell complained of is that given in Mr. Grigblay's report. As I explained, my own report to you was partly based on private messages from Mr. Grigblay. In any case the condition is not, I am quite sure, due to faulty drains or to any defect in the building work.

I am unable to say to what the defects in the Riddoppo paint are due. You will remember that I never recommended it, and Mr. Grigblay also objected to using it. As arranged, I have asked Mr. Grigblay to see what can be done.

I am very sorry indeed for the accident of the kitchen door. I have to-day written to Grigblay with instructions for alterations that will prevent anything of the kind happening again.

I have this morning inquired by telephone, and find that the breakdown of the bells was caused by a large nail driven into the wall of the pantry by one of your servants.

Yours sincerely,

Brash, we may judge, has been truculent over the telephone. The bell-wiring does not seem to have been done as well as it should. Presumably, the electric light wiring was drawn in through tubes, and the bell wires ought to have been run in the same way.

Dear Sir,   3.5.26.

We shall be obliged if you will inform Sir Leslie Brash that we cannot advise him *re* Riddoppo, as the paint is composed of ingredients which are a trade secret, and we know nothing of it. He will remember that we refused to take responsibility for painting with same and only did so by his orders on the understanding that he took responsibility for the results.

Yours faithfully,

If, as Grigblay claims, he is not responsible for the defects in Riddoppo, it would be a grave error in judgment for him to offer any opinion on the nature or cause of them, and much more unwise for him to have anything to do with reparation.

SPINLOVE TO BRASH

Dear Sir Leslie Brash,   4.5.26.
I wrote to Mr. Grigblay asking him to see what could be done to make good defects in the paint, and I enclose copy of his letter in reply.

Yours sincerely,

Spinlove has no business to pass on Grigblay's disclaimer without comment or explanation. His duty, as architect and arbiter under the contract, is to master the facts, to balance the scales between owner and builder, and to uphold the rights of each.

BRASH TO SPINLOVE

Dear Mr. Spinlove,   7.5.26.
Although I have in the past had no occasion to form a particularly favourable opinion of Mr. Grigblay's good manners, I confess that I was completely taken aback with surprise at the high-handed style in which he has indited his communication to you intimating his refusal to make himself amenable to my desire that he should apply himself to the reparation of the failure of the paint; but you must permit me to say that I was even more astonished at the detached aloofness of your communication covering its transmission. What the man intends to signify by saying that I, *I* of all people, who have had nothing to do with it, am responsible for the disintegration of Riddoppo—unless he is going off his head, which is precisely what I should anticipate of the fellow—I entirely fail to comprehend. What have I to do with the "results" of his work?

Riddoppo Boils Up

This, you must permit me to intimate, is a most preposterously impudent suggestion for a builder to propound, and I take strong objection to your affirmative acquiescence in such a monstrous proposition. I desire that you will at once require Mr. Grigblay to perform his duties, for I divine that the reserve held back by me as security for the reparation of defects is to reimburse me for losses due to unjustifiable refusals. I am not, I apprehend, to be at the mercy of the contractor!

Yours sincerely,

Brash is precipitating disaster, for he has evidently forgotten the circumstances in which he ordered Grigblay to paint with Riddoppo.

SPINLOVE TO GRIGBLAY

Dear Sirs,   8.5.26.

I sent Sir Leslie Brash a copy of your letter on the subject of Riddoppo, and I have received one from him in which he disclaims responsibility for the failure of the paint, as he has had nothing to do with it, and renews his request that you will give immediate attention to the matter.

Yours faithfully,

This letter strengthens the earlier impression that Spinlove is held by other activities and is tired of Honeywood. He has, however, adopted an untenable position in standing aside while builder and owner fight the matter out for themselves.

GRIGBLAY TO SPINLOVE

Dear Sir,   10.5.26.

We will thank you to kindly note and to politely inform Sir Leslie Brash that Riddoppo paint is his own concern and no sort of business of ours, as he knows well enough without being told. We used the stuff by his orders on the undertaking he gave to accept full responsibility for results of same, after we had objected and refused to take responsibility, which please note and see correspondence.

59

Riddoppo Boils Up

We also will thank you to respectfully point out to your client that we called attention to the defects he has just discovered for himself, nearly six months ago, and warned him before the painting was finished what would happen, and he ordered us to go on and finish in spite; and also politely inform him with our respectful compliments that it will save him a bit of unnecessary trouble if he gives up trying to put the blame for his own obstinacy on to us, and kindly note that we politely refuse to have anything further to do with his mistakes, having completed our contract to instructions; and decline to pickle off, burn off, scrape off, hack off or touch up or have any further hand with new novelty super or other painting at Honeywood of any kind whatever or for any consideration whatever; and if Sir Leslie Brash wants our advice, the advice we respectfully send him is to leave off trying to put the blame where it does not belong, and ask those to set him right who set him wrong, and that is the people who manufactured the paint and supplied to us at his orders.

Yours faithfully,

Grigblay is warming up, and no wonder! This "respectful" and "polite" message is evidently dictated by him. The general run of letters from his firm is apparently the work of a secretary.

SPINLOVE TO BRASH

Dear Sir Leslie Brash,   11.5.26.

I sent Mr. Grigblay your message, and his reply is much what I expected. He disclaims all responsibility for Riddoppo on the ground that you accepted responsibility when you ordered him to use it. He recommends that you should apply to the manufacturers, or to the suppliers, for advice on the matter.

I do not know what more I can do for I know nothing of the composition of the paint, which is a secret. As you will remember, I always advised against its use and disclaimed responsibility for the result.

Yours sincerely,

60

Riddoppo Boils Up

It is ridiculous for Spinlove to suppose that he can stand aside as though he were the disinterested spectator of a dog fight. At the same time, it must be admitted that the line he takes is strictly consistent with his disclaimer of responsibility, so that, except that he is precipitating a break with his employer, he has not prejudiced his own nor Grigblay's position as we had good reason to fear he might.

BRASH TO SPINLOVE

Dear Mr. Spinlove,   12.5.26.

I was astonished to peruse your communication transmitting Mr. Grigblay's impertinent asseverations of refusal and denials of responsibility. Am I to understand that you are desirous of taking sides with the preposterous attack of the builder upon me? Have I to remind you that, as my accredited architect, it is incumbent upon you to protect my interests and enforce on the contractor the due observance of his obligatory duties? If so, I apprehend I have been seriously mistaken in the character of the gentleman to whom I have entrusted the management of my building operations. The paint in the house is displaying disastrous signs of ocular disintegration which develop increasingly, and my architect refuses to stir a finger in the matter because he objected to the paint and is "not responsible" forsooth!

The whole matter is perfectly unendurable and beyond bearing, and I desire that you will intimate to Mr. Grigblay, with necessary emphasis, that unless he forthwith immediately agrees to restore and renew the defective paint in a properly permanent and workmanlike manner, I shall engage the services of some other building contractor to do the work, and subtract the amount of the cost as a deduction from the next payment I am asked to make to him, for I divine that the security retained by me is designed to be applicable to this purpose.

                                        Yours sincerely,

In the event of a builder refusing, or failing to satisfy his covenant, to make good defects, the retention money may be

61

applied as Brash proposes; but it can only be so applied after formal warning and notification to the builder, and only if the defect in question is due to improper workmanship or materials for which the builder is responsible.

SPINLOVE TO BRASH

Dear Sir Leslie Brash,   14.5.26.

I think you must have forgotten what occurred at the time you directed me to order Grigblay to paint with Riddoppo, and I therefore enclose copies of various letters that passed, including—in case you may not have kept copies of them—your letters to me.

It seems clear that Grigblay cannot be held responsible for the failure of the paint. He also asks you to excuse him from expressing an opinion of the cause of the defects or from having anything to do with renovations, and for the reason I gave, namely, that he knows nothing of the paint, the ingredients of which are a trade secret. When you read the letters you will see that Grigblay called attention to defects before the painting was finished, but that you ordered him to complete; and you will also see that I always strongly objected to the use of Riddoppo and disclaimed responsibility for the results of using it.

Yours sincerely,

Spinlove is certainly keeping on safe ground, but his detachment seems chiefly due to his being sick of Honeywood. The proper action for him to take would be to study the case exhaustively and give the best advice he can, and—instead of leaving his client to find his own way—guide him to the wisest course and, possibly, contrive a compromise. However, Grigblay is too wary ever to have anything more to do with Riddoppo either on the walls of Honeywood Grange or in the tin.

LADY BRASH TO SPINLOVE

Dear Mr. Spinlove,

We have a small party here on Friday and hope you will come to tennis in the afternoon and stay the night.

Riddoppo Boils Up

It is all getting into the carpets and I shall have to take them up if it goes on and they do not stop it and so *dreadfully* noisy to walk on! ! I hope they will do it soon and have finished with once for ever. It is all so very trying isn't it and so stuffy, it seems as if we should never be able to settle down but Mr. Grigblay says wait for the summer so I suppose we must it will not be long now I am thankful to say.

How beautiful all the blossom has been lately.

Yours sincerely,

Monday.

BRASH TO SPINLOVE

Dear Mr. Spinlove,   17.5.26.

I have re-perused your communication and the transmitted copies of enclosed correspondence a second time. My previous recollection of the matter had, as you correctly divine, escaped my memory, but Mr. Grigblay's proposition that by intimating willingness to take responsibility for ordering I made myself liable for the eventual default of persons other than myself is —you must permit me to point out—most excessively preposterous, as I shall get an early opportunity of requesting my legal advisers to authoritatively confirm. If, as Mr. Grigblay impudently contends, the liability for defective blemishes is not his responsibility, then it is the responsibility of the manufacturer, and they must decide the dispute between themselves. My precise directions to yourself are that the progressive disintegration shall be immediately arrested and necessary reparations proceeded with without delay. The matter is now *imperatively urgent*, as the little flakes of paint cannot be removed by brushing the carpet, and have to be individually picked off with the thumb and finger, a duty so laboriously irksome to the domestic staff that it is performed in a perfunctory manner, and particles of Riddoppo are, for this cause, on all sides being *trodden into the carpets* with resultant consequences you may conjecture.

As I do not apprehend that I have at any time intimated that I regard you as responsible for the disintegration, your disclaimer of responsibility appears to me—if you will permit me to be perfectly frank—somewhat unnecessarily premature; nor do I perceive, as you intimate that you disclaimed liability for any prognosticated eventual results.

Yours faithfully,

Brash's gracious intimation of his "willingness to take responsibility for ordering" was in these words: "I do not know what the man [Grigblay] means by 'responsibility' and—if I may be permitted to be perfectly frank—I do not care. I give the order and the responsibility for giving the order is mine. Mr. Grigblay's responsibility is to do what he is told at once."

The history of the matter as recorded in The Honeywood File *is briefly as follows:*

Brash writes to Spinlove giving glowing advertisement accounts of a wonderful New Novelty Super-Paint called Riddoppo, and directing Spinlove to use it. Spinlove objects that he knows nothing of Riddoppo and that the well-tried paint specified by him gives the best possible results. Brash grows peppery, and retorts that for Spinlove "to asseverate condemnation of a paint of which he admits he knows nothing, is a little wanting in logical reasoning", and insists on Riddoppo being used. Spinlove gives the order to Grigblay, who replies that he knows nothing of Riddoppo and has failed to obtain any satisfactory accounts of it, and that he "cannot accept responsibility for same". Brash, on hearing this, objects, angrily, at being "dictated to"; and delivers himself as first above quoted. Spinlove thereupon writes to Grigblay: "I am instructed by Sir Leslie Brash to order you to paint with Riddoppo. Sir Leslie Brash accepts all responsibility."

Those are the facts; and if, as they appear to show, Brash is responsible for the paint having been ordered, then, in that case, Grigblay is responsible to Brash for properly applying the paint; Brash is responsible to Grigblay for the integrity of the paint; the manufacturers are responsible to Brash, Brash is responsible to Spinlove, Spinlove to Brash, Spinlove to Grigblay, and Grigblay to Spinlove—all in different degrees and on different issues —so that when Grigblay described the approaching disaster as a "mix up" his term was not inappropriate. If Brash had not interfered there is no doubt that Spinlove, with Grigblay's experience and integrity to back him, would have completed the house with

64

*sound paintwork; but had things by any chance gone wrong,
Brash would then have been secured under the contract, and his
remedy would have been the simple one of requiring Grigblay to
repaint. He has brought all this trouble on his own head.*

SPINLOVE TO BRASH

Dear Sir Leslie Brash,   18.5.26.
    I have told Mr. Grigblay the position you are taking. I will
not reply to your letter as we shall be able to talk matters over
during the week-end.

With kind regards,
Yours sincerely,

SPINLOVE TO GRIGBLAY

Dear Sirs,   19.5.26.
    I communicated the contents of your letter to Sir Leslie
Brash and sent him copies of the earlier correspondence. He
says that in ordering Riddoppo he did not make himself
responsible for defects due to improper materials or workmanship. He calls on you to make good at once as the carpets are
being spoilt; and holds that the matter is for you and the paint
manufacturer to settle between you. He is consulting his
solicitors to decide what action to take in the event of your
refusing to make good.

Yours faithfully,

*Spinlove is not content to stand aside and watch the dogfight:
he must, it seems, throw the animals one at the other.*

GRIGBLAY TO SPINLOVE

Dear Sir,   20.5.26.
    We note Sir Leslie Brash's views on responsibility for the
failure of the paint, and have nothing to add to our last *re*
same.

Yours faithfully,

GRIGBLAY IS CONFIDENTIAL

(HOLOGRAPH) GRIGBLAY TO SPINLOVE

Sir,   24.5.26.

I happened along Honeywood way and looked in, as Jossling is clearing up after finishing road which I hope is to your approval, and I just write to drop you a hint that the old gentleman is still worrying over his defective drains, as I gather you have nothing to do with a sanitary expert he has called in. There was a very young gentleman, with two handy-men to help him, had been putting the water test on the vertical soil and filling the pans to the brims, and so on up to the second floor servants', like a piano-tuner at work, till he had near 30 foot head of water above the first man-hole—so Jossling told me—and enough to burst the pipes. I found him down at the disconnecting chamber with a parcel of rockets and boxes of matches to find out with smoke how much damage he had done with water.

The drains don't ventilate Mr. Grigblay he says, I've put three rockets in and been waiting half an hour and I can't see any smoke out at top yet. You're in too great a hurry I told him; you keep at it another hour or two with all the rockets you've got there, and you'll see a bit of smoke right enough. This sucking expert had wetted all the pipes right up, and made them stone cold, and then expected to find a nice draught! However, a fashionable gentleman drove up in a saloon and rang the front bell; Jarrad, of Quince and Jarrad, patronized by Royalty—I've seen something of their doings before now. Jarrad didn't get asked in to tea, it seems, for he soon came round to find out how his young hopeful's drain-bursting experiments were getting on; and then they brought a pressure pump and other gear from the saloon and so I left him to go running his nose round the joints like a terrier dog, and rub the skin off same as he does at his Royal Palace, to try and catch a whiff of smoke after he's pumped up the ten pounds or whatever the pressure is they keep on their mercury gauges and contraptions. I hope no harm will come, Sir, but his kind are very mischievous fellows that get their living finding fault with other people's work, and the more faults they find the bigger men they hold themselves out to be. I thought best to let you know what was going forward, and if you hear any complaints perhaps our good friend Mr. Potch will have a kind word or two to say to Mr. Jarrad or to anyone else who claims he knows better ways of finding fault with other people's drains than what Potch does.

Apologizing for troubling you but thought you better know what is afoot.

Yours truly,

Brash, as we have noticed, commonly does not know the right thing to do; or, when he knows, frequently does not do it. He ought to have told Spinlove he wanted the drains tested by an independent authority, and either left Spinlove to nominate some-one or directed him to employ Quince and Jarrad. To go to the firm behind his architect's back is, if not a definitely hostile step, a sharp reminder to Spinlove that he has lost his employer's confidence. Brash's insensitiveness, however, probably exonerates him from any intention of wronging Spinlove; and Spinlove has invited this treatment by his unaccommodating attitude and his impatience at the suggestion that all is not as it should be. Grigblay's apprehensions are justified, though his contempt for Messrs. Quince and Jarrad is not at all likely to be. Mr. Potch is the District Surveyor who brought Spinlove much trouble while the house was being built.

(PERSONAL) SPINLOVE TO GRIGBLAY

Dear Mr. Grigblay, 26.5.26.
Yes, you are correct—I have heard nothing of any drain-testing; but as I am sure everything is right no amount of testing can find anything wrong.

I am obliged to you for writing.

Yours truly,

Spinlove is in a fool's paradise indeed, if he can welcome the approach of the sworn tormentor of drains—for to that dire body I divine Quince and Jarrad to belong.

SUMMARY OF VARIATIONS

GRIGBLAY TO SPINLOVE

Dear Sir,   29.5.26.

As requested, we send you herewith summary of variations and shall be glad to receive certificate for £1,300 further on account. We have heavy commitments just at this time, and as the amount fell due in the middle of February last we shall be glad to receive your certificate and Sir Leslie Brash's cheque without further delay. The account, we may point out, now stands as follows:

	£	s.	d.
Contract	18,440	0	0
By variations account	1,892	14	7
	20,332	14	7
Less 5 per cent retention	1,016	11	6
	19,316	3	1
Already certified	18,000	0	0
Due February 10th	1,316	3	1

This is the third or fourth application Grigblay has made for payment on account of extras in respect of which Spinlove has previously certified only for £500.

(ENCLOSURE) GRIGBLAY TO SPINLOVE

INTERIM SUMMARY OF VARIATIONS

[I have numbered the items and added in italics the thoughts likely to be awakened in Spinlove.]

Summary of Variations

AMOUNT OF CONTRACT £18,440 0 0

1. Alteration to kitchen .. .. .. say   400 0 0
   ("*My goodness! It cannot possibly amount to as much as that! I told Brash 'about £100' —but that was before I had made the working drawings. Tinge must measure carefully, Damn!*")

2. Piping ditch (Day-work account) 114 5 6
   ("*Damn! I told Brash £20. They must have included other work on the time-sheets. I ought to have insisted on the day-work vouchers being sent in regularly. Tinge must check carefully.*")

3. Pulling down and altering partitions and restoring (Day-work) 137 9 0
   ("*Pity it is not more. Serves B. right for letting Lady B. interfere.*")

4. Extension and alteration of drains (day-work)   84 17 6
   ("*That must be the fish-tank extension. No business of mine, thank goodness!*")

5. Extra price picked facings (Hoochkoft) ..   92 0 0
   ("*What the . . . ! Why, they agreed to send picked after I refused to allow extra! No go, my friends!*")

6. Cutting out defective and making good (Day-work) 8 14 0
   ("*Hoochkoft and Grigblay can settle that between them. I told H. I would not have the soft under-burnt bricks, and G. that he was not to use them.*")

7. Raking and pointing to order in lieu of plain struck joint (Day-work) 49 6 3
   ("*Frost got at the joints. That's all right— Act of God. Tinge had better fix rate and measure. No justification for day-work— besides, how could they separate the time when the joint was struck as the bricks were laid?*")

8. 795 yds. sup. pointing to order in lieu of plain struck joint at 4½d. per ft. 134 3 0
   ("*Oh, I see! So the last item was for raking and pointing joints damaged. Oh! Right!—but Tinge must check the measure and rates.*")

69

Summary of Variations

9. Work in draining cellar (Day-work) 84 17 9
> (*"Oh, Lor! Twice what I expected! All that tunnelling through walls, I suppose! Wish I had checked day-work vouchers at the time."*)

10. Extra foundations to order (Day-work) ..   66 3 9
> (*"What's this? 'To order'? Not mine. There was a little give and take, certainly. Tinge would have measured the whole if there had been talk of any extra. No go, my lad!"*)

11. Timber garage outhouse (as estimated) ..   372 10 0
> (*"Very cheap too and a clinking design I will say. Old B. very pleased. A decent old boy."*)

12. Extension of washing-place (Day-work) ..   54 9 0
> (*"Why couldn't B. take my advice and include it with the building? He was sure to want it. Would have saved him money. Must be measured, anyhow. Day-work is all nonsense."*)

13. Terrace steps (special charge as notified) ..   11 6 3
> (*"Don't know anything of this. Lady B. perhaps."*)

14. Alterations to back stairs to order (Day-work)   41 12 0
> (*"That mistake of mine! They've charged far too much. Must question it."*)

15. Alterations to ground-floor window heads (Day-work) 65 10 0
> (*"I won't allow it. It was Grigblay's mistake, not mine. Anyhow I never sanctioned an extra."*)

16. Repairs and new bottoming to Entrance Road (as estimated) 62 0 0
> (*"A low charge. Wish I had got estimates for everything; but how the deuce can one, with all the interferences and hurry?"*)

17. Renewing two broken catch pits (Day-work) ..   4 13 0
> (*"They ought to have included for these when they estimated for the road repair. Out it goes!"*)

18. Oak floor to kitchen passage (To order) ..   14 12 0
> (*"Lady B. I forgot this. They never had order for extra."*)

19. Waterproofing chimneys (estimate) 42 10 0
> (*"Not done yet."*)

Summary of Variations

20. Various minor works and attendances   ..   192 6 8
("Ridiculous! I must have particulars. They must show the orders for all extras.")

	2,033	5 8

EXTRAS ON PROVISIONS

("Expected this. Not altogether my fault.")

21. Grates and range (Chiddle, etc.)	22 0 0	
22. Electric wiring (Poggle)	21 5 0	

("I couldn't know they would want so many points.")

23. Electric light fittings 48 4 6
("Well, I told Brash what was allowed.")

24. Sanitary fittings (Wide)   ..   53 17 0
("He did it with his eyes open.")

25. Radiators (additions and alterations) 28 0 0

26. Locks and furniture 32 4 9
("I cut this too fine.")

27. Casements and glazing (Watkins)   13 10 6

28. Special opening gear (do.)   ..   27 7 0
("This was absolutely neces- sary.")

29. Extra journey money *re* do.   ..   11 13 3
("When Lady B. sent the man away, I suppose.")

30. Balance of small variations   ..   21 13 8
("What does this refer to?")

Total	279 15 8	2,033 5 8
Profit	48 3 0	

("What a nuisance! Tinge must check the profit charge carefully.")

	327 18 8	327 18 8

Total additions		2,361 4 4

("Oh, I say!")

71

Summary of Variations

31. General contingencies	100	0	0				
("*I thought it was £300—but now I remember I cut off £200 when I was trying to get down the contract price. By Jove, that's unlucky! Damn!*")							
32. Well (omitted)	135	8	0				
("*I wish I had not cut down that provision so much.*")							
33. Saving on ram and piping, etc., in lieu of pump	21	0	0				
("*I expected a much larger saving. Oh, dear! This must include the special pipe and tank linings the analyst recommended. That is not my fault, anyway.*")							
34. Omission of return terrace wall say	100	0	0				
35. Entrance gates	4	2	4				
("*Every little helps.*")							
36. Omission of sun dial	59	1	0				
37. Various credits and allowances ..	32	4	5				
Total	451	15	9	2,361	4	4	
Profit	16	14	0				
("*Why have they allowed such small profit?*")							
Total omissions	468	9	9	468	9	9	
Total extra cost				1,892	14	7	

("*Oh, Lor! There will be an awful row about this! Brash has no idea of how things are. Anyhow, it's not my fault. I saved him the cost of the well, too. Let's see! How much of all this am I actually responsible for?*")

Summary of Variations

So far as may be judged, the cost of making good omissions and defects due to oversights and mistakes of the architect is just about £400; and if Spinlove had provided in the contract against water driving into the chimneys and rising in the cellar, and so forth, the contract price would have been increased, so that his guilt in inflating costs is represented by an even smaller sum. In fact, having regard to the unavoidable small accidents and unforseeable contingencies and interferences that attend all building operations, a man of far more experience than Spinlove would be well satisfied to have no larger sum to account for. Spinlove has unfortunately misled Brash with inadequate estimates given off-hand, but it did not appear that Brash attached importance to those estimates, nor that he would have abandoned the work had he been given exact ones. Spinlove has also let the account get out of hand: he has not kept himself informed of the state of affairs; he has neglected to enforce the contract condition that extras shall be formally authorized, as such, at the time the work is done; and he has not enforced the condition requiring that day-work vouchers, showing the time and materials expended on additional work which from its nature cannot be estimated by measurement, shall be rendered week by week. This is bad; but so many alterations were made by Brash, and there were so many interferences with the contract arrangements, that some excuse may be made for Spinlove. He did, in fact, warn Brash at the beginning of the building operations that, if the contract arrangements were interfered with, it would be impossible to safeguard extras.

The most indigestible part of the account is, however, the large excess of expenditure over the sums provided in the contract as "provisions" to meet the cost of work done by specialists, and of fittings subject to choice. These appear under the subheading "Extras on Provisions". The provision for general contingencies (item 31) was reduced by Spinlove from three to one hundred pounds, when he was trying to bring down the amount of the tender to a figure commensurate with Brash's swallow; and it seems likely that he pared down the provisional sums originally allowed by him at the same time, and with the same object. It is a great temptation to an architect to let his hopes for the best overrule his judgment, in this way; but it is a counsel of weakness

73

and folly, or even worse; for his client supposes the contract sum covers the equipment he needs, and for the architect knowingly to mislead him for the purpose of committing him to the undertaking is dishonest. We cannot, however, take Spinlove to task, for we do not know the facts. What we do know, however, is that in the course of a year or two extras mount up, all unbeknown, in a most embarrassing way; and that building-owners, after they are habituated to the contract price and warmed with enthusiasm for the undertaking, are prone to indulge their ambitions, and sometimes even try to forget past extravagances lest they shall discourage new ones.

It will be noticed that in imagining Spinlove's reflections on the summary so obligingly drawn by Grigblay in a form that analyses the account and saves Spinlove the trouble of analysing it for himself, I have represented him as accepting Grigblay's charge for pointing to make good damage by frost. This is a peep ahead on my part.

SPINLOVE TO GRIGBLAY

Dear Sir,   31.5.26.

I have duly received your Interim Summary of Variations, for which I am obliged, but I am concerned to notice that the total is even higher than you led me to expect. There are a number of charges that want explaining and others I certainly cannot allow, and I should like Mr. Grigblay to make an appointment to meet me here to go into the account, as soon as ready; bringing with him orders for extras, day-work vouchers, etc., supporting your charges. Also particulars of "Various minor works £192", and reasons why the charge for picked bricks is made. I expressly arranged with Hoochkoft to supply at their original quoted price, as I informed you at the time.

When I have been into matters with Mr. Grigblay I will arrange for Mr. Tinge to take up the account. Some of the items charged day-work will have to go into a measured account.

Yours faithfully,

I cannot see Grigblay spending hours unravelling day-work

Summary of Variations

sheets to Spinlove's satisfaction, but perhaps he will temper the wind to the shorn lamb and send round the estimating clerk who has charge of the account. This clerk, however, would not be able to explain or justify the charges. The proper course will be for Spinlove to push his head into the papers; get explanations from the builder on obscure points; settle contentious matters with him, and then refer the account for Tinge to arrive at the exact figures.

Dear Sir Leslie Brash,   31.5.26.

I have at last received an "Interim Summary" of the account from Grigblay; the exact figure has still, I am afraid, to be determined by the quantity surveyor, and there are certain charges which I cannot agree to—at least not without explanations—but I am very sorry indeed to say that the total is a good deal more than I expected. I am afraid the extras have mounted up very much, although you were perhaps prepared for this. I enclose a brief summary showing how the account stands, but this is not the final figure which, I hope and trust, will be substantially less.

If I can give you more information will you please let me know? The final account will not be ready for several weeks, I am afraid.

I enclose note of my own charges in respect of the last two certificates, which I omitted to send at the time. Will you please accept my apologies for my forgetfulness?

                                        Yours sincerely,

This is not, I fancy, the best of all possible occasions for Spinlove to apply for payment of his fees, even though he apologizes for not having done so before; and our young friend's amiable characteristic of identifying himself with the torment his client suffers in parting with his money, is here particularly inappropriate. We see Spinlove crouching before a lash he in no way deserves, and which he would have no reason to fear if he did not show he expected it. He invites Brash to be dissatisfied with his architect, who tells him he had no idea the total would be so

75

*large and apologizes for the amount, thereby avowing that he was
neglectful in not keeping himself informed; and who takes responsibility for matters which do not lie at his door at all. He is
"very sorry indeed" for the total of the account; he is "afraid"
the extras have mounted up, although he supposes Brash expected
they would; he does not know how it has all happened, and he is
"afraid" the account will not be ready for several weeks, although
the delay is an unavoidable circumstance with which he has
nothing to do and only Brash's undisciplined impatience will
suffer from it. If Spinlove's purpose had been to represent himself
in the worst light he could scarcely have devised a neater or more
complete way of doing so.*

*His letter is the more absurd for the finished tact he displays
in the document that accompanies it—the "brief summary"
which is to inform Brash how the account stands. Spinlove, it will
be seen below, lumps the whole of the total balance of extras on
to Brash by the adroit device of appropriating the whole of the
credit items, totalling £468 9s. 9d., to himself, and cancelling
them out against the extra expenditure for which he is personally
responsible. The document is, in fact, not so much a statement of
account between Brash and Grigblay as an apportionment of guilt
between Brash and Spinlove. We may, I think, admire his ingenuity without being positively noisy in our applause. The facts
set forth, however, are true; the figures are exact; the information
is what Brash asked for. Brash undoubtedly ordered the extras
laid to his charge, and is responsible for the inflation of the
account by the total of them, precisely as stated. At the same
time. . . . However, the point for astonishment is that Spinlove
should cover a document so conclusive of his innocence by a letter
so eloquent of guilt.*

(ENCLOSURE) SPINLOVE TO BRASH

SUMMARY OF EXTRAS ORDERED BY
SIR LESLIE BRASH

	£	s.	d.
Approximate cost, alterations to kitchen ..	400	0	0
Piping Ditch	114	5	6

	£	s.	d.
Pulling down and restoring partitions by Lady Brash's orders	137	9	0
Extension and alterations of drains (for Aquarium)	84	17	6
New garage and washing-place	426	19	0
Time lost on Terrace steps by Sir Leslie Brash's orders	11	6	3
Repairs, new entrance road	66	13	0
Oak floor to kitchen passage (Lady Brash) ..	14	12	0
Various minor alterations	192	6	8
Grates and Ranges (excess as ordered) ..	22	0	0
Electric wiring (additional points as ordered)	21	5	0
Electric fittings (excess as ordered)	48	4	6
Sanitary fittings (excess as ordered)	53	17	0
Radiators (additions and alterations) ..	28	0	0
Special opening gear to Casements (as desired)	27	7	0
Extra journey money (men dismissed by Lady Brash)	11	13	3
Various small items	21	13	8

OTHER EXTRAS

	£	s.	d.
Restoring brickwork damaged by frost ..	183	9	3
Various small extras	26	16	0
	£1,892	14	7

BRASH ON EXTRAS

BRASH TO SPINLOVE

Dear Mr. Spinlove,   2.6.26.

Eighteen hundred and ninety-two pounds! Is *eighteen* hundred the sum you intended to intimate when you informed me you anticipated additional extras accruing to "several" hundreds? So you did not anticipate so largely augmented a figure, but supposed that I was prepared for it; and the final

amount is still to be eventually ascertained, and you *hope* it
will be a substantially reduced figure, and you will not agree
to these monstrously extortionate inflations without "explanations"! Explanations, indeed! Permit me to emphatically indicate that I will certainly require something more than mere
explanations of this scoundrelly attempt to victimize me. Is this
the gentleman of high professional attainments who undertook
to safeguard his employer's interests and protect him from the
inordinate rapacity of building contractors—whom I was always well aware to be no better than packs of thieves and
robbers? Is this the Associate of the Royal Institute of British
Architects of impeccable credentials, specially recommended
to my favourable attention for his distinguished achievements,
who allows himself to be cajoled and humbugged and swindled
as long as "explanations" are given? The matter has taken a
most serious magnification of aspect, and you may inform Mr.
Grigblay that, explanations or no explanations, I will not so
much as condescend to consider his preposterous account
unless he cuts it down by *at least one half*.

£400 for alterations to kitchen! The claim is perfectly monstrous. The kitchen arrangements, may I remind you, were not
increased in dimensions by the corrective emendations. I certainly anticipated a small extra cost to reimburse the builder
for his trouble in adapting the work he had previously performed; but four hundred pounds! and as "approximate cost"!
Does this intimation signify that, if I consent to the additional
charge, the fellow is to be at liberty to further augment the
amount?

Then, "piping ditch—£114". Will you permit me to ask
leave to remind you that you quoted me £20 for that work—
and that I hold your letter tendering the offer? *That* item of cost
of £114, at any rate, will not, I warn you in anticipation, be
amenable to any "explanations"; for I definitely repudiate any
intention of paying more than the previously stipulated sum.
"Time lost by Sir Leslie Brash's orders!" When did I order
time to be lost? Preposterous! "Various minor alterations—
two hundred pounds!" Does my architect seriously propound
the suggestion that I should disburse any sums this saucy
fellow demands without even being previously informed under

78

what pretence the exaction is extorted? "Extra journey money"
—what does that portend, may I be permitted to ask? I was
prepared for an additional extra in respect of various grates
and fittings, but what conceivable excuse is propounded why
I should be mulcted for electric wiring and casement gear and
heating radiators and drains and water-pipes; and why, may
I venture to inquire, has the fellow made no deductions for the
saving on the well and pump which you previously held out as
an inducement to me to sanction the alternative arrangement?
And why has the £300 saving disappeared, which you informed
me had been included in the contract to reimburse expenditure
for additional extra work which might eventually become
needful, and which you asseverated must be reserved for that
express purpose? Am I to understand that Mr. Grigblay has
appropriated these credits, and that you have failed to detect
the fraud?

It is necessary that I should take an early opportunity of
conferring verbally with you without delay, as the whole
matter has attained most serious proportions. Nineteen hundred pounds! It is the most monstrous and unheard-of imposi-
tion that ever was attempted; and if Mr. Grigblay or my
architect supposes that I am a gentleman who will meekly
submit to such barefaced robbery and extortion, he will regretfully find himself very greatly mistaken.

Yours truly,

*Poor old Brash! He has let himself go with a vengeance, and
it is to be hoped he felt better afterwards.*

SPINLOVE SEEKS ADVICE

SPINLOVE TO THE VICAR OF RUNCHESTER

Dear Uncle Harold,   5.6.26.
    I do not know who to turn to for advice. I have just finished
a house for a certain Sir Leslie Brash, and the enclosed is a

copy of a letter I have received from him in reply to one of mine covering a summary of the builder's Statement of Account. There is rather a heavy bill of extras, but that is not altogether my fault; and, whether it is or not, how can I allow anyone to write to me as he does? I want to do the right thing and to avoid quarrelling with him, but how is it to be done? Can you tell me what you think I ought to do? and can you write at once, please? My love to Auntie and yourself.

Your affectionate nephew,

Apparently, Brash has aroused unrighteous impulses in Spin-love, who feels the need of a little spiritual guidance to ginger up his humility, console his wounded pride, and enable him to swallow the affront without doing violence to his self-respect.

SPINLOVE TO FREDERICK DALBET

Dear Fred, 5.6.26.

Look what your friend Brash has written to me! How can I answer such a letter without hopelessly quarrelling with him? The whole bother about the extras is really his fault and not mine—or most of it is, anyway. Did you ever read such disgraceful abuse? As it was you who introduced me to Brash I feel you might be able to help smooth things over. Hurry up with your reply.

Yours,

JIM.

Spinlove's position is made difficult by the fact that he is so much younger a man than Brash; but, if he were not, Brash would scarcely have written as he did.

DALBET TO SPINLOVE

Dear Jim, 6.6.26.

I don't see what I can do. Tell the old bounder to go to blazes. I warned you he was peppery, and he has gone in off the deep end this time, that is all. He has always been nice to me—but then I am not his architect. Cheer up!

Yours,

FRED

Spinlove Seeks Advice

My dear James,   7.6.26.

We were all most pleased to hear from you again, as it seems a very long time since you wrote either to your aunt or to myself.

Patience, my dear boy, patience! Nothing is to be gained by hasty action of any kind. As you have often heard, no doubt, to forgive all is to understand all—or rather the other way about; and your wish not to quarrel with your employer, but to do the right thing, is highly commendable and just what your aunt and I would expect of you. Be not cast down; fight the good fight, and above all, as Hamlet says, "To your own self be true, and it must follow as the night the day that thou canst not then be false to any man."

I think if I were you I should be inclined to send Sir Lindsay Brosh a small token of esteem—a brace of trout if you happen to be fishing, or a souvenir of your recent travels; or failing these, possibly a copy of my *Pensées from Parnassus*, which I shall be glad to autograph and send you for this purpose. The fact that the author is a near relative would give the gift the character of a spontaneous expression of goodwill.

We gather from your letter that you are unaware that your aunt was seriously indisposed for several weeks during the winter.

Your affectionate uncle,

With all respect to the Vicar, Hamlet does not speak the words quoted and, though the maxim is admirable of its kind, it is not the kind of maxim Spinlove wants.

However valuable advice on technical points and on questions of principle may be, it is worse than useless for Spinlove to ask for direction in matters touching his personal relations with others. He must brace himself to draw the decision from his own inwards, where alone it is to be found. To turn to friends, as he here· does, is to turn tail and to confirm the indecision he seeks to escape. He expects others to understand conflicting reactions of his own soul which he cannot himself interpret.

Neither Dalbet nor Uncle Harold the Vicar has made any

attempt to put himself in the supplicant's shoes, but—as can only be expected—they show themselves much more concerned to adopt a pose flattering to their own self-esteem than to solve Spinlove's difficulty. Even if they were in possession of the whole history, and succeeded in identifying themselves with Spinlove's plight, the quarrel would be theirs and not his, for their individualities are different; and, for the same reason, their advice, however sound for themselves, would be valueless for him. The boisterous, good-humoured resentment of Dalbet, and the ingratiating affability of the Vicar, might meet their respective cases excellently had Brash become involved with them; but it would be wildly inappropriate for Spinlove either to tell Brash to go to blazes or to present him with a copy of uncle's new book.

No one can help Spinlove. So far from getting help from his friends, their letters can only increase his perplexity and aggravate his indecision. By yielding to the impulse to ask advice at all, he surrendered not only his belief in himself, but his power to decide; and he has allowed a shrinking admission of defeat to fill days which should have been applied to arriving at a decision.

BRASH TO SPINLOVE

Dear Mr. Spinlove   9.6.26.

May I be permitted to apprise you that I have received no communication from you anent my urgent request for an immediate appointment.

Yours sincerely,

GRIGBLAY TO SPINLOVE

Dear Sir,   7.6.26.

Our Mr. Tobias, chief prime-costing, will call at your office with vouchers, etc., at 11 on Wednesday, for the purpose of going into the account with you, as arranged over phone.

Yours faithfully,

Their Mr. Tobias will not be able to give Spinlove the sort of information he chiefly needs. A builder's prime-costing clerk deals only with the pricing and collection into the account of work-

men's time-sheets and merchants', storekeeper's, carters', and other vouchers allocated to it by the foreman and others. What Spinlove chiefly wants is the authority, or justification, for the various extra charges. Bloggs, the foreman, could give him the facts; but Bloggs, of course, is now in charge of other work, and perhaps far afield.

SPINLOVE TO BRASH

Dear Sir Leslie Brash,   10.6.26.

I have not replied to your letter as I have expected that on reflection you would wish to withdraw it.

Yours sincerely,

This is a capital move. The evasion is neatly managed and Brash is warned, and in such a way as to encourage him to reconsider his position.

BRASH TO SPINLOVE

Dear Mr. Spinlove,   11.6.26.

I was taken aback with natural surprise on receipt of your communication. I indited my protest in terms which the circumstances suitably warranted, and you must permit me to remind you that it is yourself I have to thank for the necessity of doing so. I consider that the suggestion of withdrawal—though it might meet the very natural desires of a professional gentleman in your situation—is not one that is properly appropriate to the occasion, and I must request an adequately complete reply without further delay.

Yours sincerely,

P.S.—I shall be obliged if you will transmit a copy of my letter as I omitted to make a transcription of it.

Brash has had eight days in which to calm down. He seems to have written his offending letter in an hour of liver-inspired fury, and has quite forgotten what he said. Spinlove ought to be able to find his cue here. It is unfortunate Brash kept no copy of his letter or he would probably have accepted Spinlove's invitation to withdraw.

83

SPINLOVE ON EXTRAS

Dear Sir Leslie Brash,   12.6.26.

As you ask, I enclose copy of your letter, and in accordance with your instructions reply to it as completely as I can.

In disparaging my concern for the large total of the extras, you forget that that concern was not on my own account but on yours, and also that it is not I who am responsible for the figure, but yourself. I warned you at the beginning that if you interfered with the work the extras would mount up, and that it would be impossible for me to keep control of the cost if you gave orders direct to the builders. You paid no attention to the warning, and now wish to saddle me with the consequences of having ignored my advice.

The value of the kitchen alteration is a question of fact to be ascertained by the quantity surveyors, and I am no more responsible for the cost of the work than I am for the ordering of it, as a moment's reflection will surely show you. The amount is an approximate figure, because the exact figure has still to be ascertained.

I regret that I misjudged the probable cost of piping the ditch, and I think that, on examination, Grigblay's figure will be found to be in error; but I did not "quote" for the work. What I did was all that any architect can offer to do, namely, to give his opinion of probable cost. Only the builder quotes (i.e. estimates or tenders), and in this case Mr. Grigblay was not called on to do so, as you did not ask for an estimate. The exact cost will be proved by vouchers recording the time and materials expended on the work, which the quantity surveyor will embody in the account when I have examined and certified them as properly to be included in it.

It is such vouchers as these, furnished by the builder, that I referred to when I spoke of "explanations". Your assumption that I used the word in a sense that made it idiotic, instead of in an exact technical sense, can only be explained by an intention to affront me.

Other items you mention it will be necessary for me to see you about, for, as the works they refer to were ordered without my knowledge, I have naturally little knowledge of them.

The £300 contingencies was cut down to £100 in order to reduce the tender to a reasonable figure; and this sum and the saving on the well, and certain other credits, have been set off, in the brief summary I sent you, against the cost of other works that became necessary. [*Ahem*!] The final Statement of Account will be laid before you when I receive it. I am not responsible for the delay, which is due to intricacies arising from the many extras and variations ordered by yourself.

The extras on wiring, radiators, water supply and drains are due to extensions and alterations of completed work ordered by you or by Lady Brash, or made necessary by interferences with other work, and they have nothing whatever to do with me. The extras on fittings is the excess of the cost of goods you yourself chose after I had informed you of the provisional amounts included in the contract to cover them.

Your aspersions on Mr. Grigblay are, so far as I know, without any kind of justification; and you have, I think, had abundant opportunities during the past two years of forming a very different opinion of him.

I think, Sir Leslie, that you wrote in haste and in anger, and that you will wish to make amends for references to myself which seem to me openly contemptuous and intended for no other purpose than to affront me. In that confidence I will here merely say that, however mean an opinion you may hold of my capacities, I think I am entitled to a chance of explaining technical matters before being abused because you yourself do not happen to understand them.

Yours sincerely,

This is a remarkable letter for Spinlove to have written; but although some of his explanations are thin, we have before noticed that he always comes out strongest when his indignation is involved. We have also observed Mr. Spinlove to be a temperamental person, torn by conflicting impulses of vanity and prudence, in whom self-control is schooled by terror. Here, however, we find him expressing himself forcibly, as the circumstances require, but with restraint and cool purpose, and enough of courtesy—in presuming good intentions in his opponent—as to rob the frankness of his retort of offensiveness. This letter of Spinlove's, however, as well as that to which it replies, has a colour foreign to professional correspondence: they suggest a quarrel between men whose relations are proof against frank interchanges.

BRASH TO SPINLOVE

My dear Mr. Spinlove,   13.6.26.

I certainly was not aware of the asperity of language into which my natural rancour at the very inflated extortions of Mr. Grigblay betrayed me, and I desire to entirely withdraw my disparaging inferences anent yourself, which I greatly regret and for which I offer you my profuse apologies. They certainly are such as I had no intention of intimating, nor do they represent my opinion; in fact, I have to regretfully admit that I wrote hastily and in a moment of heated indignation, and I hope you will entirely eliminate from your mind all memory of my accidental and quite unpremeditated lapse from discreet language.

As regards the various matters expounded in your communication, I still consider that your elucidation is—if you will permit me to say so—very far from completely satisfactory, and it is imperatively desirable that I should discuss the whole aspect of the situation with you.

I enclose cheque for £270 further on account of your fees. You will comprehend that until some explanation of the inflated sum upon which the percentage is computed was forthcoming, this disbursement was not one I could reasonably contemplate.

Yours sincerely,

It is to be noticed that by putting himself in the wrong in one matter, and having to make a withdrawal, Brash has disorganized his whole line, and is even reduced to paying up as a step towards re-establishing his fortifications. This, however, is not the first occasion when Brash has justified Dalbet's original description of him as a "real good sort". He here again reveals himself as a man whose foibles overlie generous instincts.

A Sanitary Consultant

Dear Sir Leslie Brash,   15.6.26.

Many thanks indeed for your extremely kind letter. I need
not tell you what very great pleasure it gave me. Of course,
I am delighted to accept your apology and withdrawal, and
will now forget all about the matter—in fact, I have already
put it entirely out of my mind, and I am only sorry I felt
obliged to make the protest, although I feel sure you will
realize I could scarcely avoid doing so or I should not, I need
hardly say, have put you to so much trouble.

I confirm appointment with your clerk by telephone to-day
to see you here on Wednesday morning next. I shall before then
have discussed matters with the builder.

I enclose form of receipt for cheque, for which I am much
obliged.

Yours sincerely,

This is much more like the Spinlove of old acquaintance.

A SANITARY CONSULTANT

Dear Mr. Spinlove,   14.6.26.

I write to intimate that some weeks ago a medical practitioner, called in to attend a member of the domestic staff who
had developed asthmatic symptoms, informed Lady Brash that
attacks of this disorder may be provoked by *defective sanitary
provisions*. This practitioner is not our own medical adviser,
but is employed by me to minister to the domestic staff, and
since his responsibilities are small his fees are, of course, low;
but I understand he has good credentials and is well thought
of by the local population, among whom—and this is of special
import—he *must have gained exceptional experience of the effect*

87

of obnoxious effluviums. His statement to Lady Brash has, therefore—you will not be surprised to hear—definitely established my most unfavourable prognostications.

As you had previously intimated inability to determine what curative measures to adopt, and Mr. Grigblay had no recommendations to propose, I communicated with Messrs. Quince and Jarrad, Consulting Sanitary Specialists. These gentlemen are employed by certain of my acquaintances, and also by Royalty and by members of the aristocracy, and *any* opinion of theirs is accordingly conclusively final. Mr. Jarrad attended to the matter himself personally, and made exhaustively thorough explorations and tests, and I enclose his report. I make no comment of any kind whatever. The report is exactly what I expected; the sanitary work has been disgracefully badly done, and will have to be drastically renovated—however, I will make no comment. My architect has failed me, the builder, instructed and supervised by him, has defrauded me, and it is a providential mercy that we are all alive and in relatively good health to-day; but, as I say, I make no comment, but confine myself to requesting you to *read* the report (enclosed)—simply to read what these authoritative experts say of our sanitary provisions, and then to favour me with explicit assurances that the necessary renovations will be put in hand at once, and of the date when they will be completed, as it will be necessary to vacate the house while the work is being performed. No doubt you may wish also to offer some observations justly appropriate to the occasion.

As the necessity for employing the services of Messrs. Quince and Jarrad was due to remission of care on the part of Mr. Grigblay in performing his duties, and his refusal to give attention to the emendation of defects, I shall most certainly deduct their fee of twenty guineas from the next payment due to Mr. Grigblay.

Yours sincerely,

We may conclude that under pressure from Lady Brash the doctor yielded the admission that defective drains may precipitate attacks of asthma in a person subject to them.

A Sanitary Consultant

(ENCLOSURE) QUINCE AND JARRAD TO BRASH

Sir,   12.6.26.

We have the honour to say that in accordance with your
instructions we visited Honeywood Grange on the 3rd of this
month and made an exhaustive examination of the sanitary
works, and now have the pleasure to enclose our Report.

We have the honour to be, Sir,

Your obedient servants,

*At first glance, this letter might be a command to attend a
State function at Buckingham Palace. It is beautifully typed in
green on an exquisite linen paper self-edged like a bank note, and
is headed in embossed gold lettering with an address adjoining
Cavendish Square and with the statement that Messrs. Godolphin
Quince and Hartington Jarrad are Consulting Sanitary Specialists, Patronized by Royalty and by the Nobility and Gentry.*

*The report covered by the letter extends to seven typed fool-
scap sheets, with a printed heading reproducing the intelligence
gilded on the letter, and stating, in italics, that passages typed in
red are so rendered in order to call attention to them. A glance
shows that these red letterings all refer to points to which Messrs.
Quince and Jarrad take exception; that there are a considerable
number of such passages; and that, for greater emphasis, they
are all typed in capitals.*

*The report is evidently based on an exhaustive survey and is
the skilled work of men of highly specialized knowledge and wide
experience in a restricted field; but while Spinlove's task was to
provide Honeywood with a well-devised and soundly-executed
drainage system that was in no way unnecessarily costly, Quince
and Jarrad pursue a fantastic ideal of theoretic perfection in
which expense has no consideration. With that qualification, and
except that it makes no allowance for those differences of opinion
which exist in the theory and practice of sanitation, as in everything else, and confines itself to adverse criticism, the report is
fair. It does not, however, except by implication, say what should
be done to meet the objections raised; for the reason, no doubt,
that Messrs Quince and Jarrad were not asked to reconstruct
Honeywood's drains, but only to report on them.*

A Sanitary Consultant

*There would be no purpose in here reproducing the report,
which describes, first, the system Spinlove has adopted; second,
the layout of the drains; and third, every detail of the work. It is
the passages typed in red which have scared Brash and will
trouble his architect and which alone concern us; and as Spinlove
has to meet these criticisms, we may expect to learn all we want
to know of them from future letters.*

(PERSONAL) SPINLOVE TO GRIGBLAY

Dear Mr. Grigblay,   15.6.26.

I am much disturbed to receive the enclosed letter and report
of Quince and Jarrad from Sir Leslie Brash. They make out
that everything is wrong. Will you read and let me know what
you make of it all?

Yours truly,

*As usual, when in difficulties Spinlove looks about for advice—
a bad habit, for it is only by settling things for himself that he
will learn to make decisions. At the same time, he is right to
confer with the builder on this matter, before acting.*

(PERSONAL) GRIGBLAY TO SPINLOVE

Sir,   17.6.26.

I return herewith Quince and Jarrad's latest. It is their usual
pack of nonsense, but it may be an awkward job to get the old
gentleman to agree. I think, sir, I had better have a talk over.
I can make convenient on Saturday at 11.30 if you will kindly
confirm by phone, and oblige,

Yours truly,

*We may suppose that Spinlove gained great advantage from
his talk with Grigblay.*

SPINLOVE TO QUINCE AND JARRAD

Dear Sirs,   21.6.26.

I have received from Sir Leslie Brash your report on the
drains at Honeywood Grange, of which house I happen to be

A Sanitary Consultant

the architect. I must protest that it is most unfair of you to give
mere differences of opinion the appearance of condemnations.
You find no actual fault in the arrangements anywhere, and
yet you have led my client to believe the drainage of his house
is insanitary. You even tell him that the joint of lead waste to
gully has not been made, without troubling to look to see
whether it has been or not.

Yours faithfully,

*It was undignified of Spinlove to write this letter, and also not
worth while, for Messrs. Q. and J. probably receive a good many
like it, and some that are more violent.*

QUINCE AND JARRAD TO SPINLOVE

Sir,   22.6.26.
We have the honour to acknowledge your letter informing
us that you do not agree with our views *re* drains Honeywood
Grange, and which we may say we are not surprised to hear as
we happen to know our own business.

The differences of opinion you refer to are quite common
and have no signification whatever, being quite usual with
architects.

We have the honour to be, Sir,

Your obedient servants,

*Spinlove asked for something of this sort. Q. and J. have not
used their gold-embossed bank-note stationery for this letter.*

SPINLOVE TO BRASH

Dear Sir Leslie Brash,   22.6.26.
I could not write to you on the subject of Messrs. Quince
and Jarrad's report until I had thoroughly investigated the
points raised.

I do not think that you yourself read the report closely, or
you would not have formed the opinion that the drains are
insanitary. Although the report is drawn in such a way as to
lead you to a contrary impression, no fault is anywhere found,

as you will see, either with the system or with the work; and attention is called to only *two "defects"*. One of those defects is not a defect in the drains at all, but a defect in Mr. Jarrad who tells you that a joint has been left unmade without troubling himself to see whether it has been or not; the second so-called "defect" is not an actual defect as, if it exists, it refers only to tests applied by Mr. Jarrad, and not to the normal use of the drains.

I am aware, Sir Leslie, that you will consider that I am on my defence, and will be reluctant to accept my views; but I am glad to say that I am not called upon to defend myself, and for your own peace of mind I ask you to hear me out with patience for I shall confine myself to showing what the report does actually say. Before I do this I should like to point out that the whole of the matters stressed by red lettering, except the two above mentioned, are mere expressions of *opinion*, and do not involve the question of sanitary soundness in any way whatever; and also that this difference of opinion is in all cases due to the fact that, while I designed the system so as to avoid unnecessary expense, Messrs. Quince and Jarrad's ideas are of the most extravagant and costly kind. I enclose the report and take the red-lettered points in their order.

"The aerobic filter might well be bigger and the tipper set 9 ins. higher. Gun metal bushes and trunnions are desirable, as in course of time rust will interfere with action of tipper."

The filter and tipper are the standard device of Wreek & Co., who are leading specialists in the work. I cut out the bronze bushes, etc., as being needlessly costly.

"We prefer detritus chambers and manholes to be lined with glazed brick. Also the effluent channels would be better in glazed ware. We recommend tallow for sealing manhole covers."

Glazed brick is expensive, and here quite unnecessary for sanitary efficacy. The rims are sealed with axle grease, which is usual. The sealing, in any case, is a counsel of perfection.

A Sanitary Consultant

"The glazed channel discharging waste from scullery sinks over grease trap is unnecessary and objectionable."

As this channel is required by the local Sanitary Authority it *is* necessary, and the Local Government Board does not agree that the arrangement is objectionable or it would not describe it in its Model Bye-laws.

"The ventilation of the drains is sluggish. We recommend the up-and-down-cast system in preference to the up-cast here employed."

Messrs. Quince and Jarrad are in a minority among sanitary engineers if they hold this opinion; the up-cast is almost universally employed. The sluggishness was due to Messrs Q. and J.'s representative having wetted and thoroughly chilled the pipes before he tested for ventilation. Mr. Grigblay will at any time demonstrate to you that the system ventilates properly.

"That lavatory wastes discharge over open rainwater heads near to windows. This arrangment is most objectionable as, when the down pipe and head get fouled, air passing up the pipe will smell offensively. We recommend lead waste pipes properly ventilated and discharging through inlets under grids of gullies as employed near the front entrance."

This condition *may* arise in the future. When it does, it can be readily cured by cleansing the pipes. It does *not exist to-day*. The arrangement I have adopted has much to recommend it, in addition to effecting great saving in cost. As nearly all the bedrooms have lavatory basins, Messrs. Quince and Jarrad's device would cover the elevations with a network of pipes with ventilating branches standing up above eaves.

"We much prefer and always recommend cast-iron waste and soil pipes in place of the lead used at Honeywood."

As in an hotel or workhouse! The associations of domestic architecture favour lead, and Messrs. Quince and Jarrad do

93

not say—and cannot say—that lead pipes are not at least as sound as any other.

"The lead bath and lavatory waste by front entrance has been merely pushed through the gully inlet and not jointed to it."

This is not the case. A flanged ring has been wiped to the lead and jointed to the stoneware in cement, as anyone could discover who wanted to know.

"The plate on clearing eye at the junction of the soil pipe vent by north-east gable has not been properly bedded, and allows foul air to escape from the drain."

I will have this plate taken off and re-bedded, but as there is, for all practical purposes, *never more pressure inside the open vent than outside*, leakage cannot take place; if there were any leakage it would be of no consequence as the whole purpose of ventilation is to prevent the air in the drain from getting poisonous, and if it became foul the position of the plate at the side of the gable and above the main eaves gutter would still make the matter of no consequence. The leak can only exist when the ends of ventilating pipes are stopped and air pumped into the drains under pressure.

I have written at some length, Sir Leslie, but at not, I hope, too great a length. If any doubts still remain of the soundness of the drains, I hope you will let me know what they are.

Yours sincerely,

This letter would have been more dignified if Spinlove had denied himself backhanders at Messrs. Quince and Jarrad, whose destruction would also have been more complete if Spinlove had made his points coolly instead of with warmth. The tone of the letter is unprofessional; but Spinlove's relations with Brash—who long ago made fervour, rather than decorum, the characteristic note of their interchanges—excuse it. Except for this he seems to have done extremely well and has given Brash grounds to be most grateful to him. With Grigblay's help and guidance (the "defect in Mr. Jarrad" obviously originated with Grigblay) he

A Sanitary Consultant

has thoroughly mastered the facts, and applied himself to make a most effective display of them; and he accomplishes a difficult task with a tact which even touches on charm—a most unusual achievement for him. It has been apparent that Spinlove is decently educated, and here we particularly see his advantage in this respect. The position is an awkward one, for Brash has been led by Spinlove's own lack of gumption to doubt his architect's capacity in matters of sanitation and, as we know, has a high opinion of Quince and Jarrad which is rooted in snobbery and therefore almost indestructible. Brash has no technical knowledge of drains, yet it is for him to decide between the conflicting opinions of architect and expert, whether his drainage arrangements are perfectly sanitary, or not; and if Spinlove cannot re-establish himself with his client and persuade him to his views, it is difficult to say what may not happen.

GRIGBLAY TO SPINLOVE

Dear Sir,   21.6.26.

You directed us to let you know if we were asked to make any structural alterations at Honeywood. Her Ladyship lately asked us to fix a grate she has bought, in the boxroom, and this we have done with a bit of pipe carried well up into the flue serving the small servants' bedroom (No. 5) on the second floor, by her Ladyship's orders. We do not know whether this is what you mean by structural work, but think well to mention the matter. Her Ladyship says the fireplace in No. 5 will never be used.

Yours faithfully,

A fireplace in a boxroom is scarcely to be found in the most lavishly equipped house, and it is a mystery how anyone could imagine any kind of use for one there. Two fireplaces connected to one flue are likely to give complete satisfaction only while neither of them is in use.

BRASH TO SPINLOVE

My dear Mr. Spinlove,   24.6.26.

I have to confess that I read your communication anent sani-

95

tation with some impatience, but after carefully reperusing your arguments I am inclined to regard Messrs. Quince and Jarrad's proposals as unnecessarily redundant. Although I make no pretence of being a sanitary expert myself, I certainly agree with you that excessive costliness of refinements are inappropriate when not visually evident. There are certain aspects of the matter I desire to discuss with you, but so far as I can judge you have demonstrably answered Messrs. Quince and Jarrad's criticisms, and you will be glad to know that the odoriferous conditions are now rapidly ameliorating; in fact, they appear to have eventually dissipated, for though Lady Brash has been expectantly apprehensive no undesirable olfactory evidences have, I understand, been lately detected.

In view of the fact that the sanitary provisions are not—as Messrs. Quince and Jarrad led me to suppose—defective, I shall expect those gentlemen to allow me a substantial discount off the heavy fee of twenty guineas they have the effrontery to ask for their superfluous services.

Lady Brash informs me that we are to anticipate the pleasure of your company during the week-end. I shall then have an opportunity of discussing various matters with you.

With kindest regards,

Yours sincerely,

This is a triumph for Spinlove. It is to be hoped that Brash is grateful to him. He certainly seems to be; but his unusual good humour may be chiefly due to his having got this tormenting question of the drains settled, and Lady Brash appeased. Why these troublesome smells should so suddenly disappear is a mystery; but then it is also a mystery why they should ever have existed—if they ever did exist outside Lady Brash's imagination.

Messrs. Quince and Jarrad, by Spinlove's showing, here cut a sorry figure; but in point of fact they belong to an order of men to whom society has been in the past greatly indebted. It has to be remembered that what are now commonplaces of sanitary decency were, sixty years ago, only taking shape in the minds of scientific inquirers; and that forty years ago the general application of modern principles of sanitation was an innovation bolstered by public panic. In those days doctors, faced with the complicated symptoms of patients who had nothing wrong with them, had only to say, "Are you sure there is nothing wrong with the drains?" to escape with honour from the field. The nobility and gentry—who, we noticed, are patrons of Quince and Jarrad —were obsessed with drains, which thereupon became fashionable just as appendicitis did a few years later. Country gentlemen talked drains over the wine after dinner, compared drains on their way home from church, and rivalled one another in the renown of their sanitary adventures. There was scarcely a house in the country which was not, according to present ideas, poisonous; and none that was what we would consider sanitary. Throughout the country, people who would spend nothing on anything else were eager to celebrate themselves with drains, and this work was in great measure done—and thoroughly well done—by the forerunners of Quince and Jarrad.

The firm's fantastic test-exactions and extravagant ideas are also, for them, unavoidable; for if after they have approved the sanitation of a house the drains are surveyed by another expert in order to satisfy the covenant of a lease or conveyance, or because of a suspicious case of illness; and this rival expert, by more exacting refinements of test or stringency of standards, reports a defect or imperfection, Quince and Jarrad might be liable for damages, and in any case the reputation upon which their very existence depends would suffer. This danger is so imminent that firms of the standing of Quince and Jarrad will apologize for the stringency of their tests and the triviality of their objections even while making them. This is perfectly understandable. The expert tells the owner exactly what sort of drains he has got; that is the expert's responsibility: the owner decides whether to risk living in the house or not; that is the owner's responsibility, and the expert's comment, "I should not hesitate to live there myself," and so forth, does not shift those responsibilities. If Spinlove is ever called upon to re-drain a house he would benefit by knowing this—however, it is not likely he will be, for old houses have nearly all now been re-drained, and new ones do not need it.

A DISPUTE

Dear Sir,   24.6.26.

As arranged in your interview with Mr. Grigblay on the 10th,
we have been in correspondence with Messrs. Hoochkoft on the
subject of refund of their charge for picking facings. We enclose
copies of letters and wait your further instructions *re* same.

As Mr. Grigblay reminded you, the bricks were selected by
you and ordered by us to your instructions without our seeing
samples, and were inspected by you on delivery. You afterwards informed us you had arranged with Hoochkoft to send
their picked quality, and we paid them for picked as per their
quotation to you.

We must again press for certificate for £1,316 3s. 1d. Mr.
Grigblay understood from you that certificate would follow,
and we expected it would be received before now as it is a long
time overdue.

Yours faithfully,

(ENCLOSURE 1) GRIGBLAY TO HOOCHKOFT

Dear Sirs,   16.6.26.

The architect objects to your charge of 28s. extra for picked
facings over your original quotation of 147s. per thou. He
states you agreed to pick over free of charge, as the bright-reds
objected to were not according to approved sample. We will
thank you accordingly for refund of £92 overcharge paid you
by us in error.

Yours faithfully,

(ENCLOSURE 2) HOOCHKOFT TO GRIGBLAY

Dear Sirs,   21.6.26.

Mr. James Spinlove gave us order for picked as per our
special quote to him of 175s. per thou. as duly invoiced by us
which please note is correct and oblige.

Yours faithfully,

A Dispute

Spinlove handled this matter badly. Instead of getting samples and quotations through the builder, he dealt direct with Hoochkoft and told Grigblay to order a certain broken-colour brick at a certain price without sending him the approved samples or otherwise letting him know what bricks he was to expect. He also did not definitely rule out a bright-red under burnt sample to which he objected, and Hoochkoft accepted the order, perceiving that they could contend that their bright-reds had not been excluded. The bright-reds, to the amount of about 15 per cent of the whole, were delivered, and were used by Grigblay until Spinlove stopped him. Spinlove then had a wrangle with Hoochkoft, who asked 35s. a thousand bricks extra for picking out the bright-reds, which charge Spinlove refused to allow on the grounds that Hoochkoft had agreed to exclude the bright-reds. Hoochkoft then reduced their claim for extra price to 28s. and, by manipulating an ambiguity, led Spinlove to write them a letter that might be interpreted as agreeing to the extra price, although the opposite was intended by him.

SPINLOVE TO HOOCHKOFT

Dear Sirs,   26.6.26.

Mr. Grigblay has sent me copy of your letter to him stating that I agreed an extra price for picked facings.

I did nothing of the kind. As you are well aware, I refused to countenance the extra. I cannot pass your account for more than the rate of 147s. a thousand originally quoted, and accepted, and I have so informed Mr. Grigblay.

Yours faithfully,

By yielding to impatience and showing bad manners Spinlove throws away the advantage he has in knowing better than to do so. If it comes to a slanging match he will have no chance against Hoochkoft. He also makes a great mistake in asserting himself before he knows what position Hoochkoft takes; for if he is forced later on to withdraw, he will lose ground that he might otherwise hold. The vehemence of his letter, too, is a sign of weakness. If he were sure of his case he would not be so noisy in proclaiming it.

99

A Dispute

Dear Sirs,   26.6.26.

As I reminded Mr. Grigblay, I did *not* agree Hoochkoft's price for picking. I gave you no authority to pay the extra, and I cannot pass the account for more than the originally quoted price of 147s.

I enclose certificate for £1,000 further on account. I should explain that Sir Leslie Brash raised great objection to the total of the account, and I could not very well draw the certificate until I had had an opportunity of explaining matters to him. Even so I am afraid he may make difficulties about honouring the certificate, and as there are various matters in dispute I do not feel able to certify for more than £1,000 at this time.

Yours faithfully,

It will be noticed that Spinlove has, by sloppy organization and lack of precision in expressing himself, not only given Hoochkoft an opening for setting up an unfair claim, but has also misled Grigblay who could have no other reason for paying Hoochkoft's extra charge than the belief that Spinlove had told him to pay it.

If Spinlove is satisfied that Grigblay is entitled to a certificate, he is bound to draw it; and the reluctance of the owner to accept the account or honour the certificate is no justification for Spinlove's holding it back.

Dear Sir Leslie Brash,   26.6.26.

Grigblay has been pressing for a further certificate on account. I held this up until I should have had an opportunity of going into the account with him and with you, although the amount—£1,316 3s. 1d.—has, in fact, been due to him since *early last February*. As some items in the account are still in dispute I have certified for £1,000 only. This leaves £1,332 14s. 7d. as security in your hands for the making good of defects, and to cover any deductions which may hereafter be made from the account.

Yours sincerely,

A Dispute

Dear Sir,   28.6.26.

We were naturally surprised at the contents of your letter. We may say that we regret the confusion that has unfortunately arisen, but you have evidently overlooked that you ordered picked as per our special quotation to you of.175s. and that we duly acknowledged same. This you will see is quite correct if you will refer to previous correspondence at the time. Trusting the above explanation will be quite satisfactory to you,

We remain, dear Sir,

Yours faithfully,

Hoochkoft are plausible rogues. They seem likely to get the better of Spinlove, who will find it difficult to believe this letter to be part of a deeply laid scheme to deceive him.

Dear Sir,   28.6.26.

We have to acknowledge certificate for £1,000.

As you sent us copy of Messrs. Hoochkoft's letter quoting 175s. for picked facings, and afterwards wrote us you had arranged with Hoochkoft to supply picked, we naturally paid their invoices in accordance and do not see how we could be expected to do otherwise. We do not see what more we can do in the matter.

Yours faithfully,

Spinlove is getting the worst of this. He has put himself into the same kind of difficulty as that in which Brash finds himself over the Riddoppo paint; that is to say, he has made two parties who should be accountable to one another each accountable to him. Experienced architects are careful to avoid dividing responsibility, and are particularly wary of sandwiching themselves between conflicting parties as Spinlove has here sandwiched himself. This, in fact, is a first principle of good organization as understood by architects.

101

A Dispute

Dear Sirs,   30.6.26.

Our early correspondence makes it perfectly clear that I objected to the bright-red samples when I accepted your tender, and that you accepted the order on the understanding that they were not to be included. When I found the bright-reds *were* being included in deliveries I at once told you consignments containing them would not be allowed on the site. When you then proposed an extra charge for picking over, I refused to agree, but called upon you to supply to approved samples and pointed out that it was no concern of mine whether this was effected by picking or otherwise. I made myself perfectly clear and I will not allow the extra charge.

Yours faithfully,

Spinlove evidently feels the need of justifying himself, or he would not enter upon a florid recapitulation of facts which he twice states are "perfectly clear". If they were perfectly clear it would not enter his head to elaborate the point. Hoochkoft will be quick to notice this, and also to notice Spinlove's naïve admission in his last sentence, that if he had failed to make himself perfectly clear he would not contest the charge.

Dear Sirs,   30.6.26.

I did *not* say I had "arranged with Hoochkoft". My words were "Hoochkoft has now agreed to pick out the soft bright-red bricks," which, in view of previous letters on the subject, is a perfectly clear statement that no charge for picking was to be made, and I therefore cannot pass the account.

It is for you to inform Messrs. Hoochkoft of my decision and require them to refund. If I had said *I* had agreed for Hoochkoft to pick, it would have been a different matter, but I did not say so.

Yours faithfully,

It is a pity Spinlove did not shorten his letter by the length of

A Dispute

its last sentence. As usual, in his doubt of himself and anxiety to be plausible, he says too much. Although he omitted to state in so many words that the picking was being done free of charge, Grigblay was, nevertheless, at fault in assuming the contrary; but Spinlove surrenders all possibility of making good his claim by gratuitously admitting that its justice depends on niceties of syntax the exploration of which causes—in me at least—sensations of vertigo. He also reveals that he is now out of his depth in his own muddle. The only ground on which Grigblay can ask a refund from Hoochkoft is that he misunderstood the architect's instructions when he paid; and the only reply which he can expect from Hoochkoft is: "We are sorry for you."

HOOCHKOFT TO SPINLOVE

Dear Sir,   2.7.26.

We were naturally astonished to receive your letter. After our definite refusal to supply picked at the price we quoted for unpicked, and your acceptance of our special rate to you of 175s., we are surprised you should consider it worth while to press this unreasonable claim against us after we have reminded you of the facts which we supposed you had overlooked, and must now consider the matter at an end so far as we are concerned.

Yours faithfully,

SPINLOVE TO HOOCHKOFT

Dear Sir,   3.7.26.

It is perfectly clear from the correspondence that facings were to be picked free of cost. You had no right to make the extra charge and Mr. Grigblay had no authority to pay it. As I shall not pass the account, it will be for you and Mr. Grigblay to settle it between you. You will hear from him.

Yours faithfully,

As has been said, there is nothing for Hoochkoft and Grigblay to settle between them. Spinlove, as agent for Brash, has either to force Hoochkoft to refund on the ground that the charge

103

should not have been made; or compel Grigblay to stand the loss on the ground that he had no authority to pay it. Failing that, Brash will have to meet the charge, unless he can prove it to be set up by the culpable negligence of his architect; in which case Spinlove would be liable to Brash for the amount.

HOOCHKOFT TO SPINLOVE

Dear Sir,   5.7.26.

We certainly have no intention of settling with Mr. Grigblay. So far as we are concerned the matter was long ago settled, and the only reason we have corresponded with you was to explain your mistake. In view of your hostile attitude the matter is now closed.

Yours faithfully,

Hoochkoft evidently realize that they cannot persuade Spinlove they have not cheated him, nor hope to retain his esteemed favours.

GRIGBLAY TO SPINLOVE

Dear Sir,   5.7.26.

We can only repeat that we acted in accordance with your instructions in paying Messrs. Hoochkoft's charge for picked. As you have kept this matter in your hands throughout we are not in a position to approach Messrs. Hoochkoft further *re* same. We have already told them your views on the matter.

Yours faithfully,

This letter, and Hoochkoft's, seem to signalize the final discomfiture of Mr. James Spinlove, A.R.I.B.A.

BRASH FORGETS HIMSELF

BRASH TO SPINLOVE

My dear Mr. Spinlove,   5.7.26.

I duly received your communication anent certificate, which

document has been transmitted to me by Mr. Grigblay, and have been for some days contemplating inditing a communication to intimate my apprehensions that, in disbursing this very substantial sum, I shall appear to acknowledge the justice of claims which still await eventual elucidation when the detailed account is produced.

Your own attitude in this matter continues to impress me as being—if you will permit me to say so—extremely inexplicable. It must be obvious to you—although natural reserve makes me hesitate to say so—that I am a gentleman of not altogether negligible weight and importance in the business world, who has attained a certain degree of social eminence and monetary affluence; and I assume that young gentlemen embarking upon professional careers with ambitions for success in their elective sphere, are aware of the directions in which advantageous opportunities are to be anticipated and final prosperity likely to eventuate; to be precise, they comprehend —if you will excuse a vernacular colloquialism—upon which side their bread is buttered.

You have on several occasions taken the opportunity to remind me that the contract allows you a very wide and free discretion in deciding points in dispute, and I am naturally surprised to notice that you consistently favour Mr. Grigblay's claims against me and urge—with considerable stiffness, you must permit me to remark—*his* views of contentious matters in preference to supporting *my* interests. I feel it my duty to a much younger gentleman who has not, I apprehend, enjoyed the opportunity of such wide experience of affairs as has been my providential good fortune, to intimate the illogical aspect of the position in which you put yourself, and the difficulty in which you place me. I meet one of my wealthy and influential acquaintances—let us suppose—who naturally refers to my building operations and asks: "How do you find your young architect, does he safeguard your interests and does he protect you from the rapacity of builders and contractors; is he a pliable and conciliatory gentleman?" How am I to answer that question in such a way as to encourage my influential friend's confidence in your professional capacities, while you keep me in serious doubts of the matter? This you will, I apprehend, regard as a subject deserving your thoughtful consideration, as it is obviously apparent that it has escaped your attention.

Believe me, my dear Mr. Spinlove,

Yours very sincerely,

The greasy affability of Brash's protestation—which so far as I can recall is without precedent—is evidently employed to give a gloss of magnanimity to a dirty purpose. The thing, however, is not quite what one would have expected of old Brash, and it is only fair to put the best interpretation upon it that circumstances allow. If Spinlove made clear to Brash that under the terms of a building contract the architect is constituted final arbiter of technical matters, and that his discretion is also decisive in many that are not technical, then it is perfidy of a detestable kind for Brash to use the power his years and station give him to subvert the honesty of the younger man; but we do not know that Spinlove made this clear to Brash, and the spectacle we have had of Brash's many flounderings makes it quite possible that he did not know what the obligations of an architect are. Brash may, perhaps, have regarded Spinlove as his agent in the ordinary sense of one whose services are remunerated by a commission, and did not understand that his architect's obligations to the builder were as binding, in fact and in honour, as his obligations to his client. At the same time, it is clear that Brash was conscious of meanness in tempting Spinlove to favour his interests.

SPINLOVE TO BRASH

Dear Sir Leslie Brash, 9.7.26.

As I explained in my last letter, I held back the certificate until Grigblay should have proved that he was entitled to it. Your honouring the certificate does not prejudice your right to challenge Grigblay's charges; but, in any case, responsibility for drawing the certificate is mine. Under the terms of the contract Grigblay can claim payment of all sums certified, and as he has been kept waiting a long time I hope you will make it convenient to send him a cheque at once.

I have some difficulty in understanding the drift of your letter. I do not think you need assurances that I am watching your interests closely to the best of my ability. It is also my duty to see that you are not called upon to pay any charge which is not properly substantiated. You cannot mean to suggest that I should unfairly interpret the contract against the builder in your interests, and disallow his just claims, in order to win your favour; yet that is the impression your letter gives. Will you, therefore, be so good as to explain what it is you have in mind?

Yours sincerely,

Here, again, what are we to understand? Has Spinlove failed to see the purpose of Brash's letter, or has he perfectly under-stood it and framed such a reply that Brash can make a graceful retreat? As Spinlove does not respond to, but rather repulses Brash's pose of cordiality, the latter explanation is probable; but it may be that, without knowing exactly what Brash intended, Spinlove so dislikes the implication of the letter that he yields to a healthy impulse and asks Brash what the devil he does mean.

BRASH TO SPINLOVE

Dear Mr. Spinlove,   10.7.26.

It is scarcely necessary for me to intimate that nothing was farther from my intentions when I indited my last communica-tion than to suggest that you should "unfairly interpret the contract" or "disallow the builder's just claims". As you very naturally divine, I certainly have no such desires and would be the last person to consent to any such nefarious proposition. I am a gentleman who has always disbursed his just liabilities without demur and *up to the hilt* as it is sufficiently self-evident I shall be required to do on this occasion by Mr. Grigblay with the due approbation of my architect. At the same time I appre-hend that it is within the prerogatives of the employer to indi-cate an aspect of the situation which it is clearly advantageous for his architect to comprehend. A judicial deportment is obviously an appropriate desideratum for a young gentleman engaging in the sphere of professional activities.

It will, I anticipate, signalize to you that I am pliably amen-able to appeals of logical reason when I intimate that I have

107

to-day transmitted cheque for one thousand pounds to Mr. Grigblay. I also enclose cheque for £60 in satisfaction of your own fees in respect of that disbursement.

Yours sincerely,

Brash appears to be sulky, and even a little embittered, at being taken up by Spinlove. His letter is a clever one: although it disclaims the sinister implications of its predecessor it, in fact, stresses them.

BRICK DISPUTE RENEWED

(PERSONAL) GRIGBLAY TO SPINLOVE

Sir,   10.7.26.

I have been looking into this matter of Hoochkoft's facings. You will understand it is no business of mine what understanding you came to with them, but as you cannot agree the matter I venture to drop you a hint that you have no occasion to argue it as those reds you objected to were under-burnt bricks that the fire hadn't properly reached and, as you know, some that got built in began to go almost at once. Hoochkoft cannot hold out that those soft reds were fit for what they sold them for, which is high-class facings—and which was their warranty or I am much mistaken. I enclose just a little statement that perhaps you may be interested to see and to have a word with Messrs. Hoochkoft about; but as I say it is no business of mine. It is lucky for them you had the softs thrown out or where would they be now!

Apologizing for troubling you but thought you might like the information.

Yours truly,

Brick Dispute Renewed

(ENCLOSURE) GRIGBLAY TO SPINLOVE

SIR LESLIE BRASH
DR. TO JOHN GRIGBLAY, BUILDER

EXTRAS ON FACINGS

SUPPLIED BY MESSRS. HOOCHKOFT AND CO., LTD.

	£	s.	d.
Paid Messrs. Hoochkoft for picking out defective under-burnt bricks	92	0	0
Paid Messrs. Hoochkoft for 1,050 defective bricks delivered and not used, at 147s. ..	7	14	4
Picking over 7,000 bricks for throw-out at 28s.	9	16	0
No. 87 cutting out defective under-burnt bricks built into wall-face and making good, at 2s.	8	14	0
	£118	4	4

It is a pity that this view of the matter did not occur to Spinlove before, but it has to be remembered that his objection to the under-burnt bricks was that he did not like the colour of them. Defects only appeared in a small number which were, by oversight or misunderstanding, built into the walls; and as Spinlove held Grigblay responsible for this, and required him to cut out and replace, Hoochkoft's liability did not obtrude itself.

SPINLOVE TO GRIGBLAY

Dear Mr. Grigblay,   9.7.26.

Thank you for your letter and enclosure. I will write to Hoochkoft, but at the same time I cannot agree that you had instructions from me to pay their extra charge, and I do not depart from my decision that you are responsible for cutting out and making good defective facings, for they were built in contrary to my orders.

Yours truly,

We may suppose that Spinlove does not want to relinquish his claim against Grigblay, but this is not a happy occasion upon

109

Brick Dispute Renewed

which to insist on it. Bloggs, the foreman, did his best to interpret Spinlove's instructions in throwing out the red bricks, and it was his misfortune, and not his fault, that some of those he built in began to decay.

SPINLOVE TO HOOCHKOFT

Dear Sirs,   12.7.26.

I have just received from the builder the enclosed account of his claim against my client in respect of defective facing bricks supplied by you, and shall be glad to receive your cheque drawn in favour of Sir Leslie Brash for the sum of £118 4s. 4d. forthwith, as the matter is of long standing and the account is now being closed.

Yours faithfully,

Appearances are that Spinlove took an opportunity to consult some longer head than his own on the drafting of this letter—perhaps that of Mr. Tinge, the quantity surveyor. The words he commonly wastes are conspicuously absent, and some good influence has also restrained him from his characteristic digressions in self-justification.

HOOCHKOFT TO SPINLOVE

Dear Sir,   13.7.26.

We do not understand why Mr. Grigblay's account with Sir Leslie Brash has been sent to us, and return it herewith as we can only suppose your suggestion of a cheque in settlement is intended as a joke. The matter is ended so far as we are concerned.

Yours faithfully,

SPINLOVE TO HOOCHKOFT

Dear Sirs,   16.7.26.

I have to point out that the matter of the defective facing bricks supplied by you is by no means ended, and is very far from being a joke so far as you are concerned.

The facts are that some of the soft, bright-red under-burnt

110

facings included by you in the early consignments, and built into the walls, almost immediately began to decay and, to the number of eighty-seven, had to be cut out and replaced.

As you neglected to pick out the under-burnt bricks from early consignments totalling 7,000, this work had to be done on the site by the builder.

The under-burnt throw-outs were unusable and had to be replaced by sound bricks to the number of 1,050.

The charge you made for picking is not allowable as the bright-red under-burnt bricks were unsuitable for facings.

Mr. Grigblay's charge is the sum he paid you for picking, together with the cost of picking over in your default. The other charges are based on time and materials, and the amount paid you for defective bricks that could not be used.

The bricks offered by you, ordered by me and invoiced, are "facings"; you were under warranty to supply facings, and Sir Leslie Brash claims from you £118 to reimburse him for losses directly due to your breach of warranty. I return the account and have to repeat my request for cheque in settlement forthwith.

Yours faithfully,

It is difficult to believe that Spinlove settled the draft of this letter. The probability is that some architect friend of wide experience, or a lawyer, gave him guidance. It is to his credit that he realized he was on delicate ground; for it is most difficult in positions such as this to be lucid, and to keep to the essential facts, and to avoid prejudicing the position, or actually making it untenable, by accidental admissions or inconsistencies.

SPINLOVE TO BRASH

Dear Sir Leslie Brash,   16.7.26.

Thank you for cheque. I enclose formal receipt. I am glad you have sent Mr. Grigblay a cheque as he had grounds for feeling aggrieved at the delay.

I am obliged for your reply to my letter, but I still do not completely understand what it is that you expect of me. You seem to express dissatisfaction with my conduct of the business of settling Grigblay's account. I can only assure you that I will spare no pains to see that no improper charge is included.

Yours sincerely,

Mr. Spinlove,   17.7.26.

We now understand your new move to make us refund in order to cover your own liability to your client by now saying bright-reds were defective; but unfortunately you *told us nothing of this at the time,* but waited till your other trick failed, knowing that nothing was wrong with the bricks; and if you did have a few cut out they were sound ones and only done to bolster up a false claim against us by holding out they were defective when they were not; but very likely *none were cut out at all,* and this is just a dirty job to put responsibility on to us and get a refund because your other trick of saying you never ordered picked has gone wrong.

We return you Grigblay's account and suggest try again as this has not come off and something better is needed to humbug us.

Your most obliged humble servants,

Such contemptible devices as Hoochkoft, by return of post, here ascribes to Spinlove, could scarcely enter their heads if they did not themselves practise them. Its abusive diction and general likeness to the barking of a dog is not uncommon in some fields of business correspondence. Hoochkoft for the first time honours Spinlove by meeting him as man to man, and Spinlove should take heart.

Gentlemen,   19.7.26.

I do not know whether you intend your letter as a final disclaimer, but as there is the testimony of the builder, foreman, bricklayers and others to support me, perhaps you will prefer to reconsider your position before I advise Sir Leslie Brash to take action to enforce his claim; in which case I do not think

112

such letters as that you last sent me will help you. I enclose the account and await your reply.

> I am, Gentlemen,
> Your humble servant,

This diplomatic answer was certainly not drafted by Spinlove. It is clear he had guidance.

HOOCHKOFT REMEMBERS HIMSELF

HOOCHKOFT TO SPINLOVE

Dear Sir,   22.7.26.

Your favour of the 19th inst. with enclosure and previous correspondence has been laid before our chairman and managing director, Mr. Eli Hoochkoft, who proposes to wait on you at any time convenient to your good self for the purpose of amicably settling the matter to your satisfaction in a personal interview.

We may say that we were naturally taken aback at the contents of your previous letters, as the matters referred to were quite new to us and the official who dealt with the correspondence was under a misapprehension. Mr. Hoochkoft tenders you his apologies for same, although our suggested explanations were not intended in any way as a criticism of your good self.

> We are, dear Sir,
> Yours faithfully,

Delicacy of touch is not a strong point with Hoochkoft; in fact, one of the few disadvantages of having a hide like a rhinoceros is that you assume everyone to be sheathed with an insensibility equal to your own. Hoochkoft are quite unaware that their ingratiating affability presents the picture of deceit spurred by funk. The trick by which, after one bluff has failed, they approach the subject de novo *from a new angle, by a pretence of referring it to higher authority, is a very old one.*

Hoochkoft Remembers Himself

Gentlemen,   28.7.26.

I confirm arrangement by telephone that Mr. Hoochkoft will call to see me here at noon on Wednesday.

I am, yours faithfully,

Dear Mr. Spinlove,   5.8.26.

As promised I have carefully considered the position of my firm in the light of our friendly talk and now respond to your kind offer to entertain a payment in settlement by enclosing Treasury notes to the value of £25 in the belief that this will meet your favourable ideas. Will you kindly initial for receipt of this letter to the bearer who has been instructed to deliver it into your hands?

I trust that in the future I may be honoured by your esteemed favours, when I will make it a personal pleasure to see you receive complete satisfaction in any orders you may entrust to us and that no irregularity as that complained of occurs.

Believe me, dear Mr. Spinlove,

Yours truly,

Eli is trying to bribe Spinlove; a bribe being the giving to, and acceptance by, an agent of any gift or consideration, as an inducement to the agent to do, or forbear from doing, any act in relation to his principal's affairs. Although it is a thing the slightest hint of which all right-minded men shrink from as intolerable to their self-respect, and a violation of the rudiments of personal honour; yet bribery, in one form and another, is a common usage for greasing the wheels of business, and all architects sooner or later become aware of its detestable implications. Many men whose fields of activity involve them in the practice, excuse it by the cynical sophistry that all human actions are swayed by a coveted reward, and that in essence there is no difference between actions framed in ambition for social and political advancement or the favour of powerful men, and those where the goal is more directly money—just as it has been argued that all motives are at bottom

114

selfish, or that there is no such thing as a bald man because it is impossible to say at what point, when single hairs are plucked from the head, it becomes bald.

We lately saw Brash holding out inducements to Spinlove to betray his trust which, though morally bribery, would scarcely have made him guilty at law; but this attempt by Hoochkoft is a particularly flagrant example of the crime—for crime it is. To take or give a bribe is an offence punishable by a fine not exceeding £500, with or without imprisonment not exceeding two years. If Eli were brought before me, I should award him a fine of one hundred pounds with nine months in the second division for undisturbed meditations on bricks. He is, however, unlikely to be brought before anyone; for such nefarious understandings as he here seeks to establish are reached by each party advancing towards the proposal by hints and innuendoes to which either can readily give an innocent meaning if his overture wins no response; and it is thus usual for the illicit agreement to be reached tacitly and by implication, without anything being said that would entitle either party to affirm that a bribe had been offered or asked by the other.

Thus we find Hoochkoft sending money to Brash's agent in fulfilment of an apparently honest agreement for settlement of Brash's claim; he could—although it is a question whether any jury would agree—hold out that he had no intention of bribing. He also, it will be noticed, makes it safe for Spinlove to pocket the money and decide, for any reason he chooses to give, that Brash's claim is untenable. There is the evidence of no third person; and there is no record, such as a cheque or bank notes would set up, that the money has changed hands. There is nothing but Hoochkoft's oath that he sent Spinlove the money against Spinlove's that he never received it, and vice versa, to establish the fact; and as both would be equally guilty and the arrangement meets the desires of each, there would be no likely need for either of them to thus add perjury to their conspiracy to plunder Brash.

Hoochkoft Remembers Himself

Sir,   7.8.26.

I am not prepared to recommend Sir Leslie Brash to accept any such disproportionate sum as the £25 you sent me in settlement of his claim against you.

As your offer is in no way adequate to your professions at our interview, I have to say that the sum I am prepared to recommend my client to accept in full settlement is the amount paid to you in error by Mr. Grigblay for picking out defective bricks, namely £92; and I shall be glad to receive, *not cash*, but your *cheque* for this amount *drawn in favour of Mr. Grigblay*, on receipt of which I will return your Treasury notes value £25. In the event of your not accepting this offer the matter will go out of my hands.

> I am, Sir,
> Yours faithfully,

The reason Spinlove did not send back Eli's Treasury notes by the messenger who brought them is, probably, that he could not at the moment make up his mind how to handle the matter. It is just as well he did not so return them, for it would have been a gesture of wiping out the interchange, and left things as though Hoochkoft had never offered the affront. As it is, Hoochkoft is likely to have an uneasy feeling as to what may have been happening in the enemy camp in the three days' interval between his sending the notes and Spinlove's letter, and this uneasiness will be increased by Spinlove's action in holding the notes for return, instead of putting them to Hoochkoft's credit in his account with Brash. Spinlove clearly has someone guiding him in this ticklish business; and perhaps the awkwardness of dealing with the cash, and a wish to enforce decorum on Hoochkoft and hold the whip hand over him, decided his action.

It still remains unexplained why such a practised rogue as Hoochkoft should have concluded that Spinlove was open to bribery. It is clear that he was misled by Spinlove at their interview; and it is also clear that Spinlove had no intention of so misleading him. We may suppose, therefore, that it never entered Spinlove's head that Hoochkoft's aim was to find out whether he was corruptible and, if so, his price; and thus Spinlove neither encouraged Hoochkoft to show his hand nor, in his complete unconsciousness, warned him by word or look that his task was hopeless. It is easy, on this supposition, to understand that Hoochkoft's offer of a money payment to Spinlove as "a sum in friendly settlement"—or however else he disguised his true meaning—was accepted in all good faith by Spinlove as a proposal for settlement to Brash, while Hoochkoft supposed Spinlove was veiling his acceptance in the same way that he himself was veiling the proposal. The extreme innocence of Spinlove, in fact, gave Hoochkoft, who is clearly a lumbering, obtuse fellow, the idea of excessive subtlety and wariness.

It is to be noted that no sum was named at the interview. The position was threshed out, and Hoochkoft went off to consider the sum he would offer in settlement.

HOOCHKOFT TO SPINLOVE

Dear Sir,   10.8.26.

With reference to Mr. Hoochkoft's interview with you on 4th August, we now enclose cheque drawn in favour of Mr. Grigblay for the sum of £92 as refund of disputed charge for picked facings, which you state was paid in error. The acceptance of this sum to be understood to be in full settlement of Sir Leslie Brash's claim against us as per enclosed account and which is in dispute.

Yours faithfully,

And so Spinlove has won! He has made a fight in which his native tenacity and his vanity have probably served him better than his devotion to his client's interests.

There is no doubt that Hoochkoft's false step in attempting to bribe Spinlove has precipitated his decision to pay up and so avoid any chance of litigation and exposure. It is to be noticed that Hoochkoft ignores Spinlove's letter and sends the cheque as though in fulfilment of an understanding come to at Hoochkoft's interview with Spinlove. His object in this is to cover his tracks, so far as may be, and avoid any official record of the illicit project.

117

A FALSE STEP

SPINLOVE TO BRASH

Dear Sir Leslie Brash,   11.8.26.

I think you will like to know that after considerable trouble
I have at last succeeded in securing refund of ninety-two pounds
which was overpaid to the manufacturer of the facing bricks
by mistake.

With kind regards,
Yours sincerely,

*Spinlove's guardian angel seems to be resting after the heavy
task of seeing him safely through his struggle with Hoochkoft;
for though we have had many examples of Spinlove's impetuous
folly, he has never surpassed the adroit idiocy of this letter.*

*It is obviously desirable to avoid pushing poor old Brash's dis-
located nose down into the extras account, yet Spinlove here goes
out of his way to do so. Not only is any letter at all quite unnecessary, but Spinlove entirely discredits himself by vaunting his
achievement. His childish impulse was evidently to court Brash's
esteem; but to do this it was important for him to put that strange
face on his own perfections which Shakespeare tells us is the
witness of excellency. His noisy acclaim of his own scanty merit,
which he represents in the worst possible light, can only make his
client sick with distrust. If Spinlove had merely allowed the fact
to emerge without any exhibition of complacency, his client would
have been favourably impressed with his capacity and vigilance;
but what is Brash to think of an agent who writes—with kind
regards—applauding himself for making a merchant give back
money that ought never to have been paid; and who breaks the
news with "I think you will like to know . . ." as though such
glad tidings were beyond all imagining?*

*The explanation no doubt is that Spinlove, in the exhilarating
moment of victory, is moved to demolish the adverse criticism of
Brash's last letters; and writes, as he so often does, without
pausing to consider what effect he will produce.*

118

A False Step

Dear Mr. Spinlove,   13.8.26.

I was, of course, gratified to receive the intimation communicated by your missive, but you must permit me to convey the comment that the considerable difficulty you experienced in exacting repayment of an erroneous disbursement does not favourably impress me with the expeditious conclusion of negotiations for settlement. May the interrogation be permitted 1, *why* the excess amount was paid to these grasping manufacturers; 2, *how many more* of these irregular disbursements have been allowed; and 3, when—may I ask again— shall I eventually receive the detailed Statement of Account so often promised? This account, it is now obviously clear, will have to be carefully audited by qualified accountants.

My lengthy negotiations with the Riddoppo Company anent the failure of the paint are now approaching termination, and I shall shortly have further communications to make.

Yours sincerely,

Brash's auditing accountants will not be able to deal with Grigblay's statement of account, and are likely to raise many more questions than they will understand the answers to, so that the resulting turmoil will bring Brash more suffering than consolation. The proposal itself is, however, futile: Grigblay would refuse to allow interferences, and Spinlove and Tinge (the quantity surveyor) would support Grigblay; for under the contract Brash has agreed that the architect shall decide all technical matters and questions of fact, and that the quantity surveyor shall measure and value all variations, so that Brash's auditors would have no standing.

Dear Sir Leslie Brash,   14.8.26.

In reply to your questions:

(1) The manufacturer supplied bricks some of which I condemned as not up to sample. He then supplied a better quality for which he charged the builder a higher, unauthorized, price.

119

In order to secure a refund I had to make good my contention that he was not entitled to a higher rate than that first quoted.

(2) None.

(3) Directly I receive it.

Yours sincerely,

Spinlove's hackles were erect when he wrote this.

DRY ROT APPEARS

MISS PHYLLIS BRASH TO SPINLOVE

Dear Jazz, 14.8.26.

Mum is away so what about a beano on Saturday sans all parental tennis crocks; just Snooty, Biff, Woggles, Boojum, you and me—a whole afternoon of fast and furious? Boojum wants Snooty for keeps, but don't let on as it's most *frightfully serious*. Boo served *hat-fulls* of doubles last Thursday and poor Snooty dunno where she are. Buzz in early and bring tuxedos and pys as the caboodle flits to Bingham's at nine. Only the usual old rampage but Porky B with two snotties out of his old bum-boat are there on a week-end binge and we shant go home till the Hullaballoo-bala-balay. I'm *perfectly* potty but you know what I mean.

Now don't scream, but:

> There's suthin' funny amiss, Miss;
> Along by the pantery sink.

Thus our Judith cussically obsairve (see Art. Ward) jerking poetry in your honour. Seriously, the suthin' funny is decidedly dud. Dad is having the paintwork scrubbed to keep it from flaking off, and to-day the fairy hand of Judith burst the wood thingy that runs along under the sink. It is evident suthin' is amiss, for the wood is bulged, and cracked and woolly, and seems to be crumbling and it is very much rather all along under the windows in the kitchen. No one dare tell Dad except Mum,

120

and it is a shrieking necess to have suthin' done before they come back in three weeks' time. Dad joins her on rest cure next week.

Meet the posh cubby hole and patent pocket nest Mum has made of the boxroom! You really never! It's *too* dilly! Twice as good as a caravan! Copied from the "converted attic" at the Ideal Homes Exy but *ever so much nicer* as the window is simply microscopic and it is all dim and penurious, and the roof slopes so that you can only stand up near the middle but, of course, when its a case of sits there is tons of room. The windey stairs are absolutely thrilling and there is the most dinky furniture you ever, and Mum and I simple *cuddle ourselves* there. Mum bought an old dud grate she saw lying in a cottage garden for *one and ninepence*, which was a bargain as the man asked two shillings at first; and Grig's people made a fireplace with it. Mum is trying to find some old oak beams so that it will all be posher; and old panelling for the sloping part where the white comes off. We will have tea up there on Saturday.

Yours,
PUD.

Mum is going to be psychoed.

This letter has probably been preserved to us because of its intimation of dry rot; for that fell disease, which is a more fierce enemy of new houses than of old ones, is here clearly indicated.

We now learn why Lady Brash asked Grigblay to arrange a fireplace in the boxroom.

SPINLOVE TO GRIGBLAY

Dear Sir,   17.8.26.

I was at Honeywood during the week-end and it was pointed out to me that the skirting under the pantry sink is crumbling away like touch-wood. I imagined that water from the sink had rotted it, but there is no sign of wet, and the skirting along the outer wall of the kitchen is going in the same way. It is clear that the wood was not properly seasoned and it will be necessary to renew these skirtings at once.

Yours faithfully,

Dry Rot Appears

It seems that Spinlove has never seen, or smelt, dry rot; but one would think that he might have guessed what the extraordinary condition was due to. To attempt to cure the trouble by fixing new skirtings would be like trying to extinguish a fire by throwing fuel on it. The only remedy is to remove the whole of the rotted wood, to thoroughly sterilize surroundings, and to discover and end the cause of the outbreak.

GRIGBLAY TO SPINLOVE

Dear Sir,   20.8.26.

We gathered from your letter that dry rot is the trouble, and yesterday sent over our shop foreman, Hassoks, who says no great harm done but it has got into the back of the china cupboard. He pulled the vertical scotia off and there it was five feet up, but does not seem to have taken any hold. He says it has started on the edge of wood-block flooring but not gone far he thinks. The kitchen is not so bad, but there is a soft place in the skirting at foot of stairs and it sounds dead all along, Hassoks says. so it has got a hold there too. We do not know cause as Hassoks reports walls seem dry as a bone. Perhaps you would like to meet Mr. Grigblay at the house and decide what best to be done, and if you will appoint a day we will send over to take out the cupboard and open up for your inspection.

Yours faithfully,

This is a bad business; but how bad, remains to be seen.

Dry rot is a disease of timber caused by various species of fungi which feed on wood, penetrate it, and destroy it. Infection is by contact with diseased wood, or by spores latent in it, borne on the air or conveyed by dirt. If conditions favour its growth, dry rot may be regarded as inevitable; if they are unfavourable there is no danger. Favourable conditions are the coincidence of damp with warmth and lack of ventilation; and it is particularly the responsibility of architects and builders, as the law decrees, to so design and build that those conditions shall not anywhere arise. As warmth is always present in a building, and it is impossible to ventilate every cranny of it, damp is regarded as the prime cause of dry rot. The need for entire prevention of damp is, therefore, always in the mind of the architect, the builder, the clerk of works and the foreman in charge. Ventilation, by carrying away evaporation, is a safeguard against "damp".

The beauty of dry rot—in the opinion of its admirers—is that when it once gets going it sends out, with devastating rapidity, thread-like tendrils which carry moisture, yards from the source, over the surface of walls and even though them, and which multiply to form mats of dense, cobwebby filament that collect moisture from the air and so set up and maintain new centres of growth from which new foraging tendrils spread. Thus the good work continues, so that one solitary brick carelessly thrown into the broken rubbish under the concrete foundation of a wood-block floor, and disposed in such a way as to conduct damp from the ground to the concrete, may set up in the wood blocks dry rot which in a few weeks will have travelled to the space behind skirtings, invaded the back of the door linings, passed into the staircase and involved the first floor before its presence is anywhere noticed.

The circumstances that give rise to dry rot are innumerable, and are a continued source of interest and pleasure to irresponsible observers; but the conditions of damp combined with warmth and lack of ventilation, are always present. A few days after a radiator is installed below a sliding sash window in an unfinished house, dry rot has started inside one of the jamb casings and involved the whole of it; eighteen months after a roof is finished by pointing the tiles without ventilating the roof-space, sagging outlines lead to the discovery that the whole of the inside surface is a mass of cobwebby fungus, and that the timbers are perished to the point of collapse; and—as made famous in the Law Courts half a century ago—the floors and joinery of a hospital have to be renewed at a cost of several thousand pounds because the wooden pegs, driven into the ground to fix the screeding-level of concrete floor-foundations, were not taken out. What exactly has happened at Honeywood we do not know; but some source of continuous dampness in contact with the skirting, or with other woodwork near to it, is indicated.

Dry Rot Appears

21.8.26.

I am coming down on Thursday to meet Grig about the pantry do. Am arranging to get all done before the two P's return, but there will be carpenters to take out the china cupboard so will you get the crockery cleared?

Apparently Spinlove has some sensitiveness about typing his superscription and subscription to this lady. It is, of course, inadvisable to delay the work, for the harm is growing, and it will occasion less upset—both physical and moral—if all is completed before "the two P's" return.

Spinlove's light-hearted assumption that the trouble can be readily cured, while he does not know the cause of it, is lamentable. It is clear that not only has he had no experience of dry rot, but that he has no knowledge of it at second hand, or he would view this manifestation of it with consternation. The rot in the pantry and kitchen may be only first evidences of an outbreak involving the whole of the ground-floor skirtings, which may itself be but the first visible flicker of flames that are raging out of sight in the floors, and which have already secretly invaded the cavities at the back of panelling and of door and window linings and of fireplace surrounds. Even this does not measure the full dimensions of the possible catastrophe, for not only has the damaged work to be restored and all parts near it to be doctored to destroy the infecting spores of the fungus, but the cause of the outbreak must be fully proved and, when proved, then entirely eradicated; and as this cause may be fundamental in the design of the structure or inherent in the materials employed, the little pieces of decayed skirting, as every experienced architect knows, may, as likely as not, signal a great calamity.

Dear Mr. Wychete,

24.8.26.

You have been so extremely kind in the past in advising me, that I hope you will not mind my troubling you, but I have a case of dry rot which I do not know how to deal with. I enclose linen prints of $\frac{1}{8}$ in. scale plan, and $\frac{1}{2}$ in. section of the outer wall.

The house has been occupied now for six months, and the deal skirting along the outside north wall of the kitchen, pantry and hall up to the stairs, is rotted, and the under edge of the Columbian pine wood-block flooring has begun to go in places. The larders, scullery and cloaks along the same front are tiled and have tiled skirtings. I should mention we pulled up some of the wood blocks, but there was no sign of rot except just at the outer edges, and no evidence of rot anywhere else; and though the growth had run up behind the china cupboard the wood was sound.

The walls behind the skirting were "bone dry", the builder said; but he was doubtful of the concrete under the block floor. We cut this away where it lies against the wall, and the builder then said he understood the cause.

If you look at the half-inch detail you will see that the damp-course lies just below the concrete foundation of the floor; but the floor was lowered $1\frac{1}{2}$ inches after the dampcourse was built, and the bottom of the concrete comes an inch *below* the damp-course. The brickwork below the dampcourse is full of water, and the builder says that damp is drawn into the concrete where its lower edge lies against the wet bricks, and that this has started the dry rot. Can this be possible? He also says that moisture creeps up between the bricks and the concrete, and gets into the brickwork above the dampcourse, but I could not see any evidence of this. Do you think he is right? I could see no sign of damp myself. Before we cut away the concrete the builder thought the trouble might be due to the rain, which beats through the outer $4\frac{1}{2}$ ins. of the hollow wall, collecting on the dampcourse and getting into the inner wall, but he forgot that the hollow goes down *below* the dampcourse.

The main question is—If the builder is right, what is to be done? He says he cannot advise me; that he built as I directed and cannot accept responsibility. I pointed out that *he* suggested lowering the floor so that the threshold of front entrance would line up with the brick joint and make a neat finish; but he says that the decision was mine and that he followed my directions in lowering the floor.

Dry Rot Appears

The north wall of the billiard-room is panelled in oak and the floor is of oak boards nailed to fillets let into concrete. The panelling is ventilated behind by openings in the skirting and in the top of the capping. There is no sign of dry rot here, and the builder says he thinks there is no danger.

I should be so very much obliged if you will tell me what you think I had better do, if it is not troubling you.

Yours sincerely,

The sketch below illustrates the positions of the floor and dampcourse described.

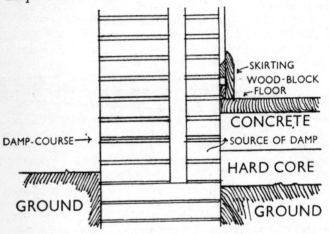

The eminent Wychete must be a good friend, indeed, to lay himself open to the fatigue of solving posers of this kind; and Spinlove must have great confidence in his opinion or he would consult a friend closer at hand instead of writing to Manchester, where, as his address indicates, Wychete operates. We know from earlier letters that the site of Honeywood slopes towards the south, and that it is only the floors on the north side that are laid directly on concrete. The others are carried on joists supported on sleeper walls.

WYCHETE ADVISES

My dear Spinlove,   26.8.26.

This is an awkward business, and if you cannot deal with it
yourself you ought to get the advice of someone on the spot;
but, of course, *you* alone are responsible to your client, and no
one but yourself can decide what course to take. The question
between you and the builder is a difficult one. If I were you
I should not press your point of view to the extent of making
him antagonistic. He may be willing to do what is necessary
without any charge, but, quite naturally, he will take no action
that will involve him in responsibility. This is the reason he
refuses to advise you, and he will not, you will find, handle
the matter as a "defect" under the terms of the contract. If he
did this, he would admit liability for the whole extent of the
damage. This may, of course, become extensive.

I do not, however, think that it will extend. In my opinion
the builder's view of the cause of the outbreak is likely to be
right, but as the growth appears not to be vigorous, I think that
the amount of damp is probably very small, and that the use
of infected wood may have led to trouble which otherwise
might not have occurred.

To make the house perfectly safe it would be necessary
to cut away the concrete floor-foundation against internal
walls, as well as external, wherever there are "solid" wood
floors—that is, over nearly half the area of the house—and
make good clear of the dampcourse; but I think the case will
be met if you replace all affected skirtings and blocks on top of
an impervious bituminous coating made continuous with the
mastic in which the wood blocks are laid, and covering walls
behind skirtings. Bellflower and Snooter Ltd. manufacture
bituminous coatings for various purposes and would advise
what best to use. You should also treat the back parts of the
china cupboard, and all contaminated work, as well as the back
of the new, with a solution of sulphate of iron. There is nothing

better for killing dry rot and it does not smell as creosote does.

If this fails, you will have to cut away the concrete. If it succeeds, you can treat any other similar outbreaks in the same way, but let us hope that there will be none. I have no doubt the ventilation of the panelling in the billiard-room will prevent any trouble there.

Ever, my dear Spinlove,
Yours sincerely,

Wychete's tactful reminder that Spinlove is responsible to his client, and that whatever action he takes must be his own decision, is much to the point. Wychete's advice—whatever it is worth— cannot lead Spinlove astray; for the reparation, if experimental, is simple; and should it be without effect, little time and money will have been wasted. There is, however, the risk that while Spinlove is dealing tentatively with this small outbreak, far-reaching growths, which immediate drastic action would prevent, may be establishing themselves secretly in other parts of the house. The decision whether to take this risk or not and, if not, what measures to adopt, devolves on Spinlove; and no one can relieve him from the need to rely on his own discretion, for that discretion is linked to a responsibility which belongs to no one but himself. It is the exercise of discretion hampered by considerations of cost, of risk, of exact justice, of conflicting interests, of uncertainty as to facts, of misunderstandings and of diverse individualities and dishonest or incapable agents, which is the chief care and preoccupation of architectural practice. To design a building, to draw and specify every part of it, and to direct its construction and see it completed with no other anxieties and dilemmas than belong to the exercise of those duties, is unknown.

SPINLOVE TO WYCHETE

My dear Mr. Wychete,   27.8.26.

Thank you extremely for your most kind letter. I am enormously obliged for your advice. I will act on it at once. Surely, as the dry rot is due to the builder's use of infected wood, the outbreak is *his* fault and he can be held responsible for making good?

> With kind regards,
> Ever yours sincerely,

Spinlove's impetuosity here again prevails to his discredit. He plainly tells Wychete that he has not troubled to read his letter.

WYCHETE TO SPINLOVE

Dear Spinlove,   28.8.26.

   I give no advice but merely make suggestions. There is no means of knowing that the wood was infected; and the "cause" of the outbreak is, in any case, *damp*.

> Yours sincerely,

Exactly! Wychete was particular in warning Spinlove that he must use his own judgment: by replying "I am taking your advice at once", Spinlove announces that he is relying on Wychete's. Wychete, naturally, will allow no such interpretation of his letter. Wychete was also particular in exculpating the builder; and if Spinlove had reflected, he would not have requited his benefactor by plaguing him to say once again what he has already been at pains to make clear.

SPINLOVE TO GRIGBLAY

Dear Sirs,   27.8.26.

   I enclose specification of work in making good where dry rot has appeared. If you see any objections to the proposals will you let me know? The work should be completed if possible before the end of next week when Sir Leslie and Lady Brash, who are away, return.

> Yours faithfully,

GRIGBLAY TO SPINLOVE

Dear Sir,   28.8.26.

   We have to acknowledge your instructions for making good

where dry rot has appeared, and will do our best to complete same before the end of next week, as requested.

Yours faithfully,

Grigblay has no intention of committing himself in any way, it will be noticed. Spinlove will realize how much support and guidance he has had in the past, now that he can get neither.

BLOGGS ON EXTRAS

GRIGBLAY TO SPINLOVE

Dear Sir,   30.8.26.

As promised you by Mr. Grigblay, we have referred to our foreman Bloggs for explanations of certain extras under "Various minor works" and other matters queried by you, and enclose sheets with his answers to same which we hope will give the information you want.

Yours faithfully,

(ENCLOSURE) GRIGBLAY TO MR. F. BLOGGS
C/O JOHN GRIGBLAY, BUILDER, BY PORTENWALSH
MEAD, BAGGERFOSS, HUNTS

Dear Fred,   7.8.26.

The architect queries extras as attached sheets. The governor wants your answers in blank spaces. No doubt you have your diary along. Enclosed is copy of Statement lettered so you can pick up easy. The jim crow was put on passenger last night. The governor says if you can't manage take along to Potters, Nottington, who will straighten while lorry waits. To be charged up against Ry.

Yours,

T. P.

Hear with OK. F. Bloggs, Aug. 28th.

Bloggs on Extras

This letter must have been sent to Spinlove pinned to the other papers, by an oversight. It shows Grigblay's business to be conducted in the old-fashioned style that still lingers, with the best traditions of the building crafts, in the provinces, where son follows father to the bench or the scaffold, and the master calls his men by their Christian names, knows the domestic circumstances of each, and distributes joints and poultry among them at Christmas. There may be somewhere in this world happier men than these, associated in more delightful work, but it is a hard thing to imagine. The tail of the letter indicates that Bloggs is in difficulties with a steel joist delivered bent from the railway.

Bloggs, it will be noted, is businesslike. He answers the letter concisely and dates his signature. The attached sheets proclaim a most studious devotion on his part, handicapped by a very gritty pencil and by india-rubber deeply involved with butter. The papers are greatly fatigued at the folds, and Bloggs has evidently lost the saucer of his teacup, but—with the help of stamp-edging —they survive, and Bloggs, as he might be trusted to do, has done the job, although it has taken him three weeks to finish it.

HONEYWOOD

The Architect queries the following. The letters in margin refer to Statement items.

A. EXTRA IN FOUNDATIONS, ETC.? ARCHITECT SAYS HE NEVER ORDERED ANY.

Sep. 20tht. 24. Architect bring along drawings of terrace, put out acause she wants steps moved further up kitchen end. It were the day her little nurse dog made to bite him so he will know it. First I must lower bench of terrace he says; then after I peg out that wont suit, so then it was three steps he ordered and that wont do neither, it got to be two he says, wich where $9\frac{5}{8}''$ and brought bench down to 7" or thereabouts above top of footings, and no harm as I could see, but I must put foundation down four courses along front and jump up with extra stepping on return he says. I put Rumbler on it and after dinner found he add got mixt and rekoned four courses has $13\frac{1}{4}''$ instead of $11\frac{5}{8}''$

131

gauge we was on, but architect passed all on 13tht see dairy hearwith for measurs has per weekly return.

Bloggs's identification of Lady Brash with "she", after an interval of six months, is eloquent of the place the lady had won for herself in his regard.

Oc. 13tht. Archtect come on to pass trenches, dont like bit of slop down drawing room end (S). He drop his pipe and I send Joe Perks for a bit of waist I add in the window of my office, so he will know all about it. He wont have me to scrape up but I must dig out 4″ to satisfy, and I level up with concrete to save jumping footings has he agreed to measure I give (see dairy) and marked with the toe of my boot for architects approval the oner see me do it and can say.

Nov 11tht. Syd broke his hand, architect was there so will know he ordered me to lower excavation for cellar floor one course, reason acause headroom to thight at door under stairs reason of lowering ground floor 1½″.

Nov. 23tht. I had bench pegs set for screed of cellar floor and he came on afternoon latish about Hoochkofs facings and left a letter on my table I sent after. He dont like top course of footings standing above screed acause of bottom being dug 3″ lower, and I must knock off to level. I says suppose inspector see what were at dam Mr. Potch he says, but after he left he came back and I haerd him shouting wehn I was in my office and put my head out to see who was and he had come back to gate and called I was to put floor back as it was and headroom were good enough, so there was that bit extra digging and hard core to level up again after, as per my weekly and see dairy.

As the due offset of footings is defined in the bye-laws, the local surveyor would object if he found a course being cut away.

B. EAVES SPROCKETS AND TILT TO RIDGE? ARCHITECT RE-MEMBERS GIVING DIRECTIONS BUT SAYS NO EXTRA.

June 6tht 1925. Architect come on roof an add me to fake a bit of eaves has per No. 41 but that dont suit, must be bigger project^n. and tilt. Well gage wehre 3½″ so he says better make it one course, so I botched it to get what he wanted but the rafter feet was all lined and cut and no tilts would carry over that far, and what finish would he have an so I says it mean cutting back feet and fix sprockets to make a job, and he says yes do it and make a job so I done it D.W. as per weekly and all stuff cut out in shop which proves it see dairy.

14 Juy tht. Tilers add left. Architect says must put more tilt to gable ends of ridges. It come on raining pretty sharp and he tore is mac standing in the door of my office wehre staple was jagged after I had to burst the door along of the boy losing the key, so he will remember. I say all I can, but it got to be done to satisfy and a nice job pulling off the ridges and all that fancy filling on face and breaking of the verges with there double undercloaks an pointing and filleting in cement, it could not only be a botch but he would have it and pleased when it were done he told me Jan 3 tht.

As the verges of the roof, where the tiling ends at gables, are slightly tilted so as to throw the water back on to the roof and prevent its being blown to run down face of gables, it is natural that the end ridge tile at gables should be given a corresponding tilt. This tilt at the end of ridge is conspicuous, and is exaggerated in the designs of some architects apparently because an upward curve of the ridge to apex of gable—the result of settlement of the roof timbers—is often seen in old houses, and has the deadly sentiment of the "dear old". The same exaggerated effect is given by artists who make drawings of houses for Christmas cards and kindred destinies. Spinlove had various fanciful notions for the roof at Honeywood, most of which were wrecked by the obstructive inertia of the British craftsman when asked to vary from accustomed usage; and one cannot help regretting that he was not similarly baulked of his extravagantly belled eaves and "old moated grange" gable ends. The devices of the building crafts, which have served the skilful and efficient use of humble material for centuries, are a pure delight to everyone who has studied them, and have come to be loved as a tradition of beautiful building; but it is the perfection with which they serve their purposes, and not the forms they present, which delight us; and to

Bloggs on Extras

*give those forms an emphasis beyond what their purpose demands,
is fatuous. It is the thing that, in the main, makes the modern villa
a monstrosity; and as it has no part in architecture, and as
Spinlove is evidently a man of educated taste, we must suppose
that his preoccupations with his ridges and eaves was to get them
to look right, and did not result in making them look wrong.
Strong associations are aroused when we view any building and,
if the style or tradition of its design awakens a certain group
of associations, it is important that every detail of the design
shall accord with that tradition and strengthen the association.
In a house with eaves, no feature is more expressive than the
degree of projection of them. As the rafter feet had been cut to
agree with the drawing (No. 41) they could not properly be used
to carry the increased stand-over of the tiles. They had to be cut
back close up to the plate, and false rafter feet, set at a slightly
flatter slope to give the required tilt, spiked to them. These are
the "sprockets" spoken of.*

C. TAKING DOWN AND REBUILDING RETURN DIES OF TERRACE
WALL. ARCHITECT STATES IT WAS YOUR MISTAKE.

Feb. 23tht. Architect come on in white trousers he left his
bat against flooring stacked in kitchen an a long job to find so
he will know wehn it were. He says break back at side of dies
had ought not to be battered same as face but plumbded, but
I reckon his drawing No. 22 showed it other way same as I had
it, and so I told him and charged D.W. has per weekly.

P.S.—There were a line on that drawing you could not tell
waht was meant for and he dont know neither so that makes
sure for if he cant say how were it my fault not to.

Privet. He says I don't know a good drawing when I see one,
an I says may be has I dont but I knows a bad one when I sees
hit I says. Privit.

*Spinlove seems to have had words with Bloggs on this matter
and not to have got the best of the exchange.*
*Bloggs's microscopic memory is clearly an immovable barrier
to all argument or question, and indicates resources of a kind that
will infallibly repulse any attempts at cross-examination. His*

134

acumen in forestalling a denial of the circumstances he adduces can only be the result of tried experience in similar contests. What foothold can Spinlove find for protesting "I remember nothing about it", when he is told the event occurred on the day he dropped his pipe in the trench, or misluid his tennis racquet? Demonstrably, Bloggs knows exactly all that happened, and Spinlove, who can remember nothing—even of the muddied pipe and the bit of cotton waste fetched from the foreman's office to cleanse it—clearly has not a leg to stand on.

This proof of the evidence of Frederick Bloggs covers five and a half laborious foolscap sheets, and I will make no further excerpts. Pinned up with these sheets are certain pages from his "dairy"; and the ungrudging liberality with which he has gutted it in the good cause is almost touching. "Leaves from a Diary" has a new meaning for me since I have seen Bloggs's. The entries are hieroglyphic and also cryptic; and if I describe the pages as having been "torn" from the book, I only do so because no more destructive-sounding word occurs to me. "Captured in Battle" best describes their appearance.

SPINLOVE TO GRIGBLAY

Dear Sir,   1.9.26.

I am obliged for your letter covering your foreman's replies to questions. I have, however to point out that in no case is the fact substantiated that work, stated to have been authorized by me, *was ordered as an extra.* As you are aware, unless work is definitely authorized as an extra *at the time it is done,* the assumption is that there was no understanding that it was to be an extra. I should be glad if Mr. Grigblay would make an appointment here to go with me into the various points raised.

I saw Mr. Tinge two days ago, who called my attention to the fact that you have charged for repointing work damaged by frost; but under the terms of the contract the responsibility for making good damage by frost is *yours.* I overlooked this, or I should have objected to the item before. I have told Mr. Tinge that it must be struck out.

Will you ring up to-morrow and let me know whether the work in making good dry rot has been completed as promised?

Yours faithfully,

Bloggs on Extras

*Spinlove is right on the point of authorization of extras; but,
actually, the terms of the contract are more rigid, for they require
that, in order to rank as an extra, work must be authorized as an
extra* in writing.

*Tinge is right, too, in the matter of damage by frost. Grigblay
contracted to "protect from damage by frost", and is therefore
responsible for making good damage due to failure to protect.*

GRIGBLAY TO SPINLOVE

Dear Sir,   3.9.26.

Mr. Grigblay will call to settle account on the 7th at 2 o'clock,
as arranged over phone.

We will ask you to note that we have on many occasions
carried out work, charged as extra in Statement and accepted
by you, on your verbal order alone; and have always accepted
your word and put in hand as desired without delaying for
written order or where should we be with all the variations
there have been ever since the work was begun, waiting for
written orders and not getting same. There are not above half
a dozen written orders from first to last, and in general the only
orders we have had have been verbal, which we have acted on
at your request and to your approval. Now that this does not
appear to please you, we shall be glad to have written authority
for extra making good dry rot as per your instructions and
oblige. The men cleared up yesterday.

If you will look at the Interim Statement we sent you, you
will find we have charged only difference in value between
plain struck joint and special pointing to your instructions and
approval.

Yours faithfully,

*Grigblay, in his own way, presents his view of the authorization
of extras with clearness—if for "verbal" we read* oral—*and the
position he takes is just. The contract stipulation that all work
that is to rank as extra shall be authorized as an extra in writing
at the time the work is done, is a good one; but like many excellent rules it can, in practice, not be always exactly followed; and
in cases such as Honeywood—which are the rule rather than the*

exception—where there are a large number of small variations, its strict enforcement would entail delays and consequent losses which no builder could be expected to tolerate. We know that Spinlove was lax in enforcing the rule and, in the circumstances, it is hard to see how it could have been enforced; but as he has accepted *as extras a number of items in the account which were not formally authorized, he cannot* object *to other claims on the grounds that they were not formally authorized, and accordingly each case will have to be settled by wranglings to decide what the facts giving rise to the work actually were. In that wrangle Grigblay will have the advantage of holding records which he can use as may best serve his ends; while Spinlove will have little but his memory with which to oppose them.*

LADY B.'s CONVERTED ATTIC

SPINLOVE TO LADY BRASH

Dear Lady Brash,   6.9.26.

As I understand you are now home again, I think I ought to write and just let you know about the new "converted attic" your daughter showed me—in fact, we all had tea up there. It is delightful, I know; so snug and cottagy with the low sloped ceiling and dingy light and the warming pans and the jolly little boxed-out chimney corner—all most ingenious, I have never seen anything at all like it before; but perhaps you do not know that it is not a *habitable room* as defined by the Regulations of the Local Government Board and required by the byelaws. The roof space arrangement, you see, was only allowed by the District Council on my undertaking that it was to be used as a boxroom or store, *only*, so that you are violating the local building regulations—breaking the law, in fact—by using the place as a habitable room. If I had not promised that the place would *not* be used as a habitable room, the District Council would have refused to allow the house to be built. You see, in order to comply with the minimum requirements of the Model

137

Lady B.'s Converted Attic

Bye-laws, the ceiling would have to be much higher, the roof-slopes much less, the window much larger and the walls, all the way down to the ground, thicker. Of course, if it were an old house built before the bye-laws were adopted, you could do as you liked; but, unfortunately, Honeywood is a new house, and if the District Council gets to hear of what has been done I am afraid there will be serious trouble. I feel I ought to write and let you know this, so that you may be prepared.

I hope you enjoyed your visits, but I'm afraid you had wretched weather during the last week.

Yours sincerely,

As Spinlove is evidently afraid of Lady Brash, and is tremulous with anxiety lest he should be misunderstood, it is clear that he only wrote in the belief that it was his duty to give the warning. What poor Lady Brash will make of the Local Government Board, the Local Building Regulations, the Requirements of the Model Bye-laws, the thundercloud imminence of the District Council and the awful admonition "Prepare for Trouble", it is hard to imagine; but the whole thing is a mare's nest—a figment of Spinlove's imperfect knowledge. If it appears that spaces allocated in the plans to boxrooms, stores, and so forth, are usable as habitable rooms, the Local Authority can require them to comply with the dimensions, lighting and ventilation ordained for habitable rooms; but it cannot prevent owners from screwing up and shuttering windows, or blocking the vent flues. The plans of Honeywood were duly approved, and the house completed and certified as conforming to the building regulations; and if Lady Brash prefers to entertain her friends in the boxroom, or to dine in the bath, or to sleep in the cupboard under the stairs, it is no business of Spinlove's, nor of the District Council's, nor of anyone —except possibly of a commissioner in lunacy.

If people are found living in conditions inimical to public health and sanitation, the Health Officer can intervene; but that is another matter.

LADY BRASH TO SPINLOVE

Dear Mr. Spinlove,   7.9.26.

I knew you would admire my Ideal Homes converted attic.

138

Lady B.'s Converted Attic

I meant it to be a great surprise, but Phyllis has told you so
now it will not be. You cannot think what a comfort it is to
get away from the servants! I just slip upstairs and know nothing of anything that is going on. Leslie prefers the lounge or
the den so we do not sit there in the evenings, I think it is because of all the stairs! ! Would it be very expensive to put in
a lift for the coals as well because there will have to be coals
in the winter although it is a delightfully *warm* room, in fact
in hot weather it is *too* warm and I cannot sit there so it will
be delightfully cosy in the winter. Can anything be done about
the noise the water makes; and is it quite *safe* when it whistles
all the time and roars and rushes as though it was going to
run over the side, particularly when Leslie comes home and is
having his bath; and then noises like a man hammering to get
in and people choking and dreadful sighs and groans and sometimes cries for help, so *alarming* if anyone was able to get up
there without being noticed, but I am sure you would not allow
such a thing for one moment.

Your letter is so very clever I could not follow it, but I should
certainly object most strongly if the District Counsel tried to
interfere; he is only a greengrocer with a *quite* small shop and
a nursery garden, and he would not *dare* go against Leslie; such
a *common* little man too, though always most civil and obliging,
but if Mr. Bunseer says *one single word* I shall go to the Stores
instantly. They send out here twice a week as he knows *perfectly
well*, and the idea of this insignificant little man interfering in
my house is a most unheard of state of things and I would never
for one moment allow it. Really I do not know what things are
coming to nowadays.

What delightful weather we are having again.

Yours very sincerely,

P.S.—Can you get me some old oak beams for it do you
think?

*Lady Brash does not appear to have been "psychoed" yet; but
she knows well how to stand at bay and, ridiculous as is her view
of the matter, she is nearer the truth than Spinlove. Mr. Bunseer
is presumably the Chairman of the District Council, or possibly*

Lady B.'s Converted Attic

a notorious member of it; at any rate local authority is, for some reason, identified with him in the lady's mind.

The boxroom is evidently cheek by jowl with the tankroom, and the noises complained of are merely manifestations of the healthy, joyous life of cisterns and of ball cocks that are out of knowledge to all who do not seek community with them. Lady Brash's realization of the Ideal Home presents a charming domestic interior: the fond wife sitting secluded and remote and lulled by the murmuring song of the cisterns, suddenly warned, by their glad outburst into full triumphant symphony, that her Leslie has returned to her and is having a bath.

Flush tanks are the source of other water-noises. The full-toned, reverberating flush tank or "water waste preventer", which is offered in great variety and at most reasonable prices by a large number of manufacturers, appears, however, to be popular; and those in search of a powerful instrument will like to know of Gladdener's "Orchestral" in D flat major with domed resonator and piccolo cadenza as finale.

Lady Brash is, of course, quite astray in supposing that warmth is inherent in her snuggery. The cause of the room's being hot in summer is that its outer fabric is ineffective as an insulator. This will also make it cold in winter, because the wide expanse of roof which allows outside warmth to pass readily in will equally readily allow interior warmth to pass out. We know that Spinlove hung his tiles to battens nailed direct to the rafters without any intervening boarding and felt, and, although the place is plastered, Lady Brash's snuggery is unlikely to bring perfect content to anyone not previously acclimatized to Arctic exploration as well as to the stoking of battleships in the Persian Gulf.

Experienced architects will recognize in this episode a trait of human nature which leads certain clients who are discerning in requiring the nicest efficiency in the arrangements made for them, to rejoice in makeshifts and discomforts of their own devising. We may be sure that Lady Brash will continue to broil or shiver in her posh cubby-hole up among the cisterns to the limits of her endurance, and, when the stimulus of novelty no longer supports her resolution, will find some other reason than the true one for her defection.

140

Lady B.'s Converted Attic

Dear Lady Brash,   9.9.26.

Of course there is no harm unless the Authorities find out about the use being made of the boxroom, but I thought you would like to know how things were.

The noises you describe are quite usual. There is no danger of any kind and you will be glad to hear there is no access to the tankroom except by the door, so that if you lock it and keep the key yourself you can be certain no one is in there.

I expect you will find you will want quite a good fire in the winter. There will not be much sun to warm the place then, will there?

A lift would no doubt be a great convenience, as you say; but I am afraid it could only be accessible from the kitchen or the dining-room, and that would not be very convenient, would it? Then, of course, it would mean taking square bits out of the dining-room and the bedrooms on the first and second floors; have you thought of that, I wonder?

Yes, the weather has been delightful, but I am sorry to see in to-day's paper that a change is coming.

Yours sincerely,

P.S.—If I come across any old oak beams for sale that will fit I will let you know, but I fear that is not very likely.

If Spinlove had any sense of humour he could not write such a letter as this; but we know he has none, and perhaps he is, on this occasion, lucky, for his nervous solicitude is the result of experience that has taught him never to appear to oppose the lady's wishes, and that any indication of decisive contrary opinion will have the effect of opposition. Spinlove writes as though the poor woman were only half-witted, but in doing so he seems—if I may obtrude the opinion—on the safe side.

Dear Mr. Spinlove,   10.9.26.

I was so much relieved to get your nice letter as Mr. Bunseer *never* comes to the house and I have now given strict orders that *no one* is allowed further than the passage and keep the cisterns locked up although I am sure he would never *dream* of doing such a thing, and I am bound to say that he is always *fresh* though the Stores is *not* but of course we rely on the garden for most of them.

They all tell me there is dry rot Mr. Grigsby has been seeing about, but I always wanted a dry one [*?house*] so I suppose now it is finished it cannot be helped if it is *too* dry, but that is better than a *damp* one for my dear mother was a martyr and a cousin as well and I take after *both*.

We are giving a small dance on the 27th as the 26th is Sunday and hope to have the pleasure of seeing you and staying the night. We dine at seven.

How quickly the evenings are drawing in though still quite light in the morning! !

Yours sincerely,

We are not, I think, to understand that the lady has any fear of Mr. Bunseer hiding in the tankroom. What she means to say is that as Bunseer never comes to the house he can learn nothing of the converted boxroom; that to make things quite safe she has forbidden any tradesman to come into the house at all, and that she has ordered the tankroom to be kept locked, but not—she is careful to let Spinlove understand—from any fear of Bunseer, whose vegetables are always fresh although those supplied by the Stores are not.

SPINLOVE TO GRIGBLAY

Dear Sir,   10.9.26.

Will you send cheque for £6 to Borter as extra on bird-bath. He came to see me some time ago and called again yesterday bringing his correspondence with the quarry company. It seems that he sent them my sketch and depended on their measures in making out his tender, but they carelessly took the scale to be 1 in. instead of $\frac{1}{2}$ in., and gave him a wrong figure so that he is out of pocket. He is in quite a small way of business, working himself with the help of two or three journeymen, and

Lady B.'s Converted Attic

I have decided he ought to be allowed the cost of the stone he used.

I am expecting to receive Mr. Grigblay's promised proposal for settlement of items still in dispute.

Yours faithfully,

Spinlove has no right to do this. It is to be hoped that neither Brash nor anyone else would wish to profit by the misfortunes of an artist who has made a beautiful thing for him with his own hands, or to take advantage of a technicality which enables him to force an individual craftsman to bear the cost of the work instead of paying for it himself; but it is not for the architect to usurp his employer's discretion and, on an impulse of vicarious generosity. make a present of his client's money as Spinlove here does. His duty, as Brash's architect (or agent) was to give Borter exact particulars; examine the tender so as to assure himself that Borter understood what was wanted and was not opening his mouth too widely; then set up an exact contract, and see that it was exactly completed. All Spinlove was entitled to do when Borter made his appeal was to master the facts and lay them before Brash with any representations he thought fit to make. If Brash then elected to pay, payment would more appropriately be made by Brash's cheque drawn in favour of Borter and transmitted by Spinlove, than by making it an extra under the contract; for it is not an extra, but a free gift by Brash; and as a gift was all Borter was entitled to ask for it is right he should understand that what he has received is a gift and nothing but a gift. I have assumed Borter's to be a genuine case; but though we may sympathize with him we need not condone his inability to take care of himself. After all, business is business. Borter and his kind bring discredit on the calling of individual craftsman which, above all others, deserves well of architects; and if Spinlove feels as I do, he will not employ Borter next time he wants a bird-bath or a sundial.

RIDDOPPO AGAIN

Dear Mr. Spinlove, 18.9.26.

My protracted absence on an unexpected prolonged round of visits to yachting and other sporting acquaintances has postponed the earlier transmission of my correspondence with Messrs. Russ and the Riddoppo Company anent the failure of the paint, which I now enclose herewith for your perusal previous to our anticipated meeting on the 25th. It would be advantageous if you would be so obliging as to allocate the forenoon of the 26th to a discussion of the proposition which will then be assisted by the convenient presence of the defective paintwork.

I am considerably astonished at the attitude now adopted by my friend Mr. Ziegfeld Swatmug, under whose personal recommendation I eventually arrived at the final decision to utilize Riddoppo; but you will see that the failure of the paint is demonstrably due to the remission of Mr. Grigblay to apply Riddoppo by methods sufficiently workmanlike to procure desirable results. This—may I be permitted to remind you— is precisely what I have all along prognosticated.

As you are aware, I have caused the disastrous consequence of the disintegration of the paint to be mitigated by the application of frequent scrubbings, and it is desirable that I should intimate for your information that this arduous duty has made it imperatively necessary to *further augment the domestic staff*, and that I am keeping an exact account of the extra disbursement occasioned. The dilapidated aspect of Riddoppo is, as you must have discerned, a perfect disgrace to *any* gentleman's house, and I desire that Mr. Grigblay should be finally informed that remedial action without further protracted delay is at once imperatively necessary.

Yours sincerely,

It will be remembered that, four months before, a deadlock was produced by Grigblay's flatly refusing to accept responsibility for, or have any hand in the restoration of, the defective Riddoppo paint; and that Brash then said he was going to take the advice of his solicitors.

(ENCLOSURE 1) RUSS AND CO., SOLICITORS, TO BRASH

Dear Sir,   28.5.26.

In accordance with instructions you gave to Mr. Russ in interview on 7th May to take Counsel's opinion, we referred the case for the opinion of Mr. Geoffrey Chawlegger, K.C., and this opinion we have now received.

We do not enclose the opinion as it is of considerable length and highly technical, but Mr. Chawlegger holds the same view of the facts as Mr. Russ expressed to you in conversation, and which may be stated as follows:

1. Your letter to your architect of 24th September 1925, instructing him to order Grigblay, the builder, to use Riddoppo paint, and stating that you accepted responsibility for so ordering after Grigblay had previously, in his letter of 22nd September 1925, objected to the paint and refused to take responsibility for the results of using it, absolves Grigblay from any liability for defects which subsequently manifested themselves, except defects which can be shown to be due to his neglect to use reasonable care in applying the paint.

2. The Riddoppo Company is responsible to you for breach of warranty if it can be shown that the paint was not suitable for the purpose for which it was supplied.

3. The Riddoppo Company is not responsible to Grigblay for breach of warranty in supplying, and Grigblay is not responsible to the Riddoppo Company for negligence in applying the paint.

4. Your right of action is against the Riddoppo Company for breach of warranty, or against Grigblay for negligence, or you may cite both and make them jointly defendants to an action for damages.

5. The architect is not responsible to you for breach of warranty by the Riddoppo Company, but action may lie against him for negligence in not seeing that the paint was

properly applied, and he may be joined as defendant in any action you may bring against the builder.

In view of this opinion we think it desirable to settle the matter by getting the parties each to agree to bear a portion of the cost of renovation; failing which we think your only course will be to make all three joint defendants of an action for damages.

Yours faithfully,

(ENCLOSURE 2) BRASH TO RUSS AND CO.

Dear Mr. Russ, 2.6.26.

I have perused your communication with some consternation as it intimates, I apprehend, that a considerable period of time must elapse before the desired renovation will be eventually completed. Is there any prohibited reason why I should not employ some person to carry out the necessary restoration of the paintwork as a preliminary to suing the defendants for the amount of my consequent disbursement?

Yours sincerely,

(ENCLOSURE 3) RUSS AND CO. TO BRASH

Dear Sirs, 5.6.26.

In the event of both Grigblay and the Riddoppo Company refusing to restore, you are entitled to have the renovations carried out and to include the cost of the work in your statement of claim in any action you may take. It is, however, imperative that the work done should be confined to putting the paintwork into the condition in which it would be if the defendants had fulfilled their obligations. It will also be advisable to have technical evidence that nothing more was done than was necessary to this end.

Yours faithfully,

(ENCLOSURE 4) BRASH TO SWATMUG

My dear Mr. Swatmug, 9.6.26.

I anticipate you will remember that some twelve months ago

you were so very obliging as to interest yourself anent a certain small domestic building-adventure of mine, and to strongly recommend a new novelty super-paint manufactured by Riddoppo, Ltd., of which you are, I think, chairman; and that you also most kindly introduced me to an official of the Riddoppo Company who gave me most invaluable advice upon the appropriately suitable variegation of tints to be selected, and for which kind assistance I had occasion to offer you my very sincere appreciation and thanks.

I regret, however, to communicate that a very brief period of time after the completion of the interior painting of my house, Riddoppo commenced to disintegrate and peel off in a most alarming manner, and it is now demonstrably evident, I am pained to intimate, that the whole work will have to be again renewed as it is in a deplorable condition and a disgrace to *any* gentleman's domicile, as you would, I am confident in thinking, most emphatically agree. The builder, who is a somewhat rough, obstreperous fellow, disclaims all responsibility as he asseverates that he used Riddoppo by my orders which—I need hardly tell you—I did not hesitate to give him after so strong a recommendation from yourself.

It will, as you will perceive, be a very great advantage to me under these distressing circumstances if you would grant me the privilege of consulting you and availing myself of your abundant stores of experienced knowledge; and if you could spare us the pleasure of your company at Honeywood for a week-end—or longer if possible—or can at any time concede us a single night of your valuable time, Lady Brash and myself would have most extreme pleasure in entertaining you.

It is a considerable interval since I had the good fortune to meet you, but I often hear from friends of the activities of your busy life which, I trust, continue to prosper.

Believe me, my dear Mr. Swatmug,

Ever yours sincerely,

(ENCLOSURE 5) BRASH TO SWATMUG

My dear Mr. Swatmug,   27.6.26.
I ventured to indite a missive to you some three weeks ago

anent the Riddoppo paint you were so very kind as to recommend for the interior decorations of an unpretentious house I was building. As I have received no expected reply, it occurs to me either that possibly you never received my letter or that, by some unfortunate disaster, yours to me has gone astray.

Lady Brash and myself have been looking forward to the pleasure of offering you the hospitality of Honeywood Grange, and live in hopes that the enjoyable event will not long be delayed.

Ever, my dear Mr. Swatmug,

Yours very sincerely,

(ENCLOSURE 6) SWATMUG TO BRASH

My dear Brash,   4.7.26.

Yes, I received your "missive" and must apologize for not having answered it before, but what with being much abroad and having several flotations in hand, and then this wretched divorce action which you must have heard of, I am afraid your letter escaped my attention.

I am pleased to have been of service to you so think nothing more about that, but I am not clear what the matter is you refer to. However, I have nothing now to do with the Riddoppo Company as I resigned from the Board when they wrote down the capital, so I fear I can be of no further use to you; but in any case I know nothing whatever about paint, though I always understood Riddoppo was a sound proposition and what you say is news to me.

I should only be too delighted if it were possible for me to accept your and your good Lady's charming invitation, but, alas! that is quite out of the question, I am sorry to say.

Yours sincerely,

A charming letter: the letter of one who knows no virtue that will not pass the test of "Does it pay?" and who has sold the goods (and the buyer) and sees no more profit in the miserable, grovelling Brash.

Riddoppo Again

(ENCLOSURE 7) BRASH TO SWATMUG

My dear Mr. Swatmug,   5.7.26.

Permit me to thank you in acknowledgment of your communication anent Riddoppo. I anticipated that, as it was at your urgent personal recommendation I adopted the use of Riddoppo, you would be desirous of assisting me in securing elimination of consequent defects; however, I comprehend that you have now no connection with the Company and that I need have no apprehension that you will interpret any action I take to secure restitution from the Company as in any way involving yourself.

Lady Brash and myself are extremely disappointed to know we may not immediately anticipate the enjoyment of a visit from you, but we still live in hopes that eventually your divers engagements may permit you to give us that pleasurable gratification.

Believe me, dear Mr. Swatmug,

Yours sincerely,

(ENCLOSURE 8) BRASH TO SECRETARY,
RIDDOPPO CO., LTD.

Dear Sir,   5.7.26.

About twelve months ago you supplied me with a quantity of your New Novelty Riddoppo Super-Paint for the interior decoration of Honeywood Grange. I regret to inform you that a very brief period after the painting was completed it commenced to disintegrate and peel away from the surface. I shall be glad if your representative will call at an early date to view the disaster, and to know what proposals you will make for immediate renovation.

Yours faithfully,

(ENCLOSURE 9) BRASH TO RIDDOPPO CO., LTD.

Dear Sirs,   12.7.26.

Permit me to call your attention to my communication of 5th July anent failure of your Riddoppo paint, and to politely

149

request the favour of an immediate reply without any further procrastination.

Yours faithfully,

(ENCLOSURE 10) RIDDOPPO, LTD. (AND REDUCED)
TO L. BRASH, ESQ.

Dear Sir,   19.7.26.

We do not find that at any time we have supplied any goods to your order.

Yours faithfully,

We now may begin to understand why there was an interval of four months between the day Brash referred the question of responsibility to Russ, and that on which he wrote telling Spinlove liability lay at Grigblay's door.

It will be noticed that the Riddoppo Company describes itself as "Ltd. (and Reduced)". This means that the Company has, as Swatmug mentioned, written down—or cancelled—part of its share capital. This writing down is equivalent to cutting losses, and will enable the Company to pay that small available dividend on the reduced nominal share value which would have been swamped as a percentage on the original share capital. The fact suggests that the Riddoppo Company is struggling to keep its head above water.

(ENCLOSURE 11) BRASH TO RIDDOPPO, LTD.

Dear Sirs,   20.7.26.

I beg leave to communicate the obvious intimation that your Riddoppo super-paint was not ordered by myself, nor am I aware that it is a customary habit for private gentlemen to order materials for building operations. The paint was appropriately ordered by my builder, Mr. John Grigblay, of Marlford, as—will you permit me to politely remind you?—you could perfectly well have informed yourself had you so desired.

It is also expedient you should clearly comprehend that attention to this matter brooks no further protracted delay, and that unless I immediately receive a satisfactory proposal for the restoration of the defective paint I shall employ other persons to carry out the necessary undertakings and hold you liable for the cost as well as for the disbursements I have already incurred in *augmentation of the domestic staff* necessary to the prevention of deleterious effects upon carpets, curtains and furniture.

I have also to ask your permission to intimate that you are not addressing "Mr. L." but Sir Leslie Brash Knight Bachelor, which information you could have immediately acquired from the most cursory reference to *Dod's*, *Who's Who*, the Post Office and Telephone Directories and numerous other publications.

Yours faithfully,

(ENCLOSURE 12) RIDDOPPO TO SIR L. B. K. BACHELOR

Dear Sir,   5.8.26.

We regret error in name, which was new to us, and signature hard to decipher.

We have now communicated with Mr. Grigblay and enclose copies of correspondence, which kindly note as this closes the matter so far as we are concerned, and oblige,

Yours faithfully,

(ENCLOSURE 12A) RIDDOPPO TO GRIGBLAY

Dear Sir,   26.7.26.

Sir Leslie Bachelor of Honeywood Grange has written complaining our N.N. Super-Paint ordered by you has gone wrong there, and shall be glad of particulars as this is the first we have heard of same.

Yours faithfully,

(ENCLOSURE 12B) GRIGBLAY TO RIDDOPPO

Gentlemen,   27.7.26.

We painted out Honeywood with your Riddoppo super because we were so ordered, and if you want to know what it looks like better go and see as we only carried out architects orders and it is no more business of ours and we will have no more to do with it. You may like to know we did not french polish or put fire to it or squirt any acid at it or boiling water or super-heated steam or molten lead, but if that is what is wanted there is still a bit of it left for you to get to work on.

Yours faithfully,

The last paragraph is a characteristic comment of Grigblay's on the advertisements of "Riddoppo New Novelty Super-Paint", which held out, for the encouragement of house-owners and decorators, that it was "fire and acid proof, not to be damaged by jets of boiling water and super-heated steam and capable of receiving a high polish".

(ENCLOSURE 12C) RIDDOPPO TO GRIGBLAY

Sir,   30.7.26.

We suppose your cheeky letter is because you do not know better and want to insult us because your painters do not know how to read instructions when they are printed in clear print on the tins for everyone to see and go by. The paint we sent you was in perfect condition as supplied to others, and if you have made a mess of things by not following instructions, well, that is your affair and not ours, which kindly note as this is the last we have to say to you or anyone else on this matter and oblige

Yours, etc.,

(This ends correspondence covered to Spinlove by Brash's letter of 18.9.26.)

SPINLOVE TO GRIGBLAY

Dear Sir,   29.9.26.

I enclose copy of correspondence on the subject of failure of Riddoppo, which I have to-day received from Sir Leslie Brash who considers it to be demonstrated that the defects are due to the painting not having been properly done, and in-

structs me formally to call upon you to clean off and repaint
forthwith.

Will you return enclosure by Friday morning at latest, and
let me know what answer I am to give Sir Leslie, as I am meeting him to discuss the matter on Saturday.

Yours faithfully,

*Spinlove has no business to send what are, in fact, Brash's
private papers to Grigblay. By doing so he takes Grigblay behind
the scenes and puts him in possession of his client's "case"—as
the lawyers call it.*

*The detachment Spinlove again displays in his letter can now
only be expected. The time has gone by when any architect could
hope to adjudicate.*

SPINLOVE TO BRASH

Dear Sir Leslie Brash,   21.9.26.

I am in receipt of your letter and enclosures and have written
to Grigblay. He will, I fear, without doubt refuse to make good
the paint-work, and for the reasons he before gave—namely,
that he only painted with Riddoppo when you undertook to
accept responsibility for the results. I inspected the painting on
several occasions while the work was in progress and could
find no fault with the way it was being done; in fact, Grigblay
put his foreman decorator in charge so that it should have
special attention.

I will set aside Sunday morning to go into the matter with
you, as you ask; but as Grigblay will certainly refuse to go
back on his decision to have nothing more to do with the
painting at Honeywood, and I have no experience of Riddoppo
—the composition of which is, as you know, a trade secret—I
am afraid I shall not be of much help to you.

Yours sincerely,

*We here see Spinlove again writing a letter that is not only
unnecessary but the very soul of tactlessness. The mention of his
name by Brash's solicitors as possibly liable, jointly with Grigblay,
has made him eager to exculpate himself and consolidate
Grigblay's position.*

Riddoppo Again

Dear Sir,   21.9.26.

Correspondence *re* Riddoppo returned herewith. We have nothing to add to what we have already said and shall be glad if your client will note same.

Yours faithfully,

And so Sir Leslie Brash is left hanging in the air, which is just what we have been expecting, and no more than he deserves for overriding the advice of his architect and the objections of the builder. If Spinlove had specified Riddoppo and Grigblay had used it without protest, Grigblay—and possibly Spinlove—would have been responsible to Brash; and as Brash holds a substantial sum as security for Grigblay's performance of his covenant to make good defects, he could, if Grigblay failed to restore the work, employ someone else to do so and deduct the cost from moneys to become due to Grigblay, so that his position would have been secure. A claim for damages, in that case, might still lie against the paint company for supplying defective paint; but this would be Grigblay's affair entirely and no concern of Brash's.

Dear Mr. Spinlove,   23.9.26.

With a view to obviating the painful necessity of giving unpleasantly frank indications of my feelings when I receive you, I write to intimate that when I give instructions to my professional adviser I anticipate they will be performed *without* unnecessary refractory comment.

The whole of this infernal muddle anent Riddoppo is sufficiently exasperating without the additional vexation of disparaging opinions which—may I be allowed to asseverate?—I have not invited, and do not desire.

For perfectly logical reasons I require Mr. Grigblay's final answer to my demands, which I apprehend I shall in due course receive; but I do *not* desire to be informed what in your opinion that answer is eventually likely to be; I do *not* ask to be told that Mr. Grigblay has previously obstinately refused restitution; I do *not* ask to be reminded that the fellow obstreperously desires to put the blame on me; I do *not* require to be instructed that the composition of Riddoppo is of a secret nature, and I do *not* ask you to reiterate over again that you know nothing of the paint, and for the very obvious and comprehensive reason that I am already redundantly informed upon the whole of those matters.

The only intimation that your communication conveys with which I was not previously conversant is that you espouse the contentious representations of Grigblay in opposition to your employer's interests; and that though you profess to have no acquaintance with the ingredients of which Riddoppo is composed, you asseverate complete confidence in your ability to decide the appropriate method of applying it. This—you must permit me to intimate—causes me considerable astonishment.

Yours sincerely,

We can imagine Spinlove aghast at this reception of his letter, and asking himself, "What on earth have I done now?" but although Brash's expression of irritation may not be excusable, his annoyance certainly is so. We have before observed an engaging frankness in old Brash of which this letter seems only another example. Spinlove's smug letter has exasperated him, and he acts on an impulse to let Spinlove know what he feels about it so that there need be no sour reserves in his greeting of his guest. It may be, of course, that his native pepper got the upper hand and that he let fly as we have often seen him do before; but, even so, there is a simplicity about the old boy which is disarming.

SPINLOVE TO GRIGBLAY

Dear Sir,   27.9.26.

I saw Sir Leslie Brash on Saturday and gave him your answer to his demand that you should repaint. I understand he is going to review the whole question.

Yours faithfully,

THE STATEMENT OF ACCOUNT

Dear Sir,   29.9.26.

We have now further considered the items of the Statement
of Account which remained in dispute after your interview
with Mr. Grigblay, and as we wish the account to be now
settled we offer to reduce certain of our charges, but only
supposing you meet us by allowing the others to stand; failing
which we must withdraw our offer and hold to our full claim,
as we consider our charges fair and we have already met your
views in a reasonable way, and think we are entitled to a little
consideration, as all give and no take is not the treatment we
are accustomed to receive from architects, and one way and
another this job has not been much profit to us and if we see
ourselves clear when all is done it is about as much as we can
expect.

MAKING GOOD DRY ROT

We must refuse to withdraw this item. If we did we should
be agreeing it was a defect under the contract, which we have
all along disputed and cannot take responsibility for.

*If Grigblay met the cost of this work he would involve himself
in liability for all further dry rot due to the same cause. It should
be remembered, also, that the Courts have decided that a builder's
liability for defects is not limited by the date named in the contract as terminating his liability when it can be shown that the
defect existed, or was latent, before the expiration of the time
fixed by that date. It is therefore of special importance to Grigblay that the architect should, by passing the item as an extra,
acknowledge that the cause of the dry rot is not a defect for
which the builder is responsible. It is, of course, equally important
for Spinlove that he should not exonerate Grigblay by allowing
the item to rank as an extra; but Spinlove, who is apparently
unconscious of the dreadful disaster the dry rot may portend, is*

156

The Statement of Account

probably also unconscious of the consequences of agreeing that Brash shall pay for restoring the first manifestation of it. The cost of restoring is likely to be only ten or fifteen pounds, but if it were only as many shillings Grigblay, who understands well how he stands, would be just as obstinate in claiming payment. The case, in fact, is a good instance of the considerations of policy with which architects must temper discretion—and sometimes even moral justice—in settling up building accounts. The bearing of each detail upon the interpretation of the contract as a whole is always in the mind of the experienced man.

RAKING JOINTS AND SPECIAL POINTING AFTER FROST

We are willing to knock off £17, making the charge £32 6s. 3d., which is, as near as we can measure, 4½d. a foot for special.

SPECIAL POINTING IN LIEU OF PLAIN STRUCK JOINT

This claim we cannot withdraw. We were willing to finish flat point where frost pulled out joint, and to finish new to match in place of striking off as specified; but you ordered a special pointing, and we are entitled to extra cost of special over ordinary flat, as already pointed out.

Apparently Spinlove specified that the faces should be finished by pressing the mortar out of the joints and striking off surplus with the edge of the trowel as the bricks were laid. A sharp frost spoilt some of this work while it was new, and the joints had to be raked and pointed which made it necessary for the whole of the brick faces, afterwards built, to be pointed to match. Spinlove, it seems, required a method of pointing which Grigblay claims was more costly than what properly could be required of him under the contract. The justice of this claim seems decidedly doubtful, but it is necessary to know the whole of the facts before forming an opinion. The sum involved, as shown in the Interim Statement (see page 69), is £134 3s. 0d.

ALTERATION TO GROUND-FLOOR WINDOW HEADS

We regret we cannot accept your view of this matter. Your half-inch joinery detail figured height from ground floor, but

157

The Statement of Account

this varied from datum level as the floor had been lowered 1½ in. by your orders, and we cannot accept responsibility for same.

As recorded in "The Honeywood File", Spinlove forgot that the floor had been lowered, and figured the dimensions wrongly; but he always contended that it was Grigblay's duty to see that the frames were made to fit the building. Grigblay's refusal is so worded as to support his repudiation of dry rot: he makes clear that he accepts no responsibility for the lowering of the floor.

RENEWING TWO CATCH PITS

We are willing to cut this out.

We have given the whole of these matters close attention and this is the last we have to say and hope you will now accept our offer, and not oblige us to withdraw it, since we understand Mr. Tinge has been waiting for your decision on outstanding points for a long time and has had the whole of account ready several weeks, so that this will now settle everything.

Yours faithfully,

SPINLOVE TO GRIGBLAY

Dear Sirs, 4.10.26.

I have considered your offer and decided to accept it and settle the account on your terms. I saw Mr. Tinge to-day and he says he can have the statement of account ready this week.

Yours faithfully,

Spinlove seems to have contested every inch of the ground in this long battle of the extras in a way that does justice to his conscientiousness and native tenacity. At the same time he appears to have been a little hard on Grigblay who, like every builder that takes a craftsman's pride in his work, has given a good deal more than his contract demands of him. However, the figure arrived at is likely to be a fair one; for Grigblay is well able to take care of himself, and Bloggs knows how to take care of him too—in fact, appearances are that no fly of any kind has ever settled on Bloggs.

The Statement of Account

Dear Sir, 8.10.26.

Enclosed please find Statement. Copy has been sent to Mr. Grigblay.

Yours faithfully,

Tinge, at any rate, does not waste words. The Statement of Account, which must be long and intricate, is not in the file. It is no doubt put away with the contract documents.

SPINLOVE TO GRIGBLAY

Dear Sir, 9.10.26.

I have received Statement of Account from Mr. Tinge showing total £20,242 11s. 9d. I shall be glad if you will confirm that you accept this figure.

Yours faithfully,

As Spinlove has already agreed with Grigblay the items making up the account, and Tinge is in the position of auditor, valuer, or assessor; Spinlove's invitation to Grigblay to agree the figure Tinge has arrived at is little more than a formality though, as a matter of business, a necessary one. Tinge is expressly appointed under the contract to determine the total figure; and neither Grigblay nor Spinlove can object to the account unless it should appear that Tinge has misunderstood instructions or made any mistake.

SPINLOVE TO BRASH

Dear Sir Leslie Brash, 9.10.26.

I have just received the Statement of Account and am very glad to be able to tell you that I have succeeded in saving nearly *three hundred and fifty pounds* off extras. The exact figure is £337 3s. 5d., making the account £1,555 11s. 2d., instead of £1,892 14s. 7d., which, you will remember, was the total originally shown. To this have to be added certain items which have come in since the original account was drawn up,

totalling £54 2s. 2d. ; and a few others that Grigblay accidentally omitted—value £112 1s. 8d., so that, after allowing certain
profits (£22 4s. 9d.) on the new items, the total figure shown is
£1,753 19s. 9d., which, after including quantity surveyor's fees
(£58 12s.), gives a final total of £1,802 11s. 9d. I thought you
might like to know the figures at once. With kind regards,

Yours sincerely,

*Brash must have been glad Spinlove's letter ended when it did,
for the vaunted three hundred and fifty pound gain had already
dwindled to £90, and, at the pace Spinlove was keeping, another
half-dozen lines would have brought him to a three hundred and
fifty pound loss. Whether Spinlove's is the best method of making
a saving on a building account appetizing to a client I am not
psychologist enough to determine; but I am disposed to doubt it.
If I wanted a hungry lion to receive the highest possible gratification from the gift of a cutlet, I should not first offer him a leg of
mutton and then snatch it away.*

*We have before noticed an adroitness in Spinlove on these
occasions, which is so excessive as to be almost unholy. His
persistency has no doubt saved Brash money; but the amount for
which Spinlove claims credit is the whole of the difference
between the totals of the Interim Summary and of the totals of
corresponding items in the Final Statement. This difference,
however, is not due to Spinlove, but mainly to Grigblay's wisdom
in affixing full covering figures to those items in the Summary
the exact value of which remained to be ascertained; and it is due
to his foresight that, after the inevitable omissions and additions
have been set against one another, the Final Statement shows a
saving, and not an excess, on the Interim Summary. Spinlove,
however, is perhaps unaware of this. With characteristic impul-
siveness he rushes in front of the curtain without waiting to reflect
whether he deserves the plaudits he invites. In view of his air of
masterly elucidation, it is a pity he has made a slip of ten pounds
in his manipulation of the figures. An architect who originates or
passes inaccurate figures does himself very great damage for,
obviously, his client would not entrust him with his affairs at all
unless he had confidence in their being handled with exact care.
It is to be understood that Spinlove is dealing only with the total*

of extras—£1,802 11s. 9d. This, added to the contract sum, £18,440, makes the total of the account £20,242 11s. 9d., which it may be mentioned is almost exactly the figure of probable least cost Spinlove named when the house was first projected.

GRIGBLAY TO SPINLOVE

Dear Sir,   14.10.26.
    We agree Account and Mr. Tinge's figures of total cost, £20,242 11s. 9d., and balance due, £1,242 11s. 9d. As we shall be entitled to said balance on 10th November we shall be glad to have list of any defects outstanding so that we may now get contract completed.

                                              Yours faithfully,

Grigblay has been paid by instalments a total of £19,000, and this balance due is, in main part, money held back as security for making good defects appearing within nine months of the date of completion of the work, which has been acknowledged by Spinlove to be 10th February. Grigblay evidently means to have his money directly it is due on 10th November and his intention is no doubt braced by the dispute about Riddoppo. What we have to expect is that Grigblay will demand his balance on 10th November, and that Brash will refuse payment on the ground that Riddoppo is a defect for which Grigblay is accountable.

THE SMELLS RETURN

Dear Mr. Spinlove,   10.10.26.
    They have all come back again and *more than ever*, even Phyllis says so now, and what is to be done I really do not know as after the gentleman who came about them they all went away and Leslie said that was the end, but now I do not know what he will say as Mrs. Godolphin, who is staying here, notices them very much at night and it affects her *breathing* and

I am the *same*, so it must be very bad and something must be done about it, but you will know best so will you say *at once* as it is so very unpleasant for everyone and cannot be allowed.

How very cold the weather has been of late.

Yours sincerely,

Dear Lady Brash, 11.10.26.

I understand from your letter that you still think there is something wrong with the drains, but that cannot possibly be the case as you will remember the question was definitely settled when the sanitary experts tested the drains five or six months ago. If there had been anything amiss they would certainly have discovered it, so you may dismiss the idea entirely and think no more about it. What you noticed is no doubt some smell from the kitchen. Are you sure the servants, to save trouble, do not use the range as a refuse-destructor—that is, burn fat and kitchen residues and rubbish there, instead of throwing them into the dustbin? They may do this before they leave the kitchen at night, and it may give rise to most unpleasant smells and should not be allowed, as it burns the fire-bars and cheeks.

Yes, the weather has been wretchedly cold.

Yours sincerely,

This seems a most inadequate rply to Lady Brash's letter.

Dear Mr. Spinlove, 14.10.26.

It is very kind of you to advise me not to trouble about them, but it is not the kitchen range, for I would *never* allow it and cook says she never does and it is much more in her bedroom which is why she complains so, and something must be done at once as poor Mrs. Godolphin left the house in a terrible fit of coughing as I knew she would, and even the doctor feared asthma and told her she should if it affected her so. It may still be the *drains*, he says, only no one will decide though I have

spoken to Leslie time after time, but he comes home to-
morrow I am thankful to say for something has got to be done
or we shall all have to leave too.

How chilly it is for this time of year, but the radiators are a
godsend! Would it cost much to put one in the Ideal Attic—
I wonder? The fire gives out *no heat* up there I find, but then
there are no smells *there*!

Yours sincerely,

MISS PHYLLIS BRASH TO SPINLOVE

Dear Jazz, 14.10.26.

Is it the *architecture* of the house that smells? If so, you
ought to choose a different style: the Free Tudor, as you call
it, is altogether too rather. Mum is getting herself into one of
her states over it and you ought to come down and nose
around. It is no good sounding the "all's well" any more. "All's
wrong" is the tuney, for we none of us like living in a third
class in a S.R. tunnel. You must take this seriously, please, for
it *is* serious.

Yours,
PUD.

SPINLOVE TO GRIGBLAY

Dear Sir, 15.10.26.

I enclose list of various small defects which have been standing over so that they might all be dealt with together. Sir Leslie
Brash agrees with the list, and I have sent him a copy of it.
Failure of Riddoppo was added by his orders. He understands,
of course, that you do not intend to touch the paint.

I have had further complaints of smells in the house. It
seems that they are the old "drain" smells, but they are now
stated to be much worse than they were before. I wish Mr.
Grigblay would go to the house on an early day, as he is often
in the neighbourhood, and see what it all means.

Yours faithfully,

Spinlove, as we remember, has held back the making good of defects until they should have fully developed, and so that all might be dealt with at one time; and he then, quite properly, obtained Brash's agreement to what Grigblay was to be required to do. This is a most necessary step, not only as making sure that the client's ideas will be satisfied, and protecting the builder who is entitled to know definitely and finally what is required of him; but as putting the client in mind of a fact he is liable to forget— namely, that the builder is not at his beck and call, but that there is a strict limit to the demands that can be made upon him.

It is the duty of the architect to decide what work a builder shall be called upon to do in fulfilment of his covenant to make good defects. The list represents Spinlove's requirements in this particular; and as he does not hold Grigblay to blame for the failure of Riddoppo, he ought not to include that item. It is important for an architect to maintain always a definite position and to be consistent and to act in exact accord with the forms pre- scribed by the contract; but when, as in this case, he knows he may have to justify himself to lawyers, he cannot be too cautious and circumspect. These miserable contests, however, invariably lead to cross-purposes and confusion; and we may suppose that if Spinlove had declined to put Riddoppo on the list he would have fallen out with Brash, and that he accordingly took the line of least resistance by including it and telling Grigblay it was under- stood he would ignore it. This is consistent with Spinlove's policy, throughout the whole of the affair, of sitting on the fence; but he will cut a poor figure when lawyers begin pressing their questions.

SPINLOVE TO LADY BRASH

Dear Lady Brash,   15.10.26.

I am so very sorry to know you are troubled with this unpleasant smell, and have arranged for Mr. Grigblay to call on an early day and make a thorough investigation of the cause which I am convinced cannot be far to seek.

Yours sincerely,

In spite of Pud's endorsement of her mother's complainings, it is clear that Spinlove still refuses to believe that the reported smells can be due to any defect in the building. In this, his native

The Smells Return

*tenacity seems a little misplaced. He is wise, however, to make
no reply to Lady Brash's suggestion of a radiator in the converted boxroom, for such a radiator would be likely to develop
the same defect as the fire does, and "give out no heat". "Jazz"
seems to have answered Pud's letter in his own hand, for there is
no copy of his reply on the file. He has disappointed us in this
way, before.*

Dear Sir,   16.10.26.

We are obliged for list of defects requiring attention to
complete contract and will put same in hand next week, except
making good Riddoppo which, as we have stated, is no business
of ours and which we respectfully refuse to do.

Mr. Grigblay regrets he cannot take any further action *re*
reported smells as he has already obliged once and could find
nothing amiss except mischievousness by the servants, which
has since been put right.

Yours faithfully,

*Grigblay's refusal to investigate the smells is natural. It is not
many months since he put himself to some trouble to get to the
bottom of complaints for which he could find no justification; and
Spinlove's peremptory manner of calling upon him to pacify Lady
Brash a second time—which, in any case, is Spinlove's job and
not Grigblay's—would properly dispose Grigblay to refuse the
favour even if he were otherwise inclined to grant it.*

LADY BRASH TO SPINLOVE

Dear Mr. Spinlove,   16.10.26.

I do not want Mr. Grigblay to call any more; he does not
wait to listen to me but only says there is nothing wrong and
it will be all right in the summer, and goes away and nothing is
done and all getting worse and worse every day and the fire
giving out no heat no matter how much coal so that I cannot
sit there it is so *freezing*, with the cisterns making a *new* noise
and I lie awake and keep wondering what is happening when

165

The Smells Return

I am not there, so will you send some *proper* person *at once* to say what it all means, as Leslie comes home to-morrow and will naturally want to know why it all is when he hears about it. You have been *most* kind and considerate I know, but now at last it must really stop for I cannot bear any more.

So depressing with the leaves falling and this cold wind!

Yours sincerely,

The poor lady is fast getting into one of her "states". In spite of her rambling ambiguities we may understand that it is the smells that are the trouble. There seems to be no doubt that something is wrong; and it may be that if Spinlove had applied himself to mastering the cause of the complaint when it was first made, instead of discountenancing it and allowing the tough sensibilities of Grigblay to discredit the delicate perceptions of the lady, he would have saved his clients some annoyance, and himself much trouble.

BRASH TO SPINLOVE

Dear Mr. Spinlove,   19.10.26.

I returned yesterday from the Shire [*sic*] where I have been engaged in company with various sporting acquaintances in beguiling the wily partridge. A number of hares also fell to my bag, and I was fortunate in securing a polecat—an exploit which my host is commemorating by having the creature set up by Rowlands. The event is the subject of a paragraph in this week's *Field*, you will notice.

Your communication anent extras was forwarded on to me, and I now write to intimate my satisfaction at the amount of the final total. I confess that I anticipated that the previous summary would again be eventually increased, and my gratification at your intimation that there is a reduction of £90 on the previously estimated figure, is considerable. There is also, I have noted, the additional saving of £92 in respect of overpayment for bricks which you previously reported, making £182 in all. May I point out that the figure £1,753 should be £1,743? This error does not, however, affect the ultimate total of extras £1,802 11s. 9d., which I take to be final and to represent my inclusive liabilities excepting the residual balance of your own outstanding fees of which I shall be glad to receive particulars.

Anent the list of defects, the question of responsibility for the Riddoppo failure has the further attention of my solicitor from whom I expect shortly to receive a communication.

I must now, I regret to intimate, request your attention to a serious matter. On my return home I find that the malodorous emanations have returned with such virulence that the whole domicile is involved, our domestic staff almost in revolt, and Lady Brash so affected in health that immediate change of air is imperative and she is leaving for Brighton to-morrow.

In the past there has been some doubt as to the existence of unsavoury effluviums, but that doubt no longer persists as both my daughter and myself have experienced disgusting vapours in various parts of the house, which are particularly obnoxious at night and in the early morning. The matter now brooks no further protracted delay and, as a first step towards elimination, I request that you will on the earliest day possible come and sleep in the house and apply your trained discernments to the identification of these nauseating savours the repulsiveness of which, if they continue, will render the house permanently uninhabitable. I shall therefore anticipate a telephone message from you to-morrow signifying the earliest day on which we may expect you.

Yours sincerely,

A remarkably urbane letter under the circumstances! Brash's beguiling of the wily partridge, and his newly acquired polecat fame, seem to have given ballast to his moral equilibrium; but his surprising acceptance of the extras account must be due to other causes, and supplies an instance of the entirely unexpected that so commonly happens. It was not to be expected that a reduction of £182—as he supposes—would reconcile Brash to the claim for £1,900 which he had so hotly repudiated; yet this appears to be the case, and the explanation, stripped of the subtleties with which the psychologist would load it, seems plain. First, Brash has already exhausted his indignation at the extras; blown off all his steam; fussed away all his available fuss: he is heartily sick of the subject and, having had a respite of some weeks, has no wish to lash himself into a renewal of his grievance. This is a common weakness in men who have not the habit of self-control. Second, as he tells us, he had made up his mind that the estimate of extras supplied him would prove to be a mere stepping-stone, or half-way house, to a much larger final claim as, except for Grigblay's honest good sense in preparing the Interim Summary, it might well have been; and the fact that the worst is revealed to be so much better than was expected, has reconciled Brash to the figure and led him to forget how unacceptable it once seemed. Third, with the serious contest over the paint unsettled and the new trouble of the inexplicable smells to be disposed of, he is glad to be quit of the question of extras.

SPINLOVE TO BRASH

Dear Sir Leslie Brash,   20.10.26.

This is to confirm arrangement by telephone, that I will meet you at Charing Cross on the 5.25 to-morrow. I am astonished at what you tell me. Why these smells should suddenly reappear, and worse than formerly, is extraordinary—as indeed is the fact that there should be *any* smells. I will do my best to get to the bottom of the matter, though I cannot think that the trouble can be due to any defect in the work.

I have also to thank you for your letter. I will let you have particulars of my charges. The final payment to Grigblay falls due on 10th November, as you know.

I should mention that the refund of £92 from the brick manufacturer *is included* in the Statement of Account. I will bring the Statement with me to-morrow, for you to see.

Yours sincerely,

We may hope, for Spinlove's peace of mind, that it has not occurred to him that the smells may be those associated with extensive dry rot; but, in point of fact, the early manifestation of the smells, their complete disappearance and their sudden return, does not indicate such a source.

We may also hope that the reflection that this was the last of Spinlove's snatching exploits reconciled Brash to the vanishing of the £92 with which he had endowed himself.

The Smells Return

Dear Sir,   22.10.26.

I went yesterday to Honeywood at the urgent request of Sir
Leslie Brash to investigate the smells complained of. I am at a
loss to understand Mr. Grigblay's report to me earlier in the
year that there were no smells; for there is no doubt whatever
that the house is pervaded by a sour, stuffy atmosphere. What
the cause of this is I have no idea. The smell was described to
me as like that of a third-class carriage in a tunnel on the
Southern Railway, and I was myself once or twice reminded
of a smoky chimney; but there were no fires in the house except
the heating and hot water furnaces and the kitchen range, and
the smell is most noticed at the opposite end of the house, particularly in the bedrooms; in fact, the stuffy odour can be at
once detected in Nos. 9, 10, 12, 15 and 16 if they are kept shut
up for a few hours, but it is scarcely noticeable—if at all—
anywhere downstairs. I slept in the small spare room (No. 9
on plan) with the windows shut, and the disgusting atmosphere
was proved when in the morning I opened the windows and
breathed fresh air. I was conscious of an oppressive sensation
in my chest and a listless enervated feeling when I first got up,
and I had a slight headache.

I may say that Sir Leslie Brash naturally expects that the
state of affairs shall be put an end to at once, and I will ask
Mr. Grigblay to meet me at Honeywood either at 3.30 to-
morrow afternoon, or in the course of the following day, and
I shall expect to hear from you by telephone in the morning.

Yours faithfully,

*If we had not such frequent cause to resent the peremptory,
ill-mannered tone in which Spinlove addresses those under his
direction, I should call attention to this instance of it. It is particularly to be regretted when he is addressing Grigblay to whom
he has been in the past greatly indebted.*

A CONSULTING CHEMIST

(HOLOGRAPH) GRIGBLAY TO SPINLOVE

Sir,   23.10.26.

I was away all to-day, but your letter was sent up to the
house so I should see it to-night. I understand they rang up
from the office to let you know I could not meet you to-day,
and I now write to let you know I cannot meet you to-morrow
and for the following reason.

I may have as good a nose as most, but I don't hold out to
have a better and there is no use my joining in any sniffing
match up at Honeywood, for that, if you will pardon me, is all
it would amount to. If what you say is fact—and I do not
doubt it is, for you will find that I dropped a hint of the same
in the report I made last spring—I can make a guess what is
the matter, and it is no small matter either; but the first thing
is to find out whether the trouble is what we think, and to do
that we want something a lot better than any nose, and that
is a "detector", and my advice, sir, is to ask Mr. F. T. Pricehard, Consulting Analyst (somewhere in Westminster he used
to be), to send down and test the air same as they do in mines,
and he will tell us what the fumes are—if there are any—or if
it's dead mice he will tell us that. He will not charge a large
fee, and if the trouble's any fault of mine I will pay it, and if
not I take it the old gentleman will.

You will excuse me telling you what I think best, but if Sir
Leslie wants the trouble put right the first thing is to find out
what trouble it is, and if Pricehard can't say, nobody can.

> I am, sir,
>
> Yours faithfully,

*In the report referred to, Grigblay attributes a stuffy smell he
noticed to down-draught in the flues carrying smoky air from
adjoining chimney-pots into certain rooms; and it now seems that
he suspects the present smells to derive from smoke fumes. The*

170

A Consulting Chemist

"detector" he refers to is a simple apparatus for the ready measuring of the deadly monoxide gas that accumulates in sewers, coal mines, and other places. Pricehard's methods, however, would be more exact than those made possible by the use of such an instrument.

SPINLOVE TO GRIGBLAY

Dear Mr. Grigblay,   25.10.26.

Thank you for your letter. I have spoken to Sir Leslie, and have to-day sent instructions to Mr. Pricehard.

Yours truly,

SPINLOVE TO PRICEHARD

Dear Sir,   25.10.26.

In confirmation of arrangements made over the telephone to-day, I enclose the full history of the "smells" at Honeywood and particulars of the construction of the building. Plans showing drains and all service pipes are hanging in the kitchen passage.

Sir Leslie Brash has arranged for doors and windows of bedrooms to be kept shut on Thursday, and will send his car to meet the 2.5 from Charing Cross at Wedgefield Junction.

Yours faithfully,

PRICEHARD TO SPINLOVE

Dear Sir,   6.11.26.

I enclose report which gives analysis of samples of air taken in the rooms at Honeywood Grange specified in the report, at the times and under the conditions described.

The slight trace of sulphur dioxide (SO_2) would account for the smell noticeable. The presence of sulphuretted hydrogen (H_2S) was not revealed by the ordinary tests used. Carbon dioxide (CO_2) 0·048 is scarcely more than would be found in normal air. Carbon monoxide (CO) 0·015 (in the worst sample) would be likely to produce headache, giddiness and oppression, after some hours.

I am of opinion that fumes from closed coke fires are present in all the samples of air I took. There are two such coke furnaces in the house, that of the heating service and that of the hot-water supply, either of which might be the source of such fumes; but I am not in a position to say how those fumes are dispersed through parts of the house remote from the furnaces.

I enclose note of my charges.

Yours faithfully,

So Lady Brash is vindicated at last! Carbon monoxide, which is colourless and without smell, is in high favour with suicides who find their most exacting needs supplied at a quite trifling cost by the public gas companies; but an architect who lays on a continuous supply of it to the bedrooms is likely to be regarded as officious. If the percentage Spinlove appears to have arranged for at Honeywood had been 0·15 instead of 0·015, no one would be likely to have survived one night.

Pricehard's investigation probably took the form of drawing samples of the suspected air through burettes with ball-bellows until the original air in the burette was displaced by the tainted air, and then closing the cocks at each end of the burettes. The contents of the burettes, each of which would have a capacity of about 200 c.cs., would then be analysed in the laboratory.

(HOLOGRAPH) GRIGBLAY TO SPINLOVE

Sir,   6.11.26.

I write confidentially to let you know, as I don't suppose you have any hand in the matter, that I have received a letter from Russ & Coy., solicitors, threatening proceedings for the failure of this new novelty patent supercrawling and crocodiling paint your client insist I use; but there are others can employ solicitors besides Sir Leslie Brash as he will find out. I never put anyone into Court myself, and never was brought there except for once, and the man who put me there has been sorry ever since and so will this one be; for I have learnt a bit, these last months, about the successes of the Riddoppo Company with their wonderful extra super face-cream, or whatever it is, and if they have any customers left now, they won't have any after I have done with them. No one had ought to be better pleased than me for the old gentleman to go on and see what he will get for his trouble; but I am a poor man and have my work to attend to, and it will do me no good being in all the papers and I think it hard I should have all this trouble put on me because I used the stuff on the understanding I was not responsible, which I should never have done except to oblige; so I just take the liberty to write and ask you, sir—as you know how things are—to drop a hint to Sir Leslie and put him in better mind of where he stands, for this Riddoppo soup of his has given the belly-ache to near everyone who has tasted it, and he will surely lose his case if he tries to make me responsible for the mess at Honeywood.

You will pardon me writing, but thought just as well as it will save a lot of trouble for everyone if the old gentleman can be persuaded to see reason just for once.

I am, sir,

Yours truly,

(CONFIDENTIAL) SPINLOVE TO GRIGBLAY

Dear Mr. Grigblay, 7.11.26.

As you know, I am entirely on your side in this dispute about the painting. Sir Leslie Brash well understands this, but he shows extreme impatience whenever I refer to the matter. However, he certainly ought to be told of the general failure of Riddoppo of which you speak, and I will drop him a hint of it.

I have just received Mr. Pricehard's report and will write to you to-morrow.

Yours truly,

I have several times expressed the opinion that it was long ago Spinlove's duty, as architect, to take control of the position and guide his client's discretion; and have deprecated his policy of sitting on the fence—though, in point of fact, his was no policy, but a mere instinct of weak evasion. I have now to confess, however, that his inertia has given him a position of neutrality which astute diplomacy might well fail to effect; he has avoided falling out either with Grigblay or with Brash, and has still an opportunity—*if he can but use it*—*of intervening to prevent the miserable disaster of an action at law.*

SPINLOVE TO GRIGBLAY

Dear Sir,   8.11.26.

I enclose copy of Mr. Pricehard's letter covering his report of the tests he made. The question is, How do the fumes get into remote bedrooms when they are not noticeable downstairs; and how is the nuisance to be cured? It is clear there must be some serious flaw in the building of the house, and I must call on you to find out what it is and to let me have your proposals for putting things right, and without delay; for this is a serious matter as you will see from what Mr. Pricehard says of the poisonous effect of the fumes. I am not writing to Sir Leslie on the subject until I can give him your explanation and tell him the defect is being remedied.

Yours faithfully,

Spinlove's readiness to dissociate himself from the disaster and to deny all sympathy to Grigblay, is not only wrong in policy, but has the appearance of being thoroughly bad-natured. For two years Grigblay has served Spinlove as a devoted colleague, and on many occasions has helped him out of difficulties with his wise advice and kindly forethought; and Spinlove must know perfectly well that this defect in the building, whatever it may be, is not Grigblay's fault but his misfortune. Grigblay has before endured similar treatment from Spinlove, with patience; and he no doubt understands that these gaucheries are merely due to want of self-confidence in the person he probably regards, and perhaps speaks of, as "the young gent".

MR. SNITCH TRIES IT ON

BRASH TO SPINLOVE

Dear Mr. Spinlove,   8.11.26.

I herewith transmit enclosed communication I have received

from Mr. Cohen Snitch. This is the gentleman—may I remind you—who endeavoured to foist upon me fraudulent plans of cottages which, it eventually transpired, were a purloined illegal infringement of another practitioner's copyright.

You may have observed that within the last few months a number of wretched little common villas have been springing up like mushrooms—or rather I should more appropriately say like *toadstools*—on either side of the Honeywood Hill Road after it leaves Thaddington Village. These abortions must represent the Honeywood Garden Estate the fellow speaks of. The villas so far built are all exactly similar replicas of one another, and we have been greatly annoyed to observe that they reproduce the form of the bay window, chimney and gable of the little pretty Den projection of Honeywood Grange which, as you know, is visible from our entrance gates; and the names all up the road, "Honeywood House," "Honeywood Lodge," "Honeywood Manor" are also an intolerable violation of my rights! Has it come to this, that a gentleman may scarcely call his house his own? It is clearly evident that Mr. Snitch intends to retaliate on my refusal to submit to his attempted fraudulent extortion of fees, and I shall have no hesitation whatever in taking all possible necessary steps to stop his proceedings and compel him to alter his designs or even to pull the places down. I therefore desire you will be so obliging as to notify me exactly what are the liabilities for the infringement of my copyright, of which this must be a most flagrant example.

I am even more disturbed at this threat of Mr. Barthold—who is an auctioneer and house-agent in Marlford—of covering the land up to the eastern boundary of my Honeywood property with the insupportable eyesore of shoddy bungalow abominations, though I apprehend that the whole proposal may be a monstrous pretext for bluffing me into extortionate disbursements. The price this saucy fellow asks is nearly three times the rate at which I acquired my Honeywood estate, and approximates to nine times the agricultural value—a most unheard-of proposition. The whole thing is intolerable and beyond bearing, and I have still to consider what suitable reply I can make to the man. If you have any views on this matter I shall be grateful if I may have the advantage of knowing them.

Mr. Snitch Tries It On

I regret to intimate that the repulsive emanations continue to cause us considerable discomfort, and shall be obliged by the anticipated early communication from you anent the ascertained reason of the odoriferous conditions.

Yours sincerely,

(ENCLOSURE) SNITCH TO BRASH

My dear Sir,   4.10.26.

Re Honeywood Garden Estate. I beg to think you may be interested to know that my client, Mr. Vincent Barthold, who is taking an active local line in this national housing proposition, is considering extending his development up Honeywood Hill to boundary of your property as preliminary to layout of back land with Rural Bungalow Allotments the same as has proved so popular below Westerham Hill, as extension of motor bus service to Wedgefield Junc. offers fascinating rural amenities to Londoners.

As adjoining owner, Mr. V. Barthold begs to hope you might be interested to support same and join small syndicate he is contemplating with a view to flotation of a Honeywood Dainty Houselets Co., and will be glad to hear from you privately *re* same.

Mr. Barthold is willing to dispose of part or whole of same, freehold, at from £170 (back) to £450 (front) per acre according to location.

If this proposition interests you, shall be glad to hear from you at early date as other investors are in the market, and will supply further particulars on application.

Yours faithfully,

"The Honeywood File" recounts how Brash, with the idea of reducing cost, employed this same Mr. Snitch—who practises locally as an architect and surveyor—to build a block of cottages; and how Mr. Snitch sold Brash the design of another architect which he copied, for the purpose, from an architectural magazine. Spinlove warned Brash that if he used the plans he would make himself liable to an action for infringement of copyright, and this

is what Brash has in mind when he notices features of his own house travestied in the villas of "Honeywood Garden Estate".

It is no new thing for commercial enterprise in housing to find profit in the execration its achievements provoke, by acquiring land and then coercing the owners of adjoining houses to buy it at an enhanced price under threat of building on it; and just as the highwayman was obliged sometimes to shoot so that his formula "Your money or your life" might be respected and yield a due harvest, so "Buy or we build" is by no means an empty threat, even when there is no intention of building. A cottage, however hideous, can readily be let, and is a profitable investment when it serves as a warning to rebellious mansion-owners. I know of a remote, solitary, bleak, raw red brick labourer's cottage comprising four stark walls and a drain pipe, set in a break of the hedge on a country road. Its position—which would be readily understood if cottages were jettisoned from passing aircraft—is explained by the entrance drive to a large private house on the opposite side of the road, up which the cottage stares unwinkingly like a village idiot entranced. It is there, as is notorious, in fulfilment of a threat, because the owner of the mansion refused to buy the field in which it stands.

This is a happy instance of the way commercial enterprise advances the cause of civilization by establishing blackmail as a recognized source of revenue and of increase to the wealth of the Empire. By building cheaply and rapidly, instead of in the old-fashioned way, not only are larger profits immediately accrued, but future profits are secured by the early need for renewal, and good money earned merely by refraining from building.

GRIGBLAY TO SPINLOVE

Dear Sir,   10.11.26.

What Mr. Pricehard says is pretty much what I feared. Of course there is some stupid thing been done somewhere and it will be a job to find out where, for what has happened is that fumes from the heating furnace get into the hollow of the outside walls, and one of those places it gets out again is, in my opinion, where the joists of upper floors bear on the $4\frac{1}{2}$-in.

inner thickness of outside walls, and so lets the air be drawn from the hollow into the space between joists and through joints of flooring into the bedrooms. I have had a look at the plans and you will find that those particular bedrooms is just where it can get; for the joists in those rooms run across to the outer wall and not parallel with it; and another thing that fixes it is the way these fumes came on worse than before when the heating furnace was started up again a few weeks ago, for as the work dried out in the summer the ends of joists, where they were built in, would shrink and leave a bit more room for the fumes to leak through than when the work was newly finished. The joints of flooring will not lie so close now, either. Well, we know the fault is in the heating flue, for the complaints stopped just when the fire was drawn for the summer; but where the fault is, and what to look for, is the difficulty—unless we open up the flue till we find out. I have never had the like of this happen in any building of mine. None of my bricklayers would play hanky-panky with a chimney flue or leave out a brick, which is what looks like; and Bloggs would not let them if they tried it. However, there cannot be many places where a little thing wrong would make all that difference, and Bloggs will be likely to say. I have written him to-day.

Yours faithfully,

Here, then, is the explanation of the famous "defective drains" —otherwise "odoriferous effluviums"; but the defect giving rise to the nuisance is still a mystery; for carelessness which would leave an opening from a chimney flue into a hollow wall-space would seem impossible of men employed by a builder of Grigblay's standing, or in work overlooked by Bloggs.

The subtlety with which smoke will find its way through brick-work has long ago established the parging—or plastering—of the interior of flues, and until quite recently the parge was always worked up with a proportion of cow dung which prevented it from developing cracks as a lime and sand rendering is apt to do. Fifty years ago bricklayers began to resist using this traditional parge —probably because its composition seemed ignominious; and as the mortar in which the bricks are laid, now commonly used to parge the flues, seems to be all that is required, it may well be that

BRASH IS FOILED

BRASH TO SPINLOVE

Dear Mr. Spinlove,   12.11.26.

I desire that you will be so obliging as to carefully peruse the enclosed copy of a letter I yesterday received from Mr. Russ anent Riddoppo, and of correspondence therein referred to, which I transmit herewith preparatory to your meeting me for the purpose of discussing the position of affairs on an early day. You will observe that I refrain from all comment. Such views as I have to communicate are, I apprehend, more fit to be the subject of verbal rather than of literary intercourse; but you may tell that infernal scoundrel Grigblay that if he or any of his damned workmen put so much as their noses inside my gate I will have them thrown out into the road.

Yours sincerely,

P.S.—Pray excuse a pardonable asperity of diction.

(ENCLOSURE) RUSS AND CO., SOLICITORS, TO BRASH

Dear Sir,   10.11.26.

In accordance with the instructions you gave Mr. Russ in your interview with him on 28th September, we entered into communication with Messrs. the Riddoppo Coy., Ltd. (and Reduced), and subsequently, on receipt of the Company's reply, with Mr. Marston Grigblay, and we enclose copy of the correspondence.

Before we received the letter from Mr. Grigblay's solicitors, of 3rd October, it came to our knowledge that a receiving order had been made out against the Riddoppo Coy. The firm is in liquidation, and from information in our possession we are of opinion that reorganization is extremely unlikely; that the assets will be sold for the benefit of the debenture holders, and that there will be little or nothing left for the unsecured creditors. In the circumstances we do not consider the company worth powder and shot.

In view of the position Mr. Grigblay takes and the difficulty of showing him to be responsible without the evidence of the Riddoppo Company of the soundness of the paint supplied; and in view also of the opinion given us by Mr. Chawlegger, we do not consider that you could succeed in an action against Mr. Grigblay. It seems to us, therefore, that the only course for you to take is to withdraw.

Yours faithfully,

So the end of this matter is that, for his sins, poor old Brash is left high and dry. Riddoppo, Ltd. (and Reduced) has gone bankrupt, a fate that overtakes not a small number of such ventures and which offers an additional reason why architects should be wary in experimenting in untried materials. The company's property will be sold to pay the debenture holders; creditors will get little, shareholders nothing, and the only person who is likely to have done well out of Riddoppo is perhaps Brash's influential commercial friend Mr. Ziegfeld Swatmug, who may have bought the rights from the inventor for a small sum, sold them to the public for a large one, and afterwards resigned from the board of directors and disposed of his holding.

(ENCLOSURE 1) RUSS TO SECRETARY, RIDDOPPO COY.

Dear Sir,   30.9.26.

We are instructed by Sir Leslie Brash, of Honeywood Grange, Marlford, Kent, that certain paint manufactured and supplied by your Company to Mr. John Grigblay, builder, of Marlford, for the decoration of Honeywood Grange, has proved seriously defective; and have to say that unless you can make satisfactory explanation showing the said defects not to be due to any fault in the paint you supplied or, alternatively, will at once give an undertaking to restore, renew or repaint as may be necessary for the proper completion of the work, we are instructed to take action against you for breach of warranty.

Yours faithfully,

(ENCLOSURE 2) RIDDOPPO TO RUSS

Dear Sir, 2.10.26.

The paint we supplied to Mr. Grigblay a year ago, which we understand is the cause of complaint, was our well-known New Novelty Riddoppo Super-Paint (Matt) and was in perfect condition as taken out of stock and same as supplied to others. We can demonstrate the superior quality of our Riddoppo Super-Paint, and produce evidence of painting carried out with paint taken from our stock before and after same supplied to Mr. Grigblay.

The defects are due to neglect of painters to follow instructions, which we now enclose as sent to Mr. Grigblay and all others and clearly printed on the tins.

We have no intention to renew defects, as same are due to neglect to follow instructions, and not to Riddoppo Super-Paint, and which is no business of ours.

Yours faithfully,

(ENCLOSURE 2A) PRINTED LEAFLET

NEW NOVELTY "RIDDOPPO" SUPER-PAINT

IMPORTANT. See the word "RIDDOPPO" (with 2 "d's" and 2 "p's") on every tin. NO OTHER GENUINE and if noticed should be informed at once.

N.B. These instructions must be followed if best results desired.

INSTRUCTIONS FOR USING RIDDOPPO

1. Use at a temperature of 55 degrees or over which should not be less than 40 degrees but in damp weather a higher temperature gives best results particularly for last.

2. Keep air-tight lid hermetically sealed and well stir before transferring and at once replace.

3. If copper-bound tools are used must be protected as RIDDOPPO acts as solvent and same may affect appearance.

4. All tools to be used first immerse and thoroughly cleanse in "RIDOP" (pink tin) supplied with all orders only after careful drying.

5. No paint must on any account be returned but specially in damp weather and if left overnight to be removed from pot carefully cleansed after with "RIDOP" (pink tin) before same is again re-used.

6. As damp takes longer to dry close windows or similarly open and shade from sun if same is not.

7. If ropy add "RIDOP" (pink tin) unless affected by frost though only a small amount and not otherwise or results will be unsatisfactory.

ALL TINS ARE THE PROPERTY OF THE RIDDOPPO COMPANY WHICH WHEN NOT RETURNED WILL BE CHARGED 2s.
(Issued by Riddoppo Ltd.)

————

The seven golden rules of Riddoppo!

One disadvantage of a Public School and University education (however lightly faced) is that it prevents a man from understanding directions, such as these, which offer no difficulties to Bloggs and his painters, and which Grigblay could probably read aright if he stood on his head to do it.

(ENCLOSURE 3) RUSS TO GRIGBLAY

Dear Sir,   4.10.26.

We are instructed by Sir Leslie Brash to point out that certain painting carried out by you at Honeywood Grange under your contract has developed serious defects, which you have declined to remedy after being required to do so.

The Riddoppo Company, who manufactured and supplied the paint in question, state that it was taken from stock and was in perfect condition, as supplied to other customers, and that they sent you full instructions for applying the paint, which instructions were also printed on the tins.

We are instructed to inform you that unless you can show that the failure of the paint-work is not due to defective workmanship or other fault for which you are responsible; or, alternatively, will give an undertaking immediately to restore or renew the defective paintwork to the satisfaction of the architect; Sir Leslie Brash intends to have the necessary renovations carried out by some other person and to deduct the cost of such renovations, together with certain expenses he has already incurred as a result of the defects, from the balance of moneys retained by him as security for the completion of your contract.

Yours faithfully,

(ENCLOSURE 4) GLAUBER AND WALSH (SOLICITORS) TO RUSS

Dear Sir,   8.10.26.

Our client, Mr. John Grigblay, instructs us to say, in reply to your letter to him of 4th October, that he strongly objected to use Riddoppo paint and only did so to oblige your client after receiving the written undertaking of the architect that your client accepted full responsibility for the result of the experiment; that he placed his foreman painter in charge of the work and employed only skilled decorators upon it; that the instructions supplied with the paint were exactly followed, or if not exactly followed, then followed as exactly as the ambiguous and confused wording made them possible to be understood; or, if understandable, then as exactly as painters and decorators can, or could be expected to understand and follow them; or if the said instructions were not ambiguous, then that they were redundant and fastidious and such as no practical men could observe, or if they were not, then that no warning of such defects as have occurred was given, so that these defects are not due to any failure to observe instructions, if clear instructions were given, which my client denies, but were due to the omission of warnings of dangers of which my client could have no knowledge as the paint was composed of "new and secret ingredients".

Furthermore, my client's case is that the said instructions are worded and designed to be, and in fact are, a mere device to enable Riddoppo to shelter themselves from liability for defects in their paint; which paint my client has evidence to prove is generally discredited by the building trade as a worthless imposture.

I am further instructed to say that my client contends that he has carried out his contract to paint in a skilful and workmanlike manner, and that he refuses to renovate or restore or renew or have anything more to do with any painting at Honeywood of any kind whatsoever or for any consideration whatsoever; and that my client regards the threat of an action by your client as the malicious attempt of a rich man to bully and browbeat a poor one, and will defend any action which your client may bring, to his last penny.

Yours faithfully,

(Here ends the correspondence enclosed by Russ to Brash.)
As Grigblay said—"There are others who can employ solicitors besides Sir Leslie Brash."

GRIGBLAY TO SPINLOVE

Dear Sir,   12.11.26.

As promised, we wrote to our foreman Bloggs on the subject of the run of the furnace flue, and his report is as follows:

"She start off left hand pretty quick but only as far as the top of fire lump at back. . . . Then she make a sudden turn and rise up straight, but going away backwards eight courses I reckon or may be ten, till she have nine inches to face of cellar wall. . . ."

Bloggs says this was done by your orders to prevent wine from getting chilled, and that it made the flue very tight just above so that he had difficulty in getting it over. He goes on:

"After that she start off and away she go left hand over the door of fuel and past soot door till that girder under kitchen hearth stop her; but she just lean over right hand to clear and off she go again nice and easy right up to stalk and a good one for a brush all the way after she pass the soot door. She was a bit tight below I admit, but I did the best I could and she swept beautiful and draw a treat and so I left her and do not know what the trouble can be since."

We are afraid the above does not help us much, but Mr. Grigblay is arranging to go over to Honeywood with the plans on Thursday and see what he can make.

Yours faithfully,

It is apparent that Blogg's authentic chirp is in part lost to us by the editorial conscience of the typist. I picture the omitted passages as recording Bloggs' views of the architect's demands.

He speaks of the flue as "she" out of respect and affection for flues, and for somewhat different reasons than when he used the same word to designate Lady Brash.

SPINLOVE TO BRASH

Dear Sir Leslie Brash,   14.11.26.

I have been away from the office on important business and found your letters of the 8th and 12th awaiting me on my return yesterday.

I am very sorry to hear of the building activities and really do not know what to advise. I am afraid however, that no question of infringement of your copyright arises. In the case of the block of cottages you proposed to build last year, the entire plan—which was the material part of the design—was, as you say, "purloined"; but I do not think there can be any copyright in an architectural feature, and though the villas may imitate, they cannot attempt to *reproduce* any part of your house. I am afraid, too, that you have no copyright in the word "Honeywood", as it is a place-name which was in use long before you adopted it.

As regards the proposed bungalow allotments, I do not know what to say. The only thing seems to be to buy the people out. It was, I think, considerate of them to give you the opportunity of acquiring the land. They perhaps thought you might not like to have buildings of that kind close up to your boundary.

I have received the analyst's report. He says the smells are due to fumes from the heating furnace. These must somehow get into the space of the hollow walls and are by that means distributed to remote parts of the house. I cannot understand in the least how this has happened. However, Mr. Grigblay has agreed to make no charge for putting things right, as it is a defect for which he is responsible.

I was sorry to learn the result of your negotiations for settlement of the Riddoppo dispute. I have always felt, as you know, that Grigblay could not be held responsible in view of his objection to the paint and of his consenting to use it only after you accepted responsibility for the result. This was also Mr. Chawlegger's view, you will remember, and now Mr. Russ evidently feels the same about it. It will be impossible for me to see you this week, but I will ring up early next week and arrange a meeting. I am extremely busy just now.

You asked me some time ago to let you have particulars of my charges. These I now have the pleasure of enclosing.

Yours sincerely,

This letter seems to have been written on one of the very worst of Spinlove's "bad days". Except for the directions it gives Brash on the matter of copyright, it is futile to the point of exasperation. If he had no advice to give he should have said so, instead of elaborating vacuity. Brash is well aware that he has acquired no rights in the word "Honeywood"; that he can rescue himself by "buying the people out", and that the one entirely impossible explanation of the proposal made him by Snitch is consideration for his feelings or his interests.

Spinlove's comment on the Riddoppo fiasco—"I always told you so"—and his bland assumption that the whole nuisance of the smells is satisfactorily disposed of by Grigblay's putting it right "without charge" is the very cream of tactlessness; and why he should choose this occasion of all others to tell Brash, twice over, that he is too busy to give him full attention, and to send him particulars of his charges, is beyond understanding.

As regards this matter of architectural copyright, it is only in recent years that the thing has been recognized in English Law; and there have not been enough judgments to determine how the Courts apply the test of "colourable imitation"—which establishes infringement—to plans, elevations, and architectural

186

Brash is Foiled

features. There are, however, from time to time claims by archi-
tects whose published designs for small houses have been adopted
by private building-owners. Such claims are usually settled by
the author of the design being paid the fees he would have earned
as architect for the work, and the making of them must be among
the most lucrative activities of architectural practice; but the
generality of architects have a natural repugnance to taking
advantage of simple souls whose attachment to the great ideal of
getting something for nothing has been a little too fervid.

Appearances are that Spinlove is not anxious for Brash to see
Pricehard's report. This is not surprising.

Dear Sir,   15.11.26.

I write to confirm telephone message: Mr. Grigblay to postpone visit Honeywood till further communication from Mr.
Spinlove.

Yours faithfully,
R. S. PINTLE.

Pintle is Spinlove's assistant and is presumably acting on
instructions Spinlove gave before he went away on this "impor-
tant business" of his. Brash's threat to have Grigblay "thrown
out into the road" if he came again to the house would seem to
make this intervention by Spinlove no more than merciful. What,
however, must quite properly have weighed with Spinlove is that
Brash has still to unburden himself of some deep grievance
against Grigblay and, that being the case, Spinlove cannot make
himself a party to an act by Grigblay which Brash for any reason
has sa d he will not tolerate. In human affairs things are not
unimportant because they are childish and silly: in fact, the chief
burden of life is the importance of trivialities.

GLAUBER AND WALSH TO SPINLOVE

Dear Sir,   18.11.26.

We are instructed by Mr. John Grigblay to call your attention to the fact that the final balance under our client's contract

187

with Sir Leslie Brash fell due on the 10th of this month and to request that you will at once issue the necessary certificate for the amount of £1,242 11s. 9d., as shown in the Statement of Account agreed by you on behalf of Sir Leslie Brash.

Yours faithfully,

As Grigblay has been called upon by Spinlove to make good the defect to which the escaping fumes are due, he is not yet entitled to this final balance which only becomes due after he has completed his covenant to make good defects; and as Grigblay has agreed to make good the defect it must be assumed that his solicitors wrote this letter on instructions Grigblay gave them before the defect was established. Grigblay no doubt so instructed Glauber and Walsh at the time he employed them to answer Russ's threatening letter, in view of the fact that the withholding of the certificate by Spinlove, or the refusal by Brash to honour it, would bring the Riddoppo conflict to a head by compelling Spinlove either to range himself in opposition to Brash or to join issues against Grigblay.

SPINLOVE TO GLAUBER AND WALSH

Dear Sirs,   21.11.26.
I am unable to draw certificate for final balance under Mr. Grigblay's Honeywood contract as there are still outstanding defects which he has been called upon to make good.

Yours faithfully,

This letter is either clever to the point of being cunning, or it is merely the result of shortsightedness; and from what we have seen of Spinlove the latter explanation seems the more likely. If Spinlove perceived that Glauber and Walsh wrote in ignorance of the fumes defect and for the purpose of bringing the Riddoppo dispute to a head, his reply is a most adroit evasion; for had he stated plainly that the defect which prevented his issuing the certificate was that of the fumes, he would have implied that the Riddoppo defect was not an obstacle to the issue. He has answered Glauber and Walsh and yet still retains his firm position on the fence.

Brash is Foiled

Dear Jazz,   20.11.26.

Well really, thingys are getting a bit *too* rather, don't you think? Why not jump in and do something! Poor Dad exploded when he got your letter the morning he went away, and knocked over his coffee. You should not do that. What did you say to upset him so? He told me the smells were fumes from the heating furnace; and since he went it has been like living in a refuse destructor here, and I had to tell the servants to let the fire out or I should not have been able to keep any of them in the house. Mum is pining in exile and I dare not go to her for fear of finding the house empty when I get back; Dad is thoroughly displeased with you, and I do not know what he will think if he comes back and still finds nothing done. It is just as if you did not care a blow. You really ought to get a move on.

                                                                    PUD.

As there is no reply to this letter in the folder, we must suppose that Spinlove answered it privately. In point of fact the delay is due rather to circumstances than to any neglect on his part.

Dear Sir,   21.11.26.

I write to confirm telephone message asking that you will at the first opportunity go to Honeywood with the plans, as you proposed, and find out where this defect in the furnace flue is. Something really must be done without delay as the inconvenience is increasing and great dissatisfaction is expressed.

Will you telephone which day Mr. Grigblay will go; and also let me know result of the investigation by wire or telephone?

                                            Yours faithfully,

BLOGGS LENDS A HAND

(TELEGRAM) SPINLOVE TO BLOGGS

21.11.26.

Reply paid. Can you say where defect furnace flue likely to be.—Spinlove.

SPINLOVE TO BLOGGS

Dear Mr. Bloggs,   21.11.26.

I wired to you to-day and enclose confirmation. I have seen your report on the run of the furnace flue, but what is wanted is information of the cause of the escape of fumes into the hollow wall, and of the position of the defect. Can you recall any circumstances which will throw light on the subject?

Yours truly,

It is irregular for an architect to write personally to any servant of a builder, but as Grigblay failed to tap the appropriate vat of Bloggs' garnered memories, Spinlove, in his ambition to "get a move on", is impelled to make the attempt.

(TELEGRAM) BLOGGS TO SPINLOVE

21.11.26.

Sir try Williams sweep Thadford may likely know.—Fred.

If Spinlove had no other feeling than surprise on reading that last word I do not envy him. Bloggs is known to everyone about buildings as "Fred"; he regards himself merely as "Fred", and his modesty holds him from the assertiveness of using his patronymic.

GRIGBLAY TO SPINLOVE

Dear Sir,   21.11.26.

Mr. Grigblay will arrange to go to Honeywood Friday.

Bloggs Lends a Hand

Please note that delay is no fault of ours as Mr. Grigblay proposed to go over last week, but we had message from you we were to wait your further instructions.

We should like to explain that Messrs. Glauber and Walsh's letter to you of 18th November was under a misapprehension.

Yours faithfully,

Glauber and Walsh no doubt wrote to Grigblay reporting Spinlove's refusal to issue the certificate, and asking further instructions.

The following letter has been written under the conditions of extreme torment imposed by the absorbent back of an old blue print—embossed by the hobnails of someone who once stood on it—and a pen of unimaginable antecedents. Bloggs has evidently made haste to reply by return.

BLOGGS TO SPINLOVE

Sir,   22.11.26.

Now I come to think there wehre a lanky chap Williams by name come hanging about to get the job to sweep the chimblys, I sent off but two or three days after there he was come back and says her Lady ship add give him the order, well I give you the order not to touch no fleues I says but I'll give you a nice esay job I says and that thire is the quick job of clearing off from wehre you have no call to be I says and wehre your not wanted I says. He sauce me and says I dursent let him has the half could never be rodded, but I dident think no more till one Tuesday dinner after the day the riging come and took the gate post, and there was the little hand cart he had standing— What's this here I ask some of them—Oh thats the chap too sweep the fleues they says and theire I found him right up the furnice acause she told him to, and grined dirty at me acause he could not pass is rods with a grate big coreing iron he had haeving and pokeing and never thinking thire wehre a soot door. It made me fare mad with half a bussel of parge and mortar he had raked down and I pretty near had to frog marsh him before he would take himself off. Well thire it was been

191

and done and had to be left you cant get inside a fleue to parge but never thought no harm would come.

Yours respectfully,

"The Honeywood File" recounts how, during Brash's absence on holiday, Lady Brash became the dupe of a touting chimney-sweep; and it now appears that the defect which has been the cause of her continued complaints, and the source of so much trouble to so many persons and for so long a time, is due to no remissness on the part of either architect or builder or of anyone else, but to the lady herself, who ignored the assurances of Spinlove and allowed the vigilance of Bloggs to be eluded. It is only fair, however, to regard the catastrophe as the lady's misfortune rather than her fault.

SPINLOVE TO WILLIAMS,
CHIMNEY SWEEP, THADFORD

Dear Sir,   23.11.26.

I understand you were employed by Lady Brash to sweep chimneys at the new house at Honeywood and were stopped after you had begun on the furnace flue, and that you found an obstruction you could not clear.

I should be glad if you could tell me where the obstruction was.

Yours faithfully,

No purpose is served by Spinlove asking this question, for now it is known that the defect is probably due to violent attempts to clear the flue of an imagined obstruction, the damage is to be looked for at the place where a set-off, or bend in the flue, prevented the rods from passing. This place will probably be above the soot door spoken of—the purpose of the door being to give access when bends in a flue prevent its being wholly swept from the fireplace opening.

SPINLOVE TO GRIGBLAY

Dear Sir,   23.11.26.

I enclose copy of letter received from Bloggs, contents of which I communicated by telephone to-day.

I have written to the chimney-sweep, but perhaps **Mr.** Grigblay will be able to get in touch with him before going to Honeywood to-morrow.

Yours faithfully,

"MR. WILLIAMS, PRACTICAL CHIMNEY-SWEEP (CHIMNEYS SWEPT)" TO SPINLOVE

Sir, 25.11.26.

Replying *re* your favour, we operated on Her Ladyship's furnace as per instructions. On endeavouring to pass 18 in. brush, obstruction was encountered after six canes. Following our usual practice with refractories from fair to medium, we then made attempt with No. 1 iron, but received instructions to desist from contractor's representative before desired results obtained.

Said flue belongs class 1 unsweepables, in our opinion, being carried over too sharp at six-and-a-quarter canes.

Yours respectfully,

MR. WILLIAMS (*Chimneys Swept*).

GRIGBLAY TO SPINLOVE

Dear Sir, 25.11.26.

We beg to report we had furnace flue opened up yesterday and found defect due to damage by sweep employed by Sir Leslie Brash. We have left the flue opened up for your inspection and instructions.

Yours faithfully,

SPINLOVE TO GRIGBLAY

Dear Sirs, 26.11.26.

Please make all necessary repairs to flue at once, so that heating furnace may be brought into use. To be charged *extra*.

Yours faithfully,

GRIGBLAY TO SPINLOVE

Dear Sir, 27.11.26.

We must decline to restore damage to flue until we have

193

received your acceptance on behalf of Sir Leslie Brash that we are in no way responsible for same.

Yours faithfully,

This sort of thing is the natural consequence of bringing solicitors upon the scenes: without good faith and mutual confidence in a common purpose it would scarcely be possible ever to get any building contract carried out at all. Brash, by his conduct of the Riddoppo dispute, has made it no less than necessary for Grigblay to protect himself as he does.

(HOLOGRAPH) GRIGBLAY TO SPINLOVE

Sir,   27.11.26.

I saw your letter at office to-day, and you will have received my reply, but I will just take leave to send you private word and ask you to have a look at that flue, for where shall I be if I build up and all evidence destroyed and only my word that the damage is no business of mine but the work of the sweep acting on your client's orders? It would be a good thing if the old gentleman had a look as well, for he has been over ready to lay trouble that is nobody's fault but his own to other people's doors, and seeing is believing, and believing may save a few solicitors' letters of which there have been more than enough wasted already. Sir Leslie is expected back in a few days they tell me, so no harm to wait a bit.

From what Bloggs wrote you I broke into the flue about five feet up in the corner of the scullery, and there it was plain enough, the handy work of "Mr. Williams"—as he calls himself—who carefully raked away about two feet of the new parging, clawed the mortar out of the joints and punched a bit of a closer, that happened to come nice and handy, clean through into the hollow wall so as to leave a proper hole you can put your hand through comfortably without rubbing any skin off your knuckles. I never saw the like of it in all my experience: he would have ended by raking the house down if Bloggs had not stopped him. It is lucky it is an easy matter to put right, though it will mean a bit of pulling down before we can get at the job.

Brash Exceeds

You will pardon me writing, but thought you ought to know how things are.

Yours faithfully,

Although a building owner has no right to expect, as some do, that an architect shall give up the better part of a day to viewing one or two insignificant defects in a completed house, it is clearly Spinlove's duty, under the special circumstances, to inspect this flue so that he may satisfy himself that the damage is as Grigblay reports and, if it is, that there has been no contributory negligence in the building of the flue. Grigblay's reference to a "closer"— which is a small piece of brick built in for the purpose of overtaking the break of the joints and making the end brick of the course finish to a fair face—indicates that the bricklayers may have been at fault; for a closer would scarcely be rightly used in the position indicated. The defect may be the occasion, as Grigblay foresees, of adding fuel to Brash's grievances; and it is incumbent on Spinlove thoroughly to master the facts so that his apportionment of responsibility may be authoritative. Strictly speaking, he had no business to decide that the sweep was to blame—as he did when he authorized the repairs as an extra— without first satisfying himself of the fact by an inspection of the work. It would serve no purpose for Brash to view the damage, for he could not use his eyes unless someone were at hand to direct him in the evidence of them, and it is only Spinlove who could well give him that direction.

BRASH EXCEEDS

BRASH TO SPINLOVE

Dear Mr. Spinlove,   2.12.26.

Your communication of the 14th reached me on the day of my departure, and I now, on my return, sit down to indite my reply in the hope that you are by this time so far relieved from the pressure of your extreme preoccupation with various other interests as not to be entirely prevented from perusing it with the attention which, as your employer, I apprehend I am entitled to expect.

My unavoidably protracted delay in replying will, I conceive, be no disadvantage to the matter I have to expound, as the extreme *insouciance* of your last communication—if I may diverge into a foreign tongue to express my sense of the inappropriateness of the epistolatory style you think fit to adopt —might have precipitated a more forcible rejoinder.

The explanations I must request you to furnish, as I have already intimated, anent your attitude to the Riddoppo dispute, and anent your approval of extortionate "profits" and "fees" added in the builder's Statement of Account, and anent also your own astonishing claim for fees—I desire to postpone to the occasion of a personal interview to be conveniently arranged at Mr. Russ's office. I now address myself to you exclusively on the subject of the noxious emanations which have continuously tormented us ever since we first took up residence at Honeywood Grange. After ten months of elusive evasion and dilatory procrastination you now inform me the house has been so built that coke fumes from the heating furnace are dispersed to all parts of it, and that we are being slowly poisoned; and you intimate with a bland assurance which—you must permit me to remark—causes me most amazed astonishment, that the whole matter is now satisfactorily disposed of *because* Mr. Grigblay has signified his willingness to carry out the necessary preventative measures "*without charge*". You must permit me to asseverate that I cannot subscribe to any such fantastically preposterous view of the matter. As a consequence of Grigblay's contemptibly shoddy building and—you must allow me to point out—the negligent supervision of my architect, and his dilatory indifference to the appalling discomfort attendant on the disgusting effluviums of which we are the victims, Lady Brash has suffered in health, the domestic staff has been on the verge of revolt, and I have been involved in heavy disbursements on account of fees incurred by the necessity of recourse to the advice of medical practitioners and to the employment of sanitary consultants.

During these months you have had numerous intimations of

the repulsive odoriferous conditions, and have repeatedly reiterated assurances that no unsavoury emanations could possibly eventuate in so carefully built a house as Honeywood, and have excused yourself from the trouble of ascertaining the cause of complaint by sending Grigblay to persuade us nothing was wrong so that he might save himself the trouble of having to put anything right. Our complaints have been met by nothing but evasive procrastinations; and when, eventually, on my urgent insistence, you condescended to investigate and were compelled to admit the presence of olfactory effluviums, what did you do? You did nothing! After weeks of delay I return expecting the necessary ameliorations to have been effected in the interim of my absence, and find only that under your directions men have knocked a hole in the scullery so that the furnace cannot be used, pushed some dirty sacks into it and vacated the work.

The position of affairs is perfectly intolerable and beyond all bearing. I do not precisely know what my rights are, and I apprehend that since my architect is in the opposite camp it is not to be anticipated that he will exactly inform me of them; but it is beyond the bounds of credulity that I am to be subjected to these persistent annoyances and refractory oppositions without power to extricate myself; and unless my architect and his builder *immediately* bestir themselves to make this house a human domicile instead of a lethal chamber for cats and dogs, I shall exercise my own resources and employ others who can be depended on to carry out what they engage to perform. My eventual demands on Grigblay for compensation are a matter for contingent consideration.

Yours faithfully,

Brash is certainly deserving of sympathy, for he is gloriously unaware that the whole of the trouble is due. his wife's interferences; he also, I think, deserves sympathy in that his manful effort at self-control has not proved equal to the length of his letter; but most of our sympathy must lie with Spinlove, who has the task of answering the letter.

SPINLOVE HITS BACK

Dear Sirs, 4.12.26.

I enclose copy of letter I have received from Sir Leslie Brash, and also a copy of that to which it is a reply. As your client, by objecting to my style, appears to require me to answer him in his own, I am replying to you. It was a great shock to me to get his letter, as no doubt he intended since it is the result of ten days' reflection; and what his immediate more "forcible rejoinder" would have been I do not know, for such studied misrepresentation and abuse must need deep thought.

You are acquainted with the facts of the Riddoppo dispute, and will be able to point out to your client that I was *right* in advising him not to use the paint; *right* in supporting Mr. Grigblay's objection to using it; and *right* in saying Mr. Grigblay could not be held responsible for the failure—which was also Counsel's opinion and is your own view. Further, that it is a mere quibble to say I took sides with the builder; that if your client, at any point in the dispute, had acted on my advice he would have saved himself wasted trouble and expense; and that everything I have done has been in his interests, which, if I had acted differently, would not have been the case. The truth is that what your client resents is my being right and he wrong.

You will also be able to explain to your client that the "profits" and "fees" charged in the Statement of Account are according to custom; that every detail of the account has been audited by the Quantity Surveyor, Mr. Tinge, after authorization by me, according to the stipulations of the contract; and you can remind him that I offered to explain any points upon which he was not satisfied.

I enclose copy of the official Scale of Charges issued by the Royal Institute of British Architects, so that you will be able to show your client that my charges are in accordance with it except where they are less. I find, however, that I omitted certain services for which I am entitled to additional fees: I therefore enclose amended account in substitution for that previously sent in error.

With regard to the leakage of coke fumes, you will be able to tell your client that his ardour in abusing me for what is no one's fault but his own, outruns discretion unless he can explain: (1)—how his household has been "continuously tormented by disgusting effluviums ever since the house was occupied", when no one but Lady Brash was able to detect any smell at all, and the furnace that caused it was out of use for more than six months; and (2)—in what way I was guilty, also "continuously", of "elusive dilatory procrastination" for giving assurances that there was nothing wrong with the drains, when there was nothing wrong, or in failing to recognize a smell which it required the services of a chemist to determine.

The facts are, as your client knows, that early in the year it was suspected something was wrong with the drains. The builder investigated and found unsanitary conditions due to neglect to keep traps clear. The drains were subsequently proved sound, and there were no more complaints of smells till the 10th October. An indeterminate stuffy smell was then noticed, and at my instigation a consulting chemist was called in who, four weeks ago, reported fumes from coke fires. My dilatoriness has since then consisted in determining what and where the defect was, and in getting the work opened up. In this I have been delayed fifteen days by your client's prohibiting the builder from entering the house, and by the refusal of the builder to make good until your client accepted responsibility for the defect, which is revealed *to be a hole knocked in the flue by a chimney-sweep employed by your client*, and who eluded the foreman after being told not to touch the flues. You will, therefore, be able to point out to your client that he has misstated many facts perfectly well known to him, and that he alone is responsible for any annoyance he has suffered.

In this letter I have tried to confine myself to the business of settling up; but as Mr. Grigblay cannot answer for himself and my silence might imply acceptance of the aspersions on him, I wish to say that Mr. Grigblay has from first to last done his duty—and more than his duty; that he is a scrupulously honourable and self-respecting man and a conscientious and capable builder; that the whole of the trouble during the past months has been made by your client; and that Mr. Grigblay has far more cause for grievance against the building owner than the building owner has against him.

You will note that your client has had the forethought to write in his own hand so as to escape the consequences of libel —a most wise precaution. It may be, however, that his sense of obligations is not entirely regulated by fear of legal proceedings, and therefore, although he has made it impossible for me to enforce a withdrawal and apology, I will nevertheless pay him the compliment of demanding both.

Yours faithfully,

We have noticed before that the highly temperamental Spinlove has a bit of the Old Adam in his make-up. Like other temperamental persons, he becomes a different being under different circumstances, and it is this that explains the exuberant folly of some of his letters, the stiff-necked superciliousness of others and the passionate resentment he sometimes, as here, displays. He must have had the devil at his elbow when he wrote and rewrote and polished up and altered the first typescript of the above, for it is clear he could not have produced the thing off-hand. The stored depths of bitterness it reveals are dreadful; and it is the sort of letter that may be said to be scarcely ever written, for those who are capable of writing them know better than to indulge themselves. The arresting thing about the letter is the deliberate uprooting of the plant Spinlove has been tending for two years with such solicitude; and the discarding of Brash's esteem and friendly offices just when they were ripe for garnering. This seems inexplicable; for if Spinlove were characteristically unable to control his temper he could not have arrived at the position he has reached. The only explanation that seems possible is that there are matters affecting the relationship of Brash and his architect which this correspondence has not revealed.

The wild folly of Spinlove's action does not, however, prevent us from admiring his courage in writing the letter; and there is a manly disregard of consequences which shows him to be of finer metal than we have hitherto had reason to suppose. That the

Spinlove Hits Back

letter is not quite fair to Brash is of no consequence: the only impediment to our joy at the prospect of Brash's reading it is that Spinlove is but little over thirty and Brash is advanced in middle age—for I imagine Grigblay's "old gentleman" to be no indication of senility, but provoked by a humorous perception of frontal luxurance, tight boots, and similar abnegations of youth.

We also may sympathize with Spinlove. In what way ought he to have replied to Brash's outrageous letter? It is a very difficult question. He might, of course, have flattered Brash into reason by being submissive, giving a diplomatic answer to the various complaints, appealing for a more tolerant view of the facts and a recognition of what was due to himself; or he might have risked a letter of passionate protest, such as in early days Brash once provoked from him; but he could scarcely have done either except at the loss of his own self-respect and his claim on Brash's—and why should he make any surrender whatever?

When a letter is written under a genuine misapprehension and without any intention of offensiveness, a diplomatic answer removes the misapprehension and prostrates the offender with the realization of his transgression; but when, as in Brash's case, there is a deliberate intention to affront, and facts are wilfully distorted to bolster abuse, the problem is how best to hit back; and to hit back with effect, for it is easy for the hitter to do more damage to himself than to his adversary—as, indeed, Spinlove seems here to have done. Spinlove must have been tormented with the difficulties of his task before he struck the happy idea of addressing his reply to Russ; and if he had written coldly instead of with feeling, made no attempt at retort, and suggested the expedience of an apology without appearing to care whether it were conceded or not, he would probably have hit Brash the harder and disarmed him of the deeper grievance he has now given him cause to feel. The things that will hurt Brash are—Spinlove's disdaining to reply to him; Russ's seeing the letters; and the humiliation of being told that his various grievances are without foundation and that he is wrong and Spinlove right. Spinlove's sarcasms were not necessary, and may be expected to do him more harm than they will Brash.

A FRIEND IN NEED

Dear Jazz,   7.12.26.

What have you been doing to Dad? He is utterly furious with you and I am afraid he is going to see Mr. Russ to-day. Why do you make all this trouble? It was never like this when the house was being built, and afterwards he was so blown out and pleased with everything—but now everything is horrid. He *shouted* to-day—he hardly ever does that. Do please have a reconcilly, or I don't know what will happen. Why is not the flue put right?

Yours,

P.

P.S.—Mum comes home to-morrow, in spite of all cold and comfortless. She took the leap at Brighton—not into the sea but into a psycho-merchant's bosom, and Aunt G. says it has done her good already.

SPINLOVE TO MISS PHYLLIS BRASH

Solemnly, it is not my fault. I am most terribly sorry about it and would do *anything* to have a reconcilly, but he wrote me a most horrible letter; abusive and misrepresenting all the facts —not troubling to understand them, and actually insulting. I could not possibly take it lying down and did not know how to answer without making matters worse; so, as he proposed to refer matters to Russ, I replied to Russ. I suppose this has upset him, but Russ will put things right, I am sure. The flue will be patched up directly the word is given. I can do no more.

RUSS TO SPINLOVE

Dear Sir,   9.12.26.

On receipt of your letter and enclosures we communicated

with our client who has since called to see us and has instructed us to say that his letter to you of 2nd November was written under a misapprehension as to certain facts. He now realizes that his criticisms of your conduct were not justified, and he withdraws them and expresses his regret that he made them.

We shall be glad if you will make an appointment with Mr. Russ at this office on an early day for the purpose of explaining one or two matters arising out of the Statement of Account, and your own charges.

We have also to direct you to instruct the builder to make the necessary alterations to the flue at the earliest moment, and to inform us directly you know definitely the date when the work will be completed.

Yours faithfully,

It will be noticed that, by ignoring Spinlove's violence, Russ's formal letter conveys a more effective rebuke than any retort or comment would be likely to do. Russ has evidently persuaded Brash to a more reasonable state of mind.

SPINLOVE TO MISS PHYLLIS BRASH

10.12.26.

Since you rang up this morning a letter has come from Russ which puts everything right so far as business is concerned—apology and everything. Will you keep a lookout to-morrow morning and let me know how thingys are at your end, as I am writing him a really nice letter that I hope will put everything right. Excuse typewriter.

For "him" I read "your Father".

SPINLOVE TO RUSS AND CO.

Dear Sirs,   10.12.26.

I am much obliged for your letter and gladly accept without reserve Sir Leslie Brash's withdrawal and apology. Of course, I was bound to ask for it.

I will call and see Mr. Russ at 11 on Thursday if that will be convenient to him.

I have arranged by telephone with the builder to put the repairs to flue in hand at once. They will be finished next week, and there is no reason why the furnace should not be lighted on Friday.

Yours faithfully,

In writing "Of course, I was bound to ask him for it" Spinlove raises a doubt whether he was justified in asking, and disparages both the apology and Brash's wisdom in conceding it.

SPINLOVE TO BRASH

Dear Sir Leslie Brash,   10.12.26.

I have to-day received a most satisfactory letter from Mr. Russ which I have, of course, suitably acknowledged; but I am impelled to thank you and to tell you the great pleasure I received from the message he sends from you. I do hope that everything is now all right between us. I was in great difficulties when I received your letter as it was really altogether "too rather", as Phyllis says, and misrepresented the facts in such an extraordinary way that I could not trust myself to reply direct; and as you had threatened to call me to account with Mr. Russ I thought the best thing would be to take the bull by the horns (I am not referring to you, of course) and see if *that* would do any good—as it *has*, I am thankful to say.

I have arranged with Grigblay to get on with the flue, and you will be glad to know that he will definitely finish the work next week and that you will be able to light the furnace on Friday, certain. I understand you agree that the damage was caused by the sweep Lady Brash employed, and that no question will be raised on the point after the work is restored. As you know, Grigblay refuses to touch the flue except on the understanding that you accept responsibility for the damage.

With kind regards and best wishes,

Yours very sincerely,

So this is Spinlove's idea of a "really nice letter"! He would have been entirely right in telling Brash he received his message with great pleasure and accepted it fully and without reserve; and also in adding a light comment on some remote subject to show that he regarded the quarrel as over and out of mind; but he appears—as usual—to have written out of the feelings of the moment without any regard for the effect of his words, which will open every wound that Brash's vanity has suffered in his interview with Russ.

MISS PHYLLIS BRASH TO SPINLOVE

Dear Jazz,   11.12.26.

I spotted your screed at breakfast this morning, but I do not think Dad is going to wear it next his heart *immediately*. He put it back in the envelope after he had read it, and said nothing, but he lobstered—he does that sometimes; not anger—sort of bashfulness, don'tcherknow? What was it you said to make him? Mum is wonderful, but, 'odds architects and builders, when are we going to have the heat on? The whole household is suffering terribly from a chilblain on Mum's little finger. She is writing to you. *It's all right.*

               Yours,

                   P.

Mem: *Go and get psychoed.*

SPINLOVE TO GRIGBLAY

Dear Sir,   17.12.26.

I kept an appointment with Mr. Russ, Sir Leslie Brash's agent, yesterday, and am glad to tell you that there is no intention of proceeding against you for the Riddoppo failure. The matter has been dropped and all suggestions that you were in any way responsible withdrawn.

I enclose certificate for £1,242 11s. 9d. being final balance due under the contract as shown in the Statement of Account. The account for restoring the flue, including analyst's fee, should be rendered separately.

             Yours faithfully,

The Cat Jumps

Dear Mr. Spinlove,   13.12.26.

I am gratified by your intimation that you have received and fittingly acknowledged 'a communication from Mr. Russ, and that that communication meets with your approval.

The matter you refer to as in dispute between us is I apprehend anent the furnace flue; in which it appears we are eventually in agreement and I accordingly observe with satisfaction that you have succeeded in obtaining Mr. Grigblay's consent to undertake the work, as the result of his protracted decision in this matter has been of interest to us for a considerable time.

I suffer, I apprehend, from a certain unavoidable confusion of mind anent the various building operations which Mr. Grigblay objects to perform, and anent those others for which he refuses to take responsibility; but any compliances on his part which offer expectations that we will shortly see the last of him are most welcome.

Yours faithfully,

Brash is sulky. Spinlove has won!

THE CAT JUMPS

My dear Mr. Spinlove,   13.12.26.

Here I am again you will see, after a most enjoyable stay at Brighton with my sister, but all the time I wished I was at home which rather spoilt my visit in spite of not having a *dreadful* chilblain when I was there.

First about the *heat*. Leslie says it will never be finished, but the men are at work now so will you tell them to be a little *quicker*. There, I knew I had forgotten something. I nearly wrote to you from Brighton but it is so much easier when one is closer. Mrs. Cooper tells me they are *all the rage* just now but of course only young people do it in public and I should never *dream* though Phyllis always does. Now what would it, all cost? I should like it on the roof so as to be near the sun, with steps up and down and all closed in to make it invisible, so will you tell me and then I will ask Leslie.

Phyllis is having some friends on Saturday to celebrate the hot water she says and we hope you will stay the night. Please excuse writing, I have such a *dreadful* chilblain on my finger.

Yours very sincerely,

And Sunday night.—P.

Apparently the lady has in view a sun-bath. The benefits of psycho-analysis are not as pronounced as might have been hoped.

SPINLOVE TO GRIGBLAY

Dear Mr. Grigblay,   18.12.26.

I had a long talk with Sir Leslie during the week-end. He is sending you a cheque in final settlement to-day and with it a letter which I hope will end all memory of the upset over the painting. He now admits that he ought to have taken our advice in the first instance, and realizes that the failure of Riddoppo is in no way your fault. There has been no complaint of fumes since the furnace was relighted, and I slept for two nights in the house with windows shut and noticed nothing; so the matter is disposed of, at last!

What I am particularly writing to you about is the restoration of the paint. It is, as you know, in a dreadful state, and what is left of it will have to be thoroughly rubbed down and the whole painted anew. The family is going abroad for two months after Christmas, Sir Leslie will not be much at home and it would be a great satisfaction to him to feel the work was in your charge. I know also that, for personal reasons, it would be a pleasure to him if you would undertake the work; and it would also relieve me of great anxiety. I trust, therefore, that you will reconsider your decision to have nothing more to do with it.

Believe me,

Yours sincerely,

P.S.—Sir Leslie has decided not to have the bedrooms painted out each in a different colour, as now, but uniformly in duck's-egg white as I originally designed.

Spinlove seems to have made good use of his week-end visit.

(HOLOGRAPH) GRIGBLAY TO SPINLOVE

Sir,   19.12.26.

I am not going to say I was not glad to read your letter or that I do not know I have to thank you for the very considerate one I received yesterday from Sir Leslie Brash with his cheque for final balance. The old gentleman expresses himself in a remarkably handsome manner to one so far below him in station, and I have written him that nothing remains to be said.

The job of building Honeywood Grange has, one way and another, perhaps been a bit more of a trouble than it had any call to be; but that is what we have to expect sometimes in the building trade, and so long as the owner is satisfied, and the architect, that is all I ask, for the house is a good one and if it wasn't it wouldn't be for want of everyone concerned having had a try at making it so.

About the painting, of course I will take on the work as asked; but I shall not be able to give an estimate and I shall want a free hand to do what I think well, and I cannot guarantee perfect results although I will do my best to secure them. If you care to have it like that, it would I think, sir, be a good thing to have a talk over. I shall be in town to-morrow and can arrange to call at any time convenient after two o'clock.

Yours faithfully,

Grigblay evidently found Brash's "handsome expressions" more gracious and condescending then he had stomach for; and his sly reminder of obstruction due to the architect's solicitudes and the owner's interferences tells its own tale.

SPINLOVE TO BRASH

My dear Sir Leslie,   21.12.26.

Grigblay called to see me about the painting yesterday. He

is glad to oblige us by doing the work, but as he does not know what is involved in it he cannot give an estimate. The work will be done as Day work—i.e. at net cost plus 15 per cent to cover establishment charges and profit. This is an offer that ought certainly to be accepted.

He says he cannot actually *guarantee* perfect results, but he will spare no pains to secure them, and as he proposes to clean off the existing paint entirely, and sand-paper all vestiges of it from the wood, there is no doubt all will be well. He will arrange with you about dismantling the rooms. He would rather not undertake this.

I spoke to him about the threatened extension of villa-building up Honeywood Hill and the proposed development of the back land. He ridicules the whole idea, and says it is merely a trick to induce you to buy the land at a high price. He says that some of the villas already built are standing empty and that the work has been stopped, and that the land Barthold offered you does not belong to him. He only has a twelve months' option on it from Mr. Rallingbourne who parts with no land without particular restrictions as to the buildings to be put on it. Were there no restrictions as to the number and kind of buildings that might be put on your land when you bought it? I recall that you asked me for a set of plans to send to Mr. Rallingbourne's solicitors. Besides all this, Grigblay says there is no chance for a "Bungalow Town" anywhere near Marlford, and, if there were, nothing could be done unless the Building Byelaws were revised which the District Council would never agree to.

I saw my friend to-day, and he says the appliance I spoke of is Wealdstone's New Radio-Active Spleen and Liver Pad, made in two strengths, "strong" and "extra". He recommends the latter. They can be re-charged from any electric light plug and are stocked by Spedding, 92 Fountain Street, St. James's. My friend swears by it.

Ever yours dutifully,

The Cat Jumps

23.12.26.

My dear James—(to indite the new nomenclature),

I am much gratified and also relieved in mind at the intimation that the building propositions of Mr. Barthold are a fraudulent pretension, and as I have to-day received a peremptory reminder from Mr. Snitch, asking a reply to his previous communication, he will be sufficiently answered by my continued silence.

I had quite forgotten, as in my case it was a mere formality, that Mr. Rallingbourne makes it a prohibitive condition in his conveyances that only private houses of due importance and refinement of design shall be erected on the land.

Will you, since no alternative course seems expedient, be so obliging as to complete the necessary arrangements for Mr. Grigblay to undertake the renovation of the painting? We shall be unboundedly thankful—as you may imagine—to see a termination put to the disgraceful state of affairs which deforms the domicile and is no better than an unsightly eyesore.

I am obliged by the information you give anent the Radio Pad. I shall certainly test the efficacy of the device.

I have the pleasure to enclose cheque in final settlement of your fees. You will observe that I have augmented the amount to a round figure, but you will not, I hope, resent my indulging this friendly impulse as I apprehend that in giving me the right to do so you surrender the right to object!

The gong! I must hence and array me for the feast!

Ever, my dear boy,

Yours affectionately,

P.S.—I am requested to remind you that the performance to-morrow is timed to commence at 8.15 and *not* at 8.30 as originally intimated.

We have long suspected that something of this sort was going to happen. Apparently, in the stress of a "reconcilly" staged by Pud, barriers went down and consciences were unloaded all round; and appearances are that Brash, fitted out with a son-in-

law and a (*soi-disant*) radio-active liver pad, will take on a new lease of that benevolence which lies beneath his weakness and follies; for Brash, despite his irascibility and pomposity, is a simple soul at heart. His simplicity is well borne out if we accept the hilarious implication of the liver pad; namely, that during the unbosomings of that eventful week-end Brash was led to confess to a discontented liver, whereupon his architect promptly recommended a cure for it.

This letter, the last in the folder, by explaining itself explains also those not infrequent signs of a relationship which the correspondence did not reveal and of which Spinlove's reckless retort on Brash's strictures is the outstanding example. We cannot decide that no man would act as Spinlove did towards his prospective father-in-law, while we have no means of knowing under what circumstances he so acted. The matter, however, seems clear enough if we remember the months of badgering to which Spinlove has submitted, and suppose that when the young people's early friendship ripened to deeper feelings, Brash, finding himself in hopeless opposition to an only child and a neurotic wife, vented his irritation on the architect; and that Spinlove, secure in his position and unable to support the humiliation thrust upon him or go hat in hand to a man who considered himself at liberty to affront him, yielded to an impulse to have the thing out. In this elemental matter of pursuing a wife a man who follows his impulses at least keeps faith with his manhood; and in no other affair of life does his manhood better recommend a man.

In wishing Spinlove the best of luck we must not forget that this affair of his holds out new terrors to some who may be toying with the idea of employing an architect; and it is therefore desirable to make clear that Spinlove's behaviour in this matter is entirely "*unprofessional*".

INDEX

213